CHEMICAL ANALYSIS

Vol. 1. **The Analytical Chemistry of Industrial Poisons, Hazards, and Solvents.** *Second Edition.* By Morris B. Jacobs

Vol. 2. **Chromatographic Adsorption Analysis.** By Harold H. Strain

Vol. 3. **Colorimetric Determination of Traces of Metals.** *Third Edition.* By E. B. Sandell

Vol. 4. **Organic Reagents Used in Gravimetric and Volumetric Analysis.** By John F. Flagg

Vol. 5. **Aquametry: Application of the Karl Fischer Reagent to Quantitative Analyses Involving Water.** By John Mitchell, Jr., and Donald Milton Smith

Vol. 6. **Analysis of Insecticides and Acaricides.** By Francis A. Gunther and Roger C. Blinn

Vol. 7. **Chemical Analysis of Industrial Solvents.** By Morris B. Jacobs and Leopold Scheflan

Vol. 8. **Colorimetric Determination of Nonmetals.** Edited by David F. Boltz

Vol. 9. **Analytical Chemistry of Titanium Metals and Compounds.** By Maurice Codell

Vol. 10. **The Chemical Analysis of Air Pollutants.** By Morris B. Jacobs

Vol. 11. **X-Ray Spectrochemical Analysis.** By L. S. Birks

Vol. 12. **Systematic Analysis of Surface-Active Agents.** By Milton J. Rosen and Henry A. Goldsmith

Vol. 13. **Alternating Current Polarography and Tensammetry.** By B. Breyer and H. H. Bauer

Vol. 14. **Flame Photometry.** By R. Herrmann and J. Alkemade

Vol. 15. **The Titration of Organic Compounds.** By M. R. F. Ashworth

Vol. 16. **Complexation in Analytical Chemistry: A Guide for the Critical Selection of Analytical Methods Based on Complexation Reactions.** By Anders Ringbom

Vol. 17. **Electron Probe Microanalysis.** By L. S. Birks

Vol. 18. **Organic Complexing Reagents: Structure, Behavior, and Application to Inorganic Analysis.** By D. D. Perrin

Vol. 19. **Thermal Methods of Analysis.** By Wesley Wm. Wendlandt

other volumes in preparation

Vol. 20. **Amperometric Titrations.** By John T. Stock

CHEMICAL ANALYSIS

A SERIES OF MONOGRAPHS ON
ANALYTICAL CHEMISTRY AND ITS APPLICATIONS

Editors

P. J. ELVING • I. M. KOLTHOFF

Volume XIX

Thermal Methods of Analysis

by Wesley Wm. Wendlandt

INTERSCIENCE PUBLISHERS
A division of John Wiley & Sons, New York/London/Sydney

THERMAL METHODS
OF ANALYSIS

WESLEY WM. WENDLANDT

Department of Chemistry, Texas Technological College,
Lubbock, Texas

1964
INTERSCIENCE PUBLISHERS
a division of John Wiley & Sons, New York/London/Sydney

Library of Congress Catalog Card Number 64-24377

PREFACE

The purpose of this monograph is to acquaint chemists and other investigators with the relatively new series of instrumental techniques which are broadly classified as "thermal methods." In the past, many of these techniques involved tedious, time-consuming, manual recording methods; however, all of them are now completely automatic and employ either analog (recorder) or digital readout devices. Thus, due to automation, the instruments become capable of self-operation, improving both the accuracy and precision of the measurements as well as relinquishing both the investigator's time and patience.

These thermal methods provide a new means of solving existing chemical problems, as well as creating new ones. It is difficult for the author to think of a modern chemical laboratory without a thermobalance or differential thermal analysis apparatus. The former instrument can provide rapid information concerning the thermal stability, composition of pyrolysis intermediates, and composition of the final product, as a compound is heated to elevated temperatures. The latter apparatus can provide information concerning the enthalpy changes occurring during thermal decomposition of the compound, as well as the detection of phase transitions of various types. Both techniques yield a wealth of information in a very short period of time.

This book is not intended to be a comprehensive survey of the literature on each thermal technique. Rather, it is a critical review, as far as space permits, on each method. It is felt that the investigator should be well informed on both the *advantages* and *limitations* of each thermal technique in order to use these techniques intelligently. It must be admitted that this book is written primarily for the analytical chemist, although the techniques are useful in other fields of investigation as well.

The author would like to acknowledge his gratitude to Professors P. J. Elving and I. M. Kolthoff for their helpful advice and guidance during the preparation of the manuscript; to helpful comments from his former colleague, Dr. Edward Sturm; to Professor J. Jordan and S. T. Zenchelsky for supplying him with their personal reprints; to Mr. Irwin Dosch and Dr. Robert L. Stone for their assistance in supplying several of the badly needed photographs; and to his present and former students who made this work possible in the first place.

Also, the author would like to express his indebtedness to the Division of Research, U.S. Atomic Energy Commission; the Air Force Office of Scientific Research, U.S. Air Force; and to the Robert M. Welch Foundation, for their continual financial support of the author's work in this field.

And finally, because of their efforts above and beyond the call of duty, the author would like to acknowledge with thanks his typists, Miss Sallie Hardin, Miss Sue Richmond, and Miss Kathryn White.

WESLEY WM. WENDLANDT

Lubbock, Texas
January, 1964

CONTENTS

I. General Introduction... 1
II. Thermogravimetry... 4
    A. Introduction.. 4
    B. Some Factors Affecting Thermogravimetry............. 6
        1. Instrumental Factors........................... 7
        2. Sample Characteristics......................... 17
    C. Some Sources of Error in Thermogravimetry........... 20
        1. Sample Container Air Buoyancy................. 20
        2. Furnace Convection Currents and Turbulence....... 21
        3. Temperature Measurement and Calibration......... 23
        4. Other Errors.................................. 25
    D. Differential Thermogravimetric Analysis.............. 27
    E. Reaction Kinetics by Thermogravimetry............... 29
        1. The Isothermal Method........................ 30
        2. Non-Isothermal Methods...................... 32
    F. Fractional Thermogravimetric Analysis................ 40
    G. Miscellaneous.. 43
        1. Procedural Decomposition Temperatures........... 43
III. Automatic Recording Balances and Thermobalances.............. 48
    A. Introduction.. 48
    B. Commercial Instruments............................. 53
        1. Fisher Recording Balance Accessory............. 53
        2. Ainsworth Recording Balances................. 56
        3. Cahn RG Electrobalance....................... 58
        4. Thermo-Grav.................................. 60
        5. Mauer Recording Balance...................... 61
        6. Harrop Thermobalance......................... 61
        7. Sharples Recording Balance.................... 62
        8. Chevenard Thermobalance...................... 63
        9. Ugine-Eyraud Thermobalance.................... 67
        10. Stanton Thermobalance....................... 69
        11. Brabender Thermobalance...................... 71
        12. Sartorius Recording Balances.................. 71
        13. The Derivatograph............................ 72
    C. Noncommercial Instruments.......................... 73
    D. Differential Thermobalances.......................... 80
    E. Multiple Instruments Containing a Thermobalance...... 82
IV. Applications of Thermogravimetry.............................. 88
    A. Introduction.. 88
        1. Applications to Analytical Chemistry.............. 89
    B. Automatic Thermogravimetric Analysis............... 89
    C. Applications to Analytical Chemistry................. 91

1. The Drying and Decomposition of Sodium Carbonate   92
2. Ignition Temperatures of Aluminum Oxide..........   92
3. Complex Mixtures of Hydrates....................   95
4. Analysis of Clays and Soils.....................   96
5. Analysis of Fission Product Oxides and Nitrates.....   97
6. Analysis of Phosphor Raw Materials...............   98
7. Analysis of Calcium Silicate Hydrates for Free Lime
     and Carbonate...............................   101
8. Determination of Magnesium, Calcium, Strontium,
     and Barium..................................   101
9. Potassium Hydrogen Phthalate....................   106
10. Rare-Earth Cupferrates and Neocupferrates.........   107
11. Compounds with Dilituric Acid...................   110
12. Some Amine Molybdophosphates..................   111
13. (Ethylenedinitrilo)tetraacetic Acid and Its Deriva-
     tives.......................................   115
14. Some 2-(o-Hydroxyphenyl)Benzoxazole Metal Chelates   121
15. Amine and Metal Tetraphenylboron Compounds....   121
16. Thorium and Zirconium Salts of Some Organic Acids.   123
17. Some Metal Oxalates............................   125
V. Differential Thermal Analysis................................   132
     A. Introduction...   132
     B. Theory...   136
     C. Factors Affecting Results............................   139
          1. Sample Holder Material.........................   140
          2. Geometry of Sample Holder......................   143
          3. Thermocouples...................................   144
          4. Thermocouple Location..........................   147
          5. Heating Rate.....................................   152
          6. Furnace Atmosphere..............................   156
          7. Miscellaneous Instrumental Factors................   161
          8. Sample Particle Size............................   162
          9. Amount of Sample...............................   163
          10. Effect of Diluent...............................   165
          11. Miscellaneous Sample Effects....................   166
     D. Quantitative Differential Thermal Analysis.............   168
          1. Heats of Transition or Reaction...................   168
     E. Reaction Kinetics....................................   174
     F. Correlation of DTA and TGA Data...................   178
     G. Derivative Differential Thermal Analysis...............   180
VI. Differential Thermal Analysis Instrumentation....................   186
     A. Introduction...   186
          1. Sample Holders..................................   186
          2. Differential Temperature Detection Devices.........   190
          3. Furnaces and Furnace Temperature Controllers.....   191
          4. DC Amplifiers and Recorders....................   192
     B. Commercial DTA Instruments........................   193

C. Noncommercial DTA Instruments........................ 209
D. Multiple Instruments Containing a Differential Thermal
    Analysis Apparatus................................ 224
VII. Applications of Differential Thermal Analysis.................... 229
A. Introduction.. 229
B. Applications to Analytical Chemistry.................. 231
C. Derivative Differential Thermal Analysis.............. 264
D. Miscellaneous...................................... 268
VIII. Thermometric Titrimetry.................................... 271
A. Introduction.. 271
B. Apparatus.. 273
C. Theory... 278
D. Applications.. 283
    1. Acid–Base Reactions............................ 284
    2. Precipitation Reactions.......................... 288
    3. Complex-Formation or Complexation Reactions..... 289
    4. Oxidation–Reduction Reactions................... 291
    5. Reactions in Non-Aqueous Solvents............... 292
IX. Pyrolytic Techniques.. 297
A. Introduction.. 297
B. Gas Evolution Analysis (GEA)....................... 297
C. Analysis of Pyrolyzates by Gas Chromatography........ 308
D. Analysis of Pyrolyzates by Mass Spectrometry.......... 317
E. Analysis of Pyrolyzates by Infrared Spectroscopy....... 321
F. Miscellaneous Methods.............................. 325
    1. Linear Pyrolysis Rates of Solids.................. 325
    2. Pyrolysis of Airborne Solids..................... 327
    3. Thermal Stability Determinations................. 328
    4. Flash Pyrolysis................................. 329
X. Dynamic Reflectance Spectroscopy............................ 332
A. Introduction.. 332
B. Theory... 332
C. Instrumentation..................................... 335
D. Applications.. 340
XI. Thermal Analysis... 345
A. Introduction.. 345
B. Theory... 346
C. Experimental Techniques............................ 353
D. Errors, Limitations, and Other Factors Affecting Results.. 359
    1. Limitations of the Dynamic Method............... 359
    2. Limitations of the Static Method................. 362
    3. Comparison of Results Obtained by the Static and Dy-
       namic Methods................................. 363
    4. Recommendations.............................. 364
E. Applications to Impurity Determinations and other Prob-
    lems... 365
XII. Miscellaneous Thermal Methods............................. 373

A. Thermoluminescence................................. 373
B. Oxyluminescence................................... 380
C. Dilatometry.. 381
D. Electrical Conductivity............................. 387
E. Miscellaneous Thermal Methods..................... 390
    1. Automatic Melting Point Determination........... 390
    2. Heated Infrared Gas Cell....................... 393
    3. High-Temperature X-Ray Diffraction............. 396
Author Index.. 405
Subject Index... 417

CHAPTER I

GENERAL INTRODUCTION

With the development of each new instrumental technique, the chemist has a new tool in which to attack and/or solve chemical problems. However, there is, at times, a fairly long time interval between the date in which the technique is developed to that in which it is applied *en masse* to chemical problems. Such has been the case with many of the thermal methods discussed herein. For example, the first thermobalance was developed by Honda in 1915, yet it was not until 1947 that Duval called attention to its applications to the field of inorganic gravimetric analysis. A similar situation is noted with differential thermal analysis (DTA), which was originally conceived by Le Chatelier in 1887 and further modified by Roberts-Austen in 1899. For many years DTA was an invaluable technique for the identification of minerals, clays, metallic alloys, and so on, but was virtually ignored by the chemists. In recent years, however, DTA has been successfully applied, either by itself or in conjunction with other thermal techniques, to the elucidation of problems of chemical interest.

The term *thermal methods of analysis* will be defined in this book to include only those techniques in which some physical parameter of the system is measured as a function of temperature. In other words, the physical parameter is a *dynamic* function of temperature. Of course, every physicochemical property is measured at some given temperature; it is only when the measured property changes significantly as a function of temperature so as to yield useful information concerning the chemical system. Using the above definition then, the principal techniques discussed here will include: thermogravimetry or thermogravimetric analysis (TGA), differential thermal analysis (DTA) or thermography, gas evolution analysis (GEA) or effluent gas analysis, pyrolysis, dynamic reflectance spectroscopy (DRS), dilatometry or thermodilatometric analysis (TDA), thermoluminescence, and others. Also included here are two other important thermal techniques that do not fall under the above classifica-

1

TABLE I.1
Thermal Methods of Analysis

Name of technique	Physical parameter measured as function of temperature	Name of instrument employed
Thermogravimetric analysis	Change in mass	Thermobalance
Differential thermo-gravimetric analysis	First derivative of change in mass	Thermobalance or differential thermo-balance
Differential thermal analysis	Temperature difference between sample and reference material	DTA apparatus
Derivative differential thermal analysis	First derivative of temperature dif-ference	DTA apparatus
Differential scanning calorimetry analysis	Heat change supplied to sample	Differential calorimeter
Specific heat measure-ment	Specific heat	Differential calorimeter
Gas evolution analysis; linear pyrolysis	Gas thermal con-ductivity	Thermal conduc-tivity cell
Pyrolysis	Pyrolysis fragments	Gas chromatograph; mass spectrometer; infrared spectro-photometer; and others
Thermoluminescence; oxyluminescence	Light emission	Photomultiplier tube in thermolumines-cence apparatus
Dilatometry	Change in volume	Dilatometer
Electrical conductivity	Change in electrical resistance	Resistance bridge
High-temperature x-ray diffraction	Change in d-spacing	X-ray diffractometer
Thermometric titrimetry	Temperature change vs. time or volume of titrant	Thermometric ti-trimeter
Thermal analysis	Temperature vs. time or heat content	Calorimeter; thermal analysis apparatus
Dynamic reflectance spectroscopy	Reflectance of sample	Spectroreflectometer

tion: They are thermal analysis and thermometric titrimetry. Both of these techniques are included because they represent important methods of analysis in analytical chemistry and involve the measurement of the temperature of a system as a function of time or volume of titrant (which is related to a time function).

The various thermal techniques, the physicochemical parameters measured, and the instruments employed in their measurement are summarized in Table I.1.

It should be pointed out that, in many cases, the use of only a single thermal technique may provide insufficient information to completely solve the problem at hand. As with other instrumental methods, complementary or supplementary information, as can be supplied by the use of other thermal methods, may be needed. For example, consider the interpretation of DTA peaks. An endothermic peak in the curve may be caused by a change in state (fusion) or, perhaps, a decomposition reaction involving a gaseous product. With the aid of gas evolution analysis, one can distinguish between the two immediately since the peak due to fusion will not appear on the GEA curve. Other techniques such as TGA and x-ray diffraction may also be used to aid in this interpretation. If a gaseous product is evolved, other instruments may be used to determine its chemical composition, such as a gas chromatograph, mass spectrometer, and an infrared spectrophotometer. Indeed, it may be stated that a single thermal property is not sufficient to characterize a chemical reaction or system, but that as many thermal methods as possible be employed.

It is not very encouraging to the reader to end this first chapter on such a pessimistic note. Rather, the reader should be encouraged to use the following thermal techniques as much as possible, but he must also recognize their limitations. Each of the thermal techniques will be discussed, as thoroughly as space permits, in the following chapters. It is hoped that the following discussion will encourage more extensive research in this exciting field of investigation.

CHAPTER II

THERMOGRAVIMETRY

A. Introduction

Thermogravimetry is a technique whereby a sample is continuously weighed as it is heated at a constant, preferably linear, rate. The resulting weight change *vs.* temperature curve so obtained gives information concerning the thermal stability and composition of the original sample, the composition and thermal stability of intermediate compounds, and the composition of the residue. Much of the information obtained is of an empirical nature, such as the minimum temperature at which the weight-loss curve deviates from the base line. A great amount of exactness has been placed upon this temperature value by a number of investigators when actually it depends upon a number of factors. In fact, it is rather surprising that the agreement between minimum stability temperatures of identical samples is as close as it is, when the various pyrolysis parameters are considered. Judging from the number of different types of thermobalances (see Chap. III) and the wide variety of furnaces, sample holder geometries, and so on, the agreement appears to be miraculous.

To illustrate the principle of the technique, consider the weight-loss curve or thermogram (also known as a thermogravigram) of a hypothetical compound, $MX_2 \cdot 6H_2O$, as given in Figure II.1. It is assumed that the sample is heated in an air atmosphere at a reasonable heating rate of $5°C/min$. From A to B on the curve, the sample is stable in that there is no change in weight. At B, the sample begins to lose weight, the process being completed at C. This first weight loss, it is again assumed, is due to the evolution of the six moles of water per mole of sample, thus giving the anhydrous compound, MX_2. In actual practice, however, either the gaseous evolved product would have to be identified by analysis or the sample removed at C and subjected to analysis. Most interpretations of the curve are subjective in that if the weight change, BC, corresponds to that expected for the loss of the water molecules, then this is the

4

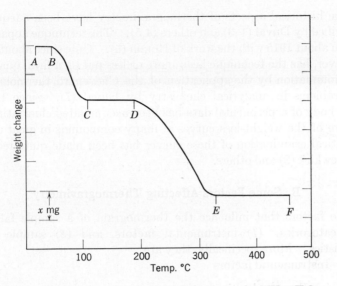

Fig. II.1. Weight-loss curve of a hypothetical sample, $MX_2 \cdot 6H_2O$.

reaction that is assigned to the transition. Admittedly, the latter method is more rapid, but also subject to false interpretation.

From C to D, the compound MX_2 is stable and gave a horizontal weight level in the curve. At D, the sample decomposed further, giving another weight level from E to F which, it is assumed, has the composition of the oxide, MO. In an air atmosphere, MO could easily be formed. Again, distance DE would correspond to the weight loss expected for the decomposition reaction.

From the various regions in the curve, the thermal stabilities of the original sample, the intermediate compound, and the final product could be ascertained, although these temperatures, as suggested previously, are quite trivial. The curve is quantitative in that the compound stoichiometry can be calculated at any temperature. The utility of the technique lies in the simplicity of the method and the information obtained from a single measurement. However, like most other laboratory techniques, at times complementary methods must be used in order to interpret the weight-loss curve. These complementary techniques include x-ray diffraction, infrared absorption spectroscopy, differential thermal analysis, gas chromatography and mass spectrometry.

The historical aspects of thermogravimetry have been adequately described by Duval (1–3) and others (4,5). The technique apparently began about 1915 with the work of Honda (6). Only since about 1947, however, has the technique been more or less put on a firm, quantitative foundation by the application of the Chevenard thermobalance to problems in analytical chemistry by Duval (7). Since 1947 a large body of experimental data has been accumulated elucidating the nature of the weight-loss curves of many compounds in great detail. A critical examination of these curves has been made quite recently by Newkirk (8) and others.

B. Some Factors Affecting Thermogravimetry

The factors that influence the thermogram of a sample fall into two categories: (1) instrumental factors, and (2) sample characteristics. More specifically, they are

(1) Instrumental factors

(a) Furnace heating rate
(b) Recording or chart speed
(c) Furnace atmosphere
(d) Geometry of sample holder and furnace
(e) Sensitivity of recording mechanism
(f) Composition of sample container

(2) Sample characteristics

(a) Amount of sample
(b) Solubility of evolved gases in sample
(c) Particle size
(d) Heat of reaction
(e) Sample packing
(f) Nature of the sample
(g) Thermal conductivity

Unfortunately, definitive studies are lacking on many of the above factors, or, if some type of a study has been made, it has been limited to only one type of thermobalance or recording system and correlations cannot be very easily made with other types of instruments. It is true, of course, that many of the above factors, such as sample holder geometry, recording speed, balance sensitivity and sample container air buoyancy, are fixed with any given thermobalance. Factors which are variable and difficult to reproduce are the sample particle size, packing, the solubility of evolved gases in the sample, furnace convection currents and electrostatic effects. In view of the above variables, it is unfortunate that some type of standard sample is not available for comparing one given experimental apparatus with another; or better yet, a "standard" thermobalance.

1. INSTRUMENTAL FACTORS

a. Heating Rate

The effect of heating rate on the weight-loss curve is to decrease the apparent decomposition temperatures with decrease in heating rate. This effect has been studied by Duval (1), Newkirk (8),

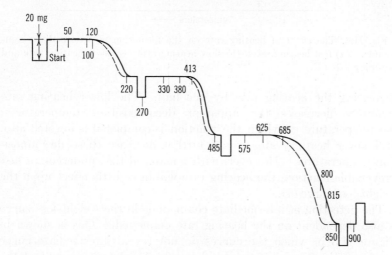

Fig. II.2. Effect of heating rate on the weight-loss curve of $CaC_2O_4 \cdot H_2O$ (8). —, 300°C/h; - - -, 150°C/h corrected for differences in scale and apparent weight gain.

Rynasiewicz and Flagg (9), Lukaszewski and Redfern (4), and Fruchart and Michel (10), and is illustrated for the decomposition of $CaC_2O_4 \cdot H_2O$ in Figure II.2.

The two curves, each plotted on the same temperature scale and corrected for apparent weight gain, show very clearly the effect of

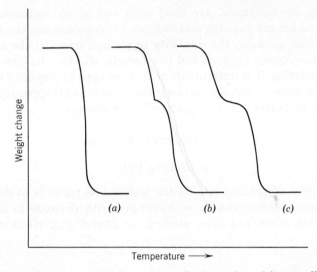

Fig. II.3. The effect of heating rate on the formation of intermediate compounds. (a) fast heating rate; (b) slow heating rate; (c) slow heating rate and recording rate (4).

decreasing the heating rate by one half. The lower heating rate definitely decreases the apparent decomposition temperatures; the temperature at which the reaction is completed is lowered also. Still lower heating rates would further decrease these decomposition temperatures However, with a material that undergoes a fast irreversible reaction, the heating rate will have little effect upon the weight-loss curve (4).

The detection of intermediate compounds in the weight-loss curve is also dependent on the heating rate employed. This is shown in Figure II.3 in which the curves do not reveal intermediate curve breaks at the fast heating rate; however, breaks are evident at the lower heating rate (4). Fruchart and Michel (10) detected intermediate compounds, with the composition, 6-, 4-, 2-, and 1-hydrate, when $NiSO_4 \cdot 7H_2O$ was heated at a rate of 0.6°C/min. A previous study at 2.5°C/min revealed only the existence of the 1-hydrate (11). A similar situation was observed with the monosalicylaldoxinezinc(II) chelate as studied by Rynasiewicz and Flagg (9) and DeClerq and Duval (12). On heating at 300°C/h a wet precipitate containing a 250% excess of water, a horizontal weight region was obtained in the curve from 215 to 290°C (9). DeClerq and Duval (12), using a higher heating rate of 380°C/h, did not detect a horizontal weight level and hence rejected the method for the determination of zinc. The latter results indicated that when samples which contain a large amount of water are studied a slow heating rate should be employed. It should also be noted that a sudden inflection in the weight-loss curve may be caused by a sudden variation in the rate of heating and hence be false (4). One method used to detect this phenomenon is to always record the furnace temperature as a function of time on a strip-chart recorder.

For resolution of thermal decomposition curves of a rather complex nature, Lukaszewski and Redfern (4) suggested the quasi-static technique. With this technique, provision is made for the interruption of the uniform temperature rise cycle and continuation of the heating at a constant fixed temperature This method gives weight-loss curves that are, in general, steeper than those obtained under dynamic conditions and provides more accurate data on the final decomposition temperatures.

Newkirk (8) has criticized the establishment of drying temperatures as the temperatures at the beginning and end of a horizontal weight level of a single weight-loss curve. As a general rule, this range is approximately correct but has been shifted upward in temperature by the effect of rate of heating. Normally this is true only for a specific thermobalance. Fortunately, even though the temperature to be assigned to a point on the curve may be indeterminate, the curves under identical conditions are usually identical.

b. Recording or Chart Speed

The recording of the weight-loss curves for either rapid or slow reactions can have a pronounced effect on the shape of the curve. The effect of chart speed on the recording of the curves of various reactions is illustrated in Figure II.4. In curve (a), there is a definite flattening of the curve as the chart speed is increased for a slow thermal decomposition reaction. In the case of a slow reaction followed by a rapid one, curve (b), the slower chart speed curve shows less resolution of the two separate steps than the faster chart speed. For a fast reaction followed by a slower one, curve (c), an effect similar to that of curve (b) was observed, namely, less curve resolution

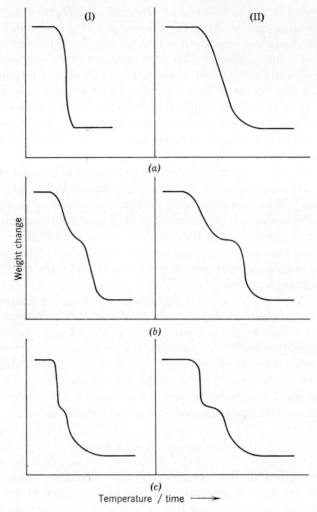

Fig. II.4. Effect of chart speed upon the shapes of weight-loss curves; (I) slow chart speed; (II) fast chart speed (4).

A resolution factor, R, has been introduced (4) which is based upon the following. For a recording chart speed of 1 cm/min and a weight-loss at time t represented on the chart by dw cm/min, the shape of the slope at time t will depend on both chart speed and weight scale in g/cm. Thus,

$$R = \tan \alpha = dw/dl$$

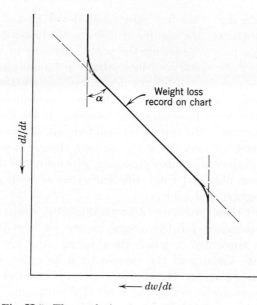

Fig. II.5. The resolution factor, R; ideally $\alpha = 45°$ (4).

in which a value of $dw/dl = 1$ or $\alpha = 45°$ is desirable for the midpoint of a reaction. These various functions are illustrated in Figure II.5.

An excessive chart speed will tend to minimize differing rates of weight loss. It is recommended that a chart speed of 6–12 in./h for a heating rate of 1–6°C/min be employed (4). With X-Y recorders, however, the chart speed on the temperature axis is controlled by the response of the instrument, and the heating rate on the weight axis is controlled by the responses of the recorder pen and the recording balance and the rate of the thermal decomposition reaction.

c. Effect of Furnace Atmosphere

The effect of different atmospheres on the weight-loss curves has been investigated by Saito (13), Richer and Vallet (14), Newkirk (8), Garn and Kessler (15,16), Garn (17), Rabatin and Card (18), Soulen and Mockrin (19), Lukaszewski (20), and Vallet (21).

In a weight-loss curve, the sample under investigation evolves a gaseous substance or reacts with a gaseous substance from the atmosphere surrounding it.   If the first case is considered, that of evolution of a gaseous substance, the sample will begin to dissociate as soon as its dissociation pressure exceeds the partial pressure of the gas or vapor in its immediate vicinity.   Since a dynamic temperature system is employed, the specific rate of the decomposition reaction will increase as well as the concentration of the ambient gas surrounding the sample due to the decomposition of the sample.   If the ambient gas concentration increases, the rate of the reaction will decrease.   However, due to convection currents in the furnace, the gas concentration around the sample is continuously changing, which is one of the reasons why thermograms obtained from different types of thermobalances are not exceedingly reproducible.

To circumvent these problems of irreproducibility, Garn and Kessler (16) have proposed for thermogravimetry in "self-generated" atmospheres an apparatus in which the evolved gases are restricted to the immediate vicinity of the sample by a long diffusion path. The evolved gases displace the ambient atmosphere and approach the partial pressure demanded by the van't Hoff equation.   Although a convincing case is presented, as a result of the studies by Guiochon (22) the method should be employed with caution.   He elucidated the effect of dissolved gases in the liquids or solids that are formed in the decomposition reaction.   This dissolved gas causes a delay in the weight-loss because during the first part of the reaction the gas concentration increases, as does the rate of evaporation of the liquid product that may be formed.   At equilibrium, the rates of formation and evaporation are equal, but the weight of the liquid, either the initial or final product, is not constant.   Moreover, as stated previously, the equilibrium concentration of the gas depends on the partial pressure of the gas in the furnace.   This gas solubility concentration is difficult to measure and eliminate, and hence, the errors connected with it are generally unknown.

Some rather pronounced differences were noted between weight-loss curves for samples obtained in a conventional manner and those obtained in a self-generated atmosphere apparatus.   The curves for lead(II) carbonate, as shown in Figure II.6, illustrate this point (16).   When the substance is decomposed in an air atmosphere, there are two distinct weight losses.   There is a slight hint that the second loss is actually two, the third loss starting at about 330°C. After the weight loss was completed at 380°C, the lead oxide present,

PbO, oxidized to Pb₃O₄ which decomposed as the temperature approached 600°C. With the self-generated atmosphere present (top of sample holder in place), the decomposition reactions were well

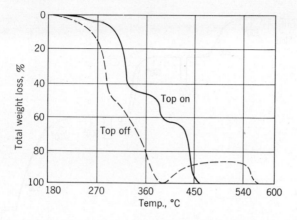

Fig. II.6. Thermal decomposition of lead carbonate in the absence and presence of a self-generated atmosphere (16).

separated and distinct. The curve breaks corresponded to the sequence.

$$PbCO_3 \rightarrow PbO \cdot PbCO_3 \rightarrow 2PbO \cdot PbCO_3 \rightarrow PbO$$

The oxidation reactions were, of course, prevented from occurring by the carbon dioxide atmosphere.

The small changes in the composition of the ambient atmosphere surrounding the sample have an effect on the weight-loss curve obtained, as was shown by Newkirk (8). The weight-loss curve of $CaC_2O_4 \cdot H_2O$ in a vented and nonvented furnace is given in Figure II.7. The dashed curve represents the decomposition reaction in a closed top (non vented) furnace, and the solid line in an opened top (vented) furnace. By venting, the apparent weight-gain correction is reduced; on plateaus, the dashed curve lies above the solid curve and the difference increases with an increase in temperature.

The effects of different gaseous atmospheres and of pressure on the weight-loss curves of maganese(II) carbonate are illustrated in Figure II.8. The higher concentration of carbon dioxide repressed the decomposition of the manganese(II) carbonate (18) as was also shown by a self-generated atmosphere study (16).   Increasing the pressure from 1 (16) to 13 atm increased the decomposition temperature by at least 140°C (18).

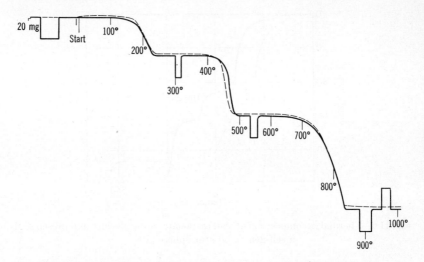

Fig. II.7. Effect of venting on the weight-loss curve of $CaC_2O_4 \cdot H_2O$ (8).   - - -, no vent; —, vent 7 mm diameter.

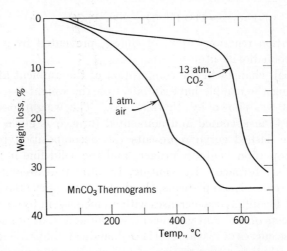

Fig. II.8. Decomposition curves of manganese(II) carbonate in air and in an atmosphere of carbon dioxide at 13 atm pressure (18).

d. Miscellaneous Effects

The geometry of the sample holder has been discussed by Garn and Kessler (16), Garn (17), Kissinger, et al. (23) Lukaszewski (20), and Duval (1). For thermogravimetry in self-generated atmospheres, the sample holder in Figure II.9 has been proposed. The

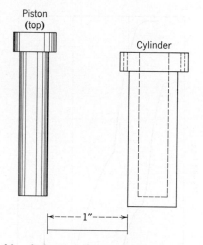

Fig. II.9. Sample holder design for thermogravimetry in self-generated atmospheres (16).

cylinder and piston devices were made from alumina. The powdered sample is placed in the cylinder and the piston inserted and pushed down firmly to make intimate contact with the sample and to displace all of the air from the cylinder. The differences between the closed cylinder and the open one have been discussed previously. The differences between the results obtained using the closed cylinder and a small shallow cup are said to be even more striking (16).

The effect of size or heat sink of the sample holder has been illustrated by Garn (17). The effect is shown on the thermal decomposition of lead carbonate as illustrated in Figure II.10. The above sample holder, which was placed on an aluminum block 1 in. in height with cylindrical surface of 3.1 sq. in., was employed. The shallow aluminum pan was of the same diameter but had an overall height of $1/16$ in. A factor of 16 in the area directly exposed to the heated furnace wall permitted more rapid heat transfer to the middle of the sample and hence more uniform temperature throughout.   It should be noted that the sample on the massive sample holder decomposed over a smaller temperature range.

The conventional sample holders employed in thermogravimetry are far from being infinite heat sinks (17).   Generally, the heat of reaction of the sample is the principal consumer of heat energy, yet

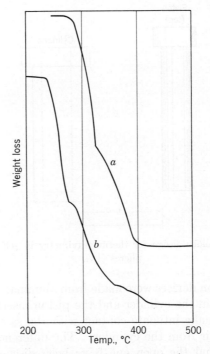

Fig. II.10. Effect of heat sink on the thermogravimetry of lead carbonate. (a) massive aluminum block; (b) thin aluminum pan.   Heating rate is about 450°C/h (17).

the sample holders are not designed to supply that heat rapidly. Garn (17) suggests that sample holders should be designed to supply this heat to the sample as rapidly as possible.

Lukaszewski (20) recommended the use of the crucible and support assembly as shown in Figure II.11.   Crucibles should be symmetrical and of minimal volume;   the support assemblies should be as small and as streamlined as possible.

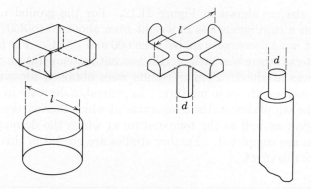

Fig. II.11. Crucible and support assembly recommended by Lukaszewski (20).

Duval (1) suggested that since the walls of the crucible are heated more strongly than the center, the use of a plate and a thin layer of sample would be the best sample holder, whereas the high-form crucible would be the worst. However, certain samples swell or spatter when heated so that the use of crucibles with high walls is necessary. Duval does not recommend a covered crucible, however, since this would cause the horizontal weight plateaus to be longer. This was illustrated with the pyrolysis of magnesium ammonium phosphate. In an open crucible, there appeared to be a discontinuity between the loss of water and the ammonia, while in the covered crucible, there appeared a short horizontal or at least a break as soon as the ammonia stopped coming off.

2. Sample Characteristics

The effect of particle size of a substance on the weight-loss curves has been elucidated by a number of investigators, among them Saito (13), Richer and Vallet (14), and Martinez (24).

In comparing the thermal decomposition curves of calcium carbonate and calcite, Richer and Vallet (14) found that the empirical decomposition temperatures obtained at the heating rate of 150°C/ h in a stream of nitrogen gas were: powdered calcium carbonate, 783°C; powdered calcite, 802°C; and a cube of calcite weighing about 350 mg 891°C.

Likewise, for a chrysotile sample, Martinez (24) found that the decomposition temperature decreased with a decrease in sample particle size, as shown in Figure II.12. For the ground material, there was a continuous loss in weight from about 50 to 850°C, with the most rapid decomposition between 600 and 700°C. For the massive material, there was little weight loss until a temperature of about 600°C was attained. Similar results were obtained for serpentine and a brucine–carbonate mixture. In general, a decrease in particle size of the sample lowers the temperatue at which thermal decomposition begins, as well as the temperature at which the decomposition reactions are completed. Further studies are needed in this area to elucidate this effect.

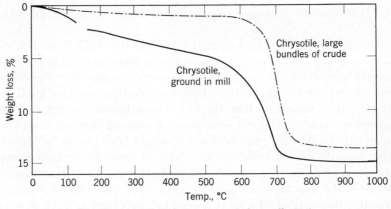

Fig. II.12. Weight-loss curves of chrysotile (24).

The effect of the heat of reaction of the sample on the weight-loss curve has been studied by Newkirk (8). The heat of reaction will affect the difference between the sample temperature and furnace temperature, causing the sample temperature to lead or lag the furnace temperature depending on whether the heat effect is exothermic or endothermic. Since these temperatures may be above 10° C or more, depending on the heating rate employed, the calculation of kinetic constants from weight-loss curves may be unavoidably and significantly in error. This effect is more thoroughly discussed in Section C of this Chapter.

The solubility of gases in solids imposes a serious limitation to the thermogravimetric method as discussed by Guiochon (22). It is difficult to eliminate or even measure, and is generally unknown.

This was shown by the heating of solid ammonium nitrate initially containing 1% nitric acid at 200°C for 3 h. At the end of this period, the sample contained 0.6% nitric acid. This acid has no catalytic effect on the decomposition of the sample, which gives no nitric acid under these conditions, so that only the slowness of its evaporation can explain these results. The concentration of this dissolved substance may be decreased to a small value by the use of wide crucibles without covers, a thin layer of sample, and a flow of inert gas through the furnace. According to Guiochon (22), this gas flow through the furnace is almost always necessary to facilitate the diffusion of gases to and from the sample.

The work of Duval (1,2) concerning the drying and ignition temperatures of analytical precipitates has had a pronounced effect on inorganic gravimetric analysis. However, a number of controversies have arisen in the literature concerning the absence or presence of various horizontal weight levels present in the pyrolysis curve. The monosalicylaldoximezinc(II) chelate can be used to illustrate this point (9). Duval always started with the wet precipitate in a small crucible and carried out the pyrolysis in a static air atmosphere. This method was said to approximate the conditions of the analyst in the actual drying or ignition of the precipitate with the exception of a constantly increasing rate of temperature rise. With precipitates containing voluminous amounts of water or other solvents, the thermobalance can give entirely erroneous results unless a very slow heating rate is employed. Again, it should be reiterated that the determination of the actual isothermal drying or ignition temperature of a precipitate from the weight-loss curve should be done with caution.

The effects of sample packing, amount of sample, and thermal conductivity of the sample on the weight-loss curve have been little studied and are generally difficult to reproduce in practice. The thermal conductivity of the sample is a function of particle size and sample packing density and will change as the reaction proceeds due to fusion of the sample, conversion to a different substance, sintering, swelling, and so on. Concerning the sample size, a different curve will be obtained on a 1 mg sample than on a 100 mg one. With many of the present recording balances, it is possible to obtain weight-loss curves on 0.5 or even 0.1 mg of a sample. The heat-sink effect would certainly be important for the small sample sizes. Much more work needs to be done in this particular area of thermogravimetry.

C. Some Sources of Error in Thermogravimetry

The sources of error in thermogravimetry can lead to considerable inaccuracies in the temperature and weight-loss or weight-gain data obtained. Accurate thermogravimetry requires that a correction be applied for these errors or at least some recognition be made as to their magnitude. Many of these errors are interrelated and hence cannot be considered separately. Full consideration must be given to all of these factors in thermogravimetry.

The possible sources of error in thermogravimetry are manifold. Among them can be listed the following:

(1) Sample container air buoyancy
(2) Furnace convection currents and turbulence
(3) Random fluctuations in the recording mechanism and balance
(4) Furnace induction effects
(5) Electrostatic effects on balance mechanism
(6) Environment of the thermobalance
(7) Condensation on sample support
(8) Temperature measurement and calibration
(9) Weight calibration of recording balance
(10) Chart paper rulings
(11) Reaction of the sample with sample container

1. SAMPLE CONTAINER AIR BUOYANCY

The effect of air buoyancy on the sample container and support mechanism has been studied by Newkirk (8), Simons et al. (25), Lukaszewski (20), Duval (1,2), and Mielenz et al. (26). Most of the studies have been made on the Chevenard thermobalance (1,2,8, 20,25,26), but the Stanton instrument has also been investigated (20).

The apparent weight-gain curve for the Chevenard thermobalance, as a function of temperature, is given in Figure II.13. In general, the weight gain is also a function of the heating rate and load, as well as temperature. On the basis of a factorial design, Simons et al. (25) worked out a table giving the apparent weight gain vs. temperature for different volumes of load on the balance. The

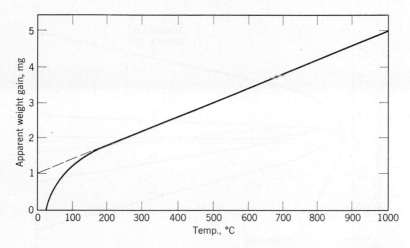

Fig. II.13. Apparent weight gain as a function of temperature for the Chevenard thermobalance (25).

apparent weight gain of a single porcelain crucible whose weight was ∼4 g and volume ∼1.5 ml ranged from 1.8 mg at 200°C to 4.2 mg at 1000°C, at a heating rate of 300°C/h. For a pair of nested crucibles weighing ∼8 g and having a volume of ∼3 ml, the range was 2.5–5.4 mg. The corresponding numbers at the heating rate of 150° C/h were 2.0–5.3 mg and 2.7–6.2 mg. These values are consistent with those reported by Mielenz et al. (26).

For a platinum sample holder, 0.7 cm square, 0.5 cm deep, and weighing 1.6 g, Lukaszewski (20) found that the increase in weight from ambient to 350°C was 0.3 ± 0.05 mg, and from 350 to 1400°C, 0.2 ± 0.05 mg, at a heating rate of 1–3°C/min. The effects of different heating rates and load sizes were also studied.

2. FURNACE CONVECTION CURRENTS AND TURBULENCE

The apparent weight gain or loss due to convection currents in the furnace has been studied by Newkirk (8) and by Lukaszewski (20).

The apparent weight loss caused by the upflowing stream of air on the sample container and the apparent weight gain due to air turbulence are determined largely by the sample crucible size and shape (8). The apparent weight changes as functions of furnace top openings are given in Figure II.14. It was found that except for

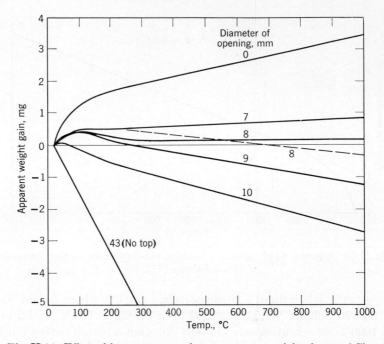

Fig. II.14. Effect of furnace top opening on apparent weight change of Chevenard thermobalance at a heating rate of 300°C/h (8).   —, One porcelain crucible, Coors 230-000 (about 4 g); - - -, two crucibles.

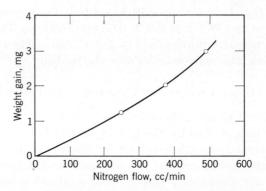

Fig. II.15. Effect of gas velocity on apparent weight gain of a porcelain crucible at room temperature on the Chevenard thermobalance (8).

a large opening, there was always an initial weight gain even when on further heating there was an overall weight loss. It was not possible to choose an opening that would give no apparent weight gain on heating over the entire temperature range. This effect is also dependent on the furnace heating rate.

When using a flowing gas atmosphere in the furnace, Newkirk (8) found an additional apparent weight gain, as shown in Figure II.15. Its magnitude was governed by the molecular weight of the gas employed.

3. TEMPERATURE MEASUREMENT AND CALIBRATION

Generally, the temperature of the sample is taken as the temperature measured by a thermocouple located either just above or below the sample container. The true temperature of the sample either lags or leads the thermocouple temperature depending on the nature of the decomposition reaction (endothermic or exothermic), the heating rate, sample thermal conductivity, geometry of the sample holder, and so on. This effect is illustrated by the curves for the sample and

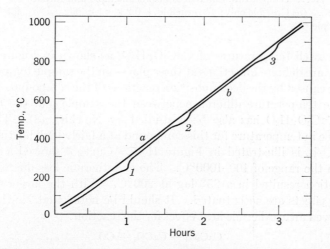

Fig. II.16. Thermowell and sample temperatures in the decomposition of $CaC_2O_4 \cdot H_2O$ in nitrogen on a Chevenard thermobalance. One gram sample heated at 300°C/h at a nitrogen flow rate of 400 ml/min. (a) Thermowell temperature ($+10°$ cal); (b) sample temperature (19). (1) $CaC_2O_4 \cdot H_2O \rightarrow Ca C_2O_4 + H_2O$; ($2$) $CaC_2O_4 \rightarrow CaCO_3 + CO$; ($3$) $CaCO_3 \rightarrow CaO + CO_2$.

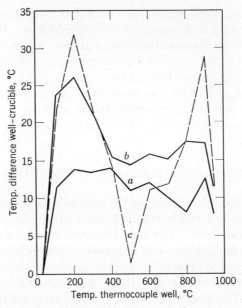

Fig. II.17. Temperature differences between sample and furnace for $CaC_2O_4 \cdot$ H_2O (8). (*a*) Crucible only; (*b*) crucible $+$ 0.2 g of sample; (*c*) crucible $+$ 0.6 g of sample (8).

thermowell temperatures of $CaC_2O_4 \cdot H_2O$, as shown in Figure II.16. There are definite inflections at three places on the sample temperature curve caused by the decomposition reactions of the compound.

The temperature difference between the sample and the furnace for $CaC_2O_4 \cdot H_2O$ has also been studied by Newkirk (8). The difference in temperature for this compound at a fairly high heating rate, 600°C/h, is illustrated in Figure II.17. Curve *a* showed a 10–14° lag in the range of 100–1000°C. The endothermic loss due to water evolution resulted in a 25° lag at 200°C. With the larger sample, these effects are accentuated. It should be noted that Newkirk (8) observed an exothermic heat effect for the reaction:

$$CaC_2O_4 \rightarrow CaCO_3 + CO$$

while Soulen and Mockrin (19) stated that it was an endothermic reaction. The discrepancy is that in an air atmosphere, which Newkirk presumably employed, carbon monoxide was oxidized to carbon dioxide by air, the oxidation reaction being highly exothermic.

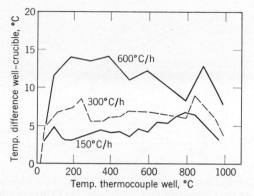

Fig. II.18. Effect of heating rate on crucible temperature (8).

The latter investigators used a nitrogen furnace atmosphere in which the oxidation reaction did not take place. This again emphasizes the importance of furnace atmosphere and its effect on the pyrolysis reactions. The decomposition of $CaC_2O_4 \cdot H_2O$ has also been studied by Wendlandt (27) using a DTA method.

By lowering the heating rate from 600 to 150°C/h, the temperature difference between the sample crucible and the furnace thermocouple decreased as was shown by Newkirk (8). The effect of heating rate on this temperature difference is illustrated in Figure II.18. The lag varied from 3 to 14° and was roughly proportional to the heating rate.

The usual precautions concerning the calibration of the thermocouple should be taken for best results in thermogravimetry. If known, corrections should always be applied to the measured temperatures, especially for reaction kinetics investigations.

4. OTHER ERRORS

A well-designed thermobalance should reduce several of the other errors to negligible values. The errors that are caused by random fluctuations of the recording mechanism, furnace induction effects, electrostatic effects, changes in thermobalance environment, and so on, can be eliminated by proper thermobalance design, construction, and location in the laboratory.

Newkirk (8) found that if the balance mechanism of the Chevenard thermobalance was not properly thermally shielded, the oil in the

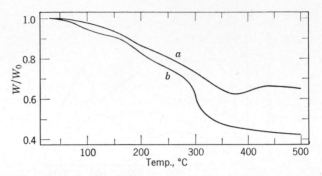

Fig. II.19. Thermal decomposition of tris(2,2'-bipyridine)chromium(III) cyanide in nitrogen on the Chevenard thermobalance. (a) Without sleeve around crucible support; W/W_0 is the fraction of original sample weight; (b) with sleeve around crucible support (19).

dash pots became warm, causing an apparent weight gain due to the decreased buoyancy of the oil. In the latest model of this balance, the oil dash pots have been replaced by a magnetic damping device (see Chap. III).

Condensation on the cool part of the sample holder support rod is another source of error. The condensate may re-evaporate as the temperature is increased and may again condense still lower on the support. This may lead to entirely false conclusions. Soulen and Mockrin (19) stated that this problem is intensified when a rapid inert flow is employed because the volatile materials are driven downward onto the support rod. The magnitude of this effect can be ascertained if the sample holder, sample, and the support assembly are weighed both before and after each run. If they differ appreciably in weight, a correction must be applied. This, of course, gives no information about the correction during the course of the run. Soulen and Mockrin (19) eliminated this problem in the Chevenard thermobalance by placing a ceramic or nickel sleeve around the crucible support. The thermal decomposition of tris(2,2'-bipyridine)chromium(III) cyanide in nitrogen was studied with and without the sleeve present. The results of the two runs are given in Figure II.19. Without the sleeve, a completely erroneous weight-loss curve was obtained for this particular compound. Of course, for compounds involving noncondensable gaseous products, this will present no problem.

Newkirk and Aliferis (28) have shown that the decomposition temperatures of sodium carbonate were lowered if the sample holder was made of silica or porcelain. The sodium carbonate reacted with the silica of the container forming sodium silicate and carbon dioxide. Little weight loss was observed when platinum or gold sample holders were used. Thus, in thermogravimetric analysis, a sample holder should be used that is inert as far as reactions with the sample, its decomposition products, or with the gaseous atmosphere present in the furnace.

Periodic calibration of the thermobalance will prevent errors on the weight axis of the recorder. Many investigators calibrate the instrument before each run by adding a known weight to the sample container.

D. Differential Thermogravimetric Analysis

In conventional thermogravimetry, the weight of a sample, w, is continuously recorded as a function of temperature, T, or time, t, or

$$w = f(T \text{ or } t) \tag{II.1}$$

Quantitative measurements of the weight changes are possible by determination of the distance, on the curve weight axis, between the two points of interest or between the two horizontal weight levels. In differential thermogravimetry, the differential of the weight change with respect to time, dw/dt, is recorded as a function of temperature or time, or

$$dw/dt = f(T \text{ or } t) \tag{II.2}$$

The curve obtained is the first derivative of the weight-change curve. A series of peaks are now obtained, instead of the stepwise curve, in which the areas under the peaks are proportional to the total weight change of the sample.

De Keyser (29,30) first suggested this technique in 1953, followed by Erdey et al. (31) and Waters (32). Further work in this area of thermogravimetry has been by Erdey (33,34), Paulik et al. (35), Waddams and Gray (36), Waters (37), Campbell et al. (38), and Erdey et al. (39).

A comparison between a conventional (a) and differential weight-loss curve (b) is given in Figure II.20. The differential curve may be

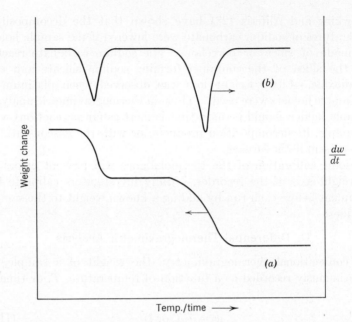

Fig. II.20. Comparison between a conventional (a) and differential weight-loss curves (b).

obtained either from the conventional curve by manual differentiation of the latter, automatic differentiation or by use of a differential recording thermobalance. The instrumentation for this technique is discussed in Chapter III. The differential weight-loss curves resemble differential thermal analysis curves and are generally used for complementary information purposes. For example, by comparison of the two curves, it is possible to distinguish between peaks that are due to loss in weight and those which are caused only by endothermic phase transitions or other reactions not involving a weight change.

The advantages of differential thermogravimetry have been summarized by Erdey et al. (31):

(1) The curves may be obtained in conjunction with TGA and DTA measurements.

(2) The curves for DTA and differential thermogravimetric analysis (DTG) are comparable, but the results of the former method indicate even those changes of state that are not accompanied by

loss in weight. The curves by the latter method are more reproducible.

(*3*) While the curves for DTA extend over a wider temperature interval, due to subsequent warming of the material after reaction, the DTG measurement indicate exactly the temperatures of the beginning, the maximum rate, and the end of the change.

(*4*) On the TGA curves, changes following each other very closely cannot be distinguished, as the corresponding stages coincide. The DTG curves of the same change indicate by sharp maxima that the thermogravimetric stages can be divided into two parts.

(*5*) The DTG curves are exactly proportional to the derivatives of the TGA curves; therefore, the area under the curves gives the change in weight precisely. Accordingly, DTG can give exact quantitative analyses.

(*6*) The DTG method can be used for the investigation of materials which for some reason or another cannot be analyzed by DTA. For example, some organic compounds melt during heating; but even so, the DTG method yields fairly good results.

E. Reaction Kinetics by Thermogravimetry

The use of thermogravimetry as a means for the elucidation of the reaction kinetics for solid- or liquid-state thermal decomposition reactions is quite attractive. The nature of *solid* → *solid* reactions is quite complex and will not be discussed in detail here (40). In general, the reactions proceed stepwise through a series of intermediate reactions that involve concomitant formation and decomposition of several solid (s) or liquid (l) phases. These *solid* → *solid* transformations have been summarized by Lukaszewski and Redfern (41):

(*1*) Reactions involving a decomposition such as:

$$A(\text{solid}) \rightarrow B(\text{solid}) + C(\text{gas})$$

(*2*) Reactions between two solid phases:

$$A(s) + B(s) \rightarrow AB(s) + C(g)$$

(*3*) Reactions confined exclusively to the solid phase:

$$A(s) + B(s) \rightarrow C(s) + D(s)$$

(4) Reactions involving participation of liquid phases at some stage:

$$A(s) \rightarrow B(s) + C(l)$$

(5) Reactions involving a solid and a gas, such as from a controlled atmosphere:

$$A(s) + B(g) \rightarrow C(s)$$

The above reactions can occur consecutively or simultaneously. Thermogravimetry is generally concerned with only a single substance so only reactions (1) and (5) are applicable. Other techniques, such as DTA, could be used for reactions (2), (3), and (4).

In general, two different methods are used in kinetics studies by thermogravimetry:

(1) The isothermal method, in which a plot of weight change vs. time is obtained, at constant temperature.

(2) The non-isothermal method, in which a plot of weight change *vs.* temperature (and/or time) is obtained, under dynamic temperature conditions at a linear rate of heating.

For both methods, the measurement of the exact *sample* temperature is of utmost importance. The previously discussed precautions of temperature measurement in thermogravimetry should be adhered to.

1. The Isothermal Method

For a reaction of type (1), the onset of the reaction involves the formation of a new phase B(s), at various points in the lattice structure of the initial compound, A(s). Decomposition will begin where local fluctuations provide favorable conditions for the formation of compound B(s). The product phase B(s) will spread out from the points (or nuclei) where the reaction initially began (41). The initiation of nuclei formation in the reactant is called the induction period of the reaction and may be induced by heating, scratching, grinding, and so on. The general form of the decomposition curve can be explained qualitatively in terms of nuclei formation and growth. The other parts of the "S" shaped or sigmoidal curve so obtained are: (a) main portion of curve where the fractional weight loss is proportional to time, and (b) the final decay period.

The rate equation introduced by Prout and Tompkins (42) is applicable to reactions of this type. It is given by

$$d\alpha/dt = k\alpha(1 - \alpha) \tag{II.3}$$

where k is the probability of nuclei chain branching and is assumed to be constant and α is the fraction decomposed at time t. From the Arrhenius equation

$$k = A \exp(-E^*/RT) \tag{II.4}$$

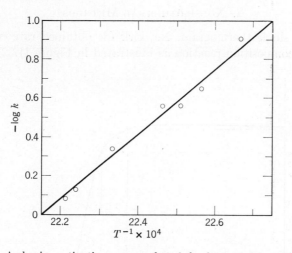

Fig. II.21. Arrhenius activation energy plot of the decomposition of [Fe(bipy)$_3$]-Br$_2$ (43).

where k is the rate constant, A is the frequency factor, and E^* the activation energy, the other pertinent quantities can be calculated.

Using the above method, Dhar and Basolo (43) studied the thermal decomposition of the metal 2,2′-bipyridine complexes [M(bipy)$_3$]Br$_2$, where M was Mn^{2+}, Fe^{2+}, Co^{2+}, Ni^{2+}, Cu^{2+}, and Zn^{2+}, under vacuum, using the Thermo-Grav thermobalance (see Chap. III). For the iron(II) complex, the dissociation reaction was

$$2[Fe(bipy)_3]Br_2(s) \rightarrow [Fe(bipy)_3][FeBr_4](s) + 3bipy\ (g)$$

for which the activation energy, E^*, was 75 kcal mole^{-1}. An Arrhenius plot for this reaction is given in Figure II.21.

In another isothermal study in which the Prout-Tompkins equation was not employed, Nathans and Wendlant (44) studied the thermal dissociation of lanthanum sulfate. For the reaction,

$$La_2(SO_4)_3 \rightarrow La_2O_2(SO_4) + 2SO_2 + O_2$$

an E^* value of 74 kcal mole^{-1} was found for the linear portion of the weight change vs. time curve. The reaction was zero order.

Other studies, too numerous to credit here, have also been carried out using this method.

2. NON-ISOTHERMAL METHODS

From a single thermogram, Newkirk (8) obtained rate constants for the decomposition reaction as illustrated in Figure II.22. For a

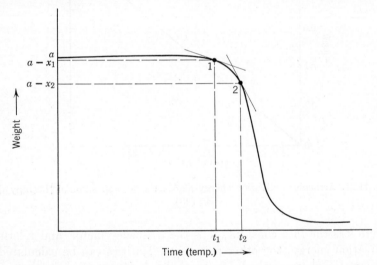

Fig. II.22. Determination of reaction rate and extent of reaction from a thermogram (8).

series of temperatures, T_1 and T_2, the sample weight remaining, $a - x_1$ and $a - x_2$, and the reaction rate, $(dx/dt)_1$ and $(dx/dt)_2$, were obtained by tangents to the curve at points 1 and 2. If the reaction is first order, then the logarithm of the reaction rate constant k, $dx/dt = k(a - x)$, when plotted against $1/T$, should yield a straight line. The results of measurements under isothermal and non-isothermal conditions yielded straight lines that were approximately parallel.

In a study concerning the kinetics of the ignition of black gun powder, Campbell and Weingarten (45) plotted the logarithm of the time-to-ignition (in seconds) vs. the reciprocal of the absolute temperature for various binary and ternary mixtures. Straight-line curves were obtained, the slopes of which enabled the activation energy of the reaction to be calculated.

An equation has been derived by Berlin and Robinson (46) which relates the decomposition temperature to the weight and surface area of the sample and from which the activation energy can be calculated if the heating rate of the sample is varied. The expression is based upon the following derivation.

In the case of a reaction in which there is an extremely rapid nucleation period followed by a rapid surface growth, the rate of decomposition is governed by the progression of the resulting interface towards the center of the crystal. The Polyani-Wigner equation thus applies to the decomposition

$$- \frac{d\mathfrak{N}}{dt} = S_2 \mathfrak{N} \nu e^{-E_2/RT} \tag{II.5}$$

where $\mathfrak{N}$ is the number of molecules at the interface, $-d\mathfrak{N}/dt$ is the number of molecules decomposing at the interface per unit of time, S_2 is the entropy factor, ν is the vibration frequency, T is the absolute temperature, and E_2 is the activation energy.

In the case of a reaction in which the loss in weight is measured, Jacobs and Tompkins (47) have derived the equation describing the rate of decomposition

$$\frac{d\alpha}{dt} = \frac{\Gamma M}{W_0 N} S_2 \nu \overline{\mathfrak{N}} A e^{-E_2/RT} \tag{II.6}$$

where α is the fraction of sample decomposed, and

$$\Gamma = \left(1 - \frac{\nu_B M_B}{\nu_A M_A} \right) - 1 \tag{II.7}$$

ν_A and ν_B are the moles of A reacting and moles of B produced, M_A and M_B are the molecular weights of reactant A and product B, M is the molecular weight of the compound undergoing decomposition,

W_0 is the initial weight of sample, N is Avogadro's number, and A is the area in cm^2 at the interface.

With investigations of the rate of decomposition of a substance by thermogravimetry, the temperature varies as a linear function of time so that

$$dt = \left(\frac{dt}{dT}\right)_c dT \qquad (II.8)$$

where $(dt/dT)_c$ is the reciprocal of the heating rate. The area between the reactants and products for a decomposition reaction involving the formation of two solid products varies with time and is a power function of the undecomposed fraction, or

$$A = A_0(1 - \alpha)^z \qquad (II.9)$$

where A_0 is the initial area of the interface.

Combining equations (II.6), (II.8), and (II.9) gives

$$\frac{d\alpha}{dT} = \frac{\Gamma M}{W_0 N} S_2 \nu \Re A_0 (1 - \alpha)^z \left(\frac{dt}{dT}\right)_c e^{-E_2/RT} \qquad (II.10)$$

By taking the logarithm of equation (II.10) and rearranging, an expression for the reciprocal of the absolute temperature is obtained:

$$\frac{1}{T} = \frac{-R}{E_2}\left[\ln\left(\frac{d\alpha}{dT}\right) - \ln(1 - \alpha)^z - \ln A_0\left(\frac{\Gamma M}{W_0 N} S_2 \nu \Re\right)\right] +$$

$$\frac{R}{E_2}\ln\left(\frac{dt}{dT}\right)_c \qquad (II.11)$$

If the quantity, T_2, is defined as the temperature at which the decomposition reaction is virtually completed, then $(1/T_2)$ plotted against $\ln(dt/dT)$ for a constant amount of sample and surface area should give a straight line with slope R/E_2 and intercept of

$$+ \frac{R}{E_2}\left[-\ln\left(\frac{d\alpha}{dT}\right) + \ln(1 - \alpha)^z + \ln A_0\left(\frac{\Gamma M}{W_0 N} \cdot S_2 W \Re\right)\right]$$

The initial weight of material and the initial area of the sample affect the position of the plot with respect to the $1/T_2$ axis. A constant rate of heating and an increase in the initial area of the sample give a slower final temperature, while an increase in the initial weight of sample gives a higher final temperature.

By varying A_0 and W_0 at a constant rate of heating, the contribution of

$$\frac{R}{E_2} \ln A_0 \left(\frac{\Gamma M}{W_0 N} S_2 W \mathfrak{N} \right)$$

to the apparent final decomposition temperature can be ascertained since both $d\alpha/dT$ and $(1 - \alpha)^z$ remain constant.

If one T_2 value and the activation energy for a certain reaction are known, the value for T_2 can be determined for any heating rate. If two values of T_2 at two different heating rates are known, the activation energy can be calculated.

Using this method, Berlin and Robinson (46) determined an activation energy of 44 kcal mole^{-1} for the thermal decomposition of calcium carbonate. This is compared to values from 31 to 95 kcal mole^{-1} previously reported in the literature. Other examples were also studied.

By far, the most widely used method for the determination of reaction kinetics of a thermal decomposition reaction is that developed by Freeman and Carroll (48). The advantage of this method is that considerably less experimental data are required than in the isothermal method, and that the kinetics can be obtained over an entire temperature range in a continuous manner without any missing regions. In addition, where a sample undergoes considerable reaction in being raised to the temperature of interest, the results obtained by an isothermal method are often questionable (48).

In the case of a decomposition reaction of type (1), the rate expression for the disappearance of reactant A from the mixture is

$$- \left(\frac{dx}{dt} \right) = kX^X \tag{II.12}$$

where X is the concentration, mole fraction, or amount of reactant A, k is the specific rate constant, and x is the order of reaction with respect to A. It is assumed that the specific rate constant can be expressed as

$$k = Ze^{-E*/RT} \tag{II.13}$$

Solving for k in equation (II.12) and substituting in equation (II.13) for k gives

$$Ze^{-E^*/RT} = -\frac{(dX/dt)}{X^X} \qquad \text{(II.14)}$$

where Z is the frequency factor, E^* the activation energy, R is the gas constant, and T the absolute temperature. The logarithmic form of equation (II.14) is differentiated with respect to dX/dt, X, and T, resulting in

$$\frac{E^*dT}{RT^2} = d\ln(-dX/dt) - xd\ln X \qquad \text{(II.15)}$$

Integrating the above gives

$$-\frac{E^*}{R}\left[\Delta\left(\frac{1}{T}\right)\right] = \Delta\ln\left(-\frac{dx}{dt}\right) - X\Delta\ln X \qquad \text{(II.16)}$$

Dividing equations (II.15) and (II.16) by $d\ln X$ and $\Delta\ln X$, respectively, gives

$$\frac{E^*dT}{RT^2 d\ln X} = \frac{d\ln(-dX/dt)}{d\ln X} - x \qquad \text{(II.17)}$$

and

$$\frac{-\dfrac{E^*}{R}\Delta\left(\dfrac{1}{T}\right)}{\Delta\ln X} = \frac{\Delta\ln(-dX/dt)}{\Delta\ln X} - x \qquad \text{(II.18)}$$

From the above, if plots of

$$\frac{dT}{T^2\log X} \quad vs. \quad \frac{d\log(-dX/dt)}{d\log X}$$

and

$$\frac{\Delta(1/T)}{\Delta\log X} \quad vs. \quad \frac{\Delta\log(-dX/dt)}{\Delta\log X}$$

are made, straight lines with slopes of $+$ or $-E^*/2.3R$ and intercepts of x should be obtained.

In actual practice, however, if the relationship between moles of reactant to weight is used

$$-\frac{dn_a}{dt} - \frac{n_0 dw}{w_c dt}$$ (II.19)

where n_0 is the initial number of moles of A, w_c is the weight loss at the completion of the reaction, w is the total loss in weight up to time, t, and n_a is the number of moles of A at time, t, and

$$W_r = w_c - w$$ (II.20)

Combining equations (II.19) and (II.20) with (II.18)

$$-\frac{(E^*/R)\,\Delta\,(1/T)}{\Delta \ln n_a} = -x + \frac{\Delta \ln (-dn_a/dt)}{\Delta \ln n_a}$$ (II.21)

the equation for calculation of the actual reaction kinetics is obtained, or

$$-\frac{\dfrac{E^*}{2.3R}\,\Delta\left(\dfrac{1}{T}\right)}{\Delta \log W_r} = -x + \frac{\Delta \log dw/dt}{\Delta \log W_r}$$ (II.22)

It should be noted that this treatment may be applied to the measurement of any physical property which is unaffected by sample temperature.

A number of decomposition reactions have been studied by this method. Included in this list are the compounds: $CaC_2O_4 \cdot H_2O$ (48); 8-quinolinol chelates of uranium and thorium (49); kaolinite (50); lanthanum, uranium, and thorium oxalates (51); $[Cr(H_2O)_6]$-sulfate, arsenate, and phosphate (52,53); divalent metal chelates (54); $[Cr(en)_3]X_3$ complexes (55); and the $[Co(NH_3)_4(H_2O)_2]X_3$ complexes (56). Markowitz and Boryta (57) found that this method could not be used to study reactions in which the sample temperature deviated considerably from that of the furnace. Such was the case with highly exothermic reactions such as the reactions of powdered metals with air, oxygen, or nitrogen.

The kinetics of volatilization of a substance in thermogravimetry has been discussed by Doyle (58). Using the thermogram illustrated in Figure II.23, where w is the apparent residual weight fraction

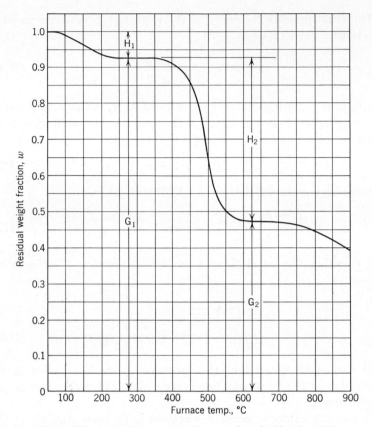

Fig. II.23. Illustrative thermogram for sample volatilization (58).

calculated on initial weight, the apparent weight fraction volatilized is

$$v = (1 - w) \qquad (\text{II.23})$$

The apparent volatilization rate is found by multiplying the thermogram slope, $-dw/dT$, by the constant heating rate, B:

$$dv/dt = -B(dw/dT) \qquad (\text{II.24})$$

For a particular volatilization step, however, the appropriate residual weight fraction is the true one, h, calculated on the total fraction volatilized during the step, rather than on the total initial weight. From Figure II.23 then

$$h = (w - G)/H \qquad (II.25)$$

where H is the total apparent weight fraction volatilized during the step and G is the apparent weight fraction remaining after the step has been completed. From equations (II.23) and (II.25),

$$dv/dt = -H(dh/dt) \qquad (II.26)$$

It should be noted that H and G are seldom as clearly defined as they are in Figure II.23; their estimation, in many cases, constitutes one of the major difficulties of kinetics calculations.

Another difficulty arises from the need to take into account the nature of the kinetic process. In general,

$$-dh/dt = rf(h) \qquad (II.27)$$

where r is the empirical rate constant for volatilization and where the specific form of $f(h)$ depends on the reaction order. The constant r must be treated as empirical because its value for a particular substance is not always uniquely determined by temperature, but may depend on the nature and geometry of the sample holder, the nature of the environmental atmosphere, etc. The potential triviality of r was constantly emphasized by Doyle (58) by use of the symbol r instead of the specific rate constant, k. Using this terminology, the Arrhenius equation for the volatilization process is

$$r = ae^{-b/RT} \qquad (II.28)$$

The constant b, at least over part of the experimental temperature range had the same value as the activation energy.

When evaluating the constants in equation (II.24), usually only a small portion of the thermogram is used, the region where the slope is neither too shallow nor too steep to be measured with sufficient precision. In fact, in the range of volatilization rates that are small compared to the heating rate, the slopes found from the thermogram are not only imprecise but also inherently inaccurate, being consistently greater than those found by an isothermal method. This effect is due to the fact that, in thermogravimetry, the dwell time at each temperature is so brief that no evidence of volatilization can accumulate in the range of small volatilization rates.

Doyle (58) used the above method for studies on the volatilization of octamethylcyclotetrasiloxane and polytetrafluoroethylene.

Soulen (59) has developed an electronic digital computer program for the calculation of reaction kinetics by the Freeman and Carroll (48) method. The program involves computation of temperature, weight, and rate of reaction from the values of dc millivolt signals originating from the thermobalance. Results of this method applied to an actual chemical reaction were not presented however.

F. Fractional Thermogravimetric Analysis

This new technique, introduced by Waters (60) in 1960, extended the scope of thermogravimetric analysis by providing information on the composition and properties of the evolved materials. The principle of fractional thermogravimetric analysis (FTA) is that one or more of the volatile components given off by the sample is selectively condensed or absorbed and simultaneously weighed with the sample by the thermobalance. The loss in weight recorded is consequently due to uncondensed or unabsorbed volatile components, which may consist of moisture, gas, or combinations of the two. The amounts of the individual components are determined from a set of curves recorded under different conditions of fractionation but exactly the same sample pyrolysis conditions.

The apparatus used for FTA is illustrated schematically in Figure II.24. The borosilicate glass bulb, a, containing the sample is heated by the furnace, b, and is connected by a finely drawn capillary tube to the small absorption tube, c. The entire glass system is suspended by the wire, e, from the beam of the thermobalance. The absorption tube contains appropriate solid reagents or absorbents in a finely divided state, and its temperature is controlled by a cooling block or a small subsidiary furnace, d.

The technique is illustrated by the FTA of sodium bicarbonate (60). This substance decomposes between 100 and 225°C with the evolution of water and carbon dioxide, or

$$2NaHCO_3(s) \rightarrow Na_2CO_3(s) + H_2O(g) + CO_2(g)$$

The FTA curves of this reaction are given in Figure II.25. Curve a measured the combined loss of water and carbon dioxide which totaled 36.6% by weight (theoretical value 36.9%), while with curve b, the water vapor was absorbed by the desiccants, silica gel, and

Anhydrone, placed in the absorption tube. The weight loss due to carbon dioxide only was found to be 25.4% (theoretical value 26.2%). In curve c, both water and carbon dioxide were absorbed giving a

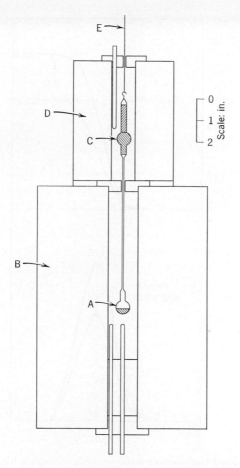

Fig. II.24. Apparatus for fractional thermogravimetric analysis (60).

total loss in sample weight of only 0.1%, which confirms the high efficiency of the absorption process.

The evolution of permanent gases could be measured either gravimetrically (above) or volumetrically. For the latter measurements, the top of the sample tube was not suspended from a thermobalance.

but was connected to a soap film gas flowmeter of 5 ml capacity. Thus, the rate of evolution of gas by volume could be obtained, generally in parallel with the gravimetric determination.

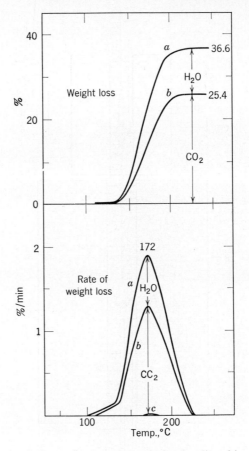

Fig. II.25. Fractional thermogravimetric analysis of sodium bicarbonate; heating rate of 3°C/min (60).

Application of the above technique to the analysis of coking coal was explored by Waters (60). This method enabled the determination of water, carbon dioxide, total volatiles, hydrogen, etc.

The limitations and sources of error of the method have also been discussed by Waters (60). Among these are:

(1) Absorption and retention of other gases by the silica gel.

(2) Effect of capillary construction on the flow of volatile matter.

(3) Deposition of a thin film of carbonaceous matter in the capillary.

The accuracy of the method was evaluated by studying the decomposition of known compounds, among them were: naphthalene, % carbon and hydrogen found, respectively, 93.0 ± 0.05 and 6.21, calculated % values were 93.7 and 6.29, respectively; calcium acetate, % volatile matter found, 35.65 ± 0.25, calculated %, 36.6.

Except for the difficulties encountered in construction of the sample and absorption tubes, the method appears to be quite useful.

G. Miscellaneous

1. PROCEDURAL DECOMPOSITION TEMPERATURES

Since the usual decomposition temperatures obtained from a thermogram are highly dependent on the experimental procedure employed, Doyle (61) has used the expression "procedural decomposition temperature" as a precaution against absently regarding such trivial data as definitive.

Two types of procedural decomposition temperatures were defined by Doyle (61). The first of these was called the "differential procedural decomposition temperature" (dpdt), which was used to define the location of "knees" in normalized thermogravimetric curves. The second type was called "integral procedural decomposition temperature" (ipdt) and was a means of summing up the entire shape of the normalized weight-loss curve.

The ipdt values are determined from a weight-loss curve as follows: The curve, as shown in Figure II.26, is divided into small squares. The area under the curve is integrated by weighing a paper cutout of the curve on an analytical balance. The weight of crosshatched region in Figure II.26 divided by the weight of the total rectangular plotting area is the total curve area, A^*, normalized with respect to both residual weight and temperature. The quantity A^* is converted to a temperature T_A^*, by

$$T_A^* = 875A^* + 25 \tag{II.28}$$

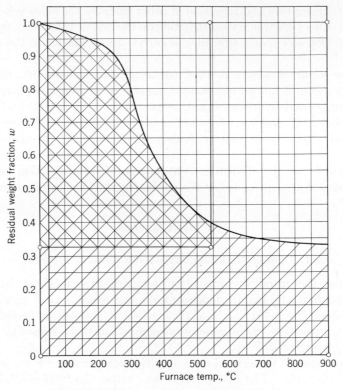

Fig. II.26. Thermogram areas, A^* and K^* (61).

In T_A^*, it is presumed that all materials volatilize below 900°C and do so at a single temperature. Thus, T_A^* represents a characteristic end-of-volatilization temperature, rather than an ipdt having practical significance. However, it does serve as a measure of refractoriness, but is not very satisfactory.

To put all materials on an equal basis with respect to experimental temperature range, as in A^*, but also with respect to their individual refractory contents, a second curve area, K^*, was defined, as illustrated by the doubly crosshatched region given in Figure II.26. In value, the lesser area, K^*, is the ratio between the doubly crosshatched area and the rectangular area bounded by the characteristic end-of-volatilization temperature, T_A^*, and the residual weight fraction at the fixed end-of-test temperature of 900°C.

Doyle (61) showed that the product A^*K^* represented a comprehensive index of intrinsic thermal stability for 54 polymers of widely different basic types. It was also shown that by substituting A^*K^* for A^* in equation (II.28) the ipdt obtained had a practical meaning as a half-volatilization temperature. Unlike ordinary half-volatilization temperatures, defined as the temperature at which half the ultimate volatilization has occurred, the ipdt based on the residual weight fraction of 900°C was appropriate whether decomposition occurred in a single step or in several consecutive steps.

As a quantity derived from curve areas, the ipdt was highly reproducible and its value was only slightly affected by small vagaries or systematic errors in the data curve, especially as contrasted with indices derived on the basis of residual weight fraction end points alone. Even small variations in heating rate do not affect it appreciably. The ipdt of several polymeric materials are given in Table II.1.

TABLE II.1

Integral Procedural Decomposition Temperatures of Some Familiar Polymers (61)

Polymer	ipdt, °C
Polystyrene	395
Maleic-hardened epoxy	405
Plexiglass	345
66 Nylon	419
Teflon	555
Kel-F	410
Viton	460
Silicone resin	505

References

1. Duval, C., *Inorganic Thermogravimetric Analysis*, 2nd ed., Elsevier, Amsterdam, 1963.
2. Duval, C., *Inorganic Thermogravimetric Analysis*, 1st ed., Elsevier, Amsterdam, 1953.
3. Duval, C., *Anal. Chem.*, **23**, 1271 (1951).
4. Lukaszewski, G. M., and J. P. Redfern, *Lab. Pract.*, **10**, 469 (1961).
5. Jacque, L., G. Guiochon, and P. Gendrel, *Bull Soc. Chim. France*, **1961**, 1061.
6. Honda, K., *Sci. Rept. Tohoku Univ.*, **4**, 97 (1915).
7. Peltier, S., and C. Duval, *Anal. Chim. Acta*, **1**, 346 (1947).
8. Newkirk, A. E., *Anal. Chem.*, **32**, 1558 (1960).

9. Rynasiewicz, J., and J. F. Flagg, *Anal. Chem.*, **26**, 1506 (1954).
10. Fruchart, R., and A. Michel, *Compt. Rend.*, **246**, 1222 (1958).
11. Demassieux, N., and C. Malard, *Compt. Rend.*, **245**, 1514 (1957).
12. DeClerq, M., and C. Duval, *Anal. Chim. Acta*, **5**, 282 (1951).
13. Saito, H., *Sci. Rept. Tohoku Univ.*, **16**, 1 (1927).
14. Richer, A., and P. Vallet, *Bull. Soc. Chim. France*, **1953**, 148.
15. Garn, P. D., and J. E. Kessler, *Anal. Chem.*, **32**, 1900 (1960).
16. Garn, P. D., and J. E. Kessler, *Anal. Chem.*, **32**, 1563 (1960).
17. Garn, P. D., *Anal. Chem.*, **33**, 1247 (1961).
18. Rabatin, J. G., and C. S. Card, *Anal. Chem.*, **31**, 1689 (1959).
19. Soulen, J. R., and I. Mockrin, *Anal. Chem.*, **33**, 1909 (1961).
20. Lukaszewski, G. M., *Nature*, **194**, 959 (1962).
21. Vallet, P., *Compt. Rend.*, **198**, 1860 (1934).
22. Guiochon, G., *Anal. Chem.*, **33**, 1124 (1961).
23. Kissinger, H. E., H. F. McMurdie, and B. S. Simpson, *J. Am. Ceram. Soc.*, **39**, 168 (1956).
24. Martinez, E., *Am. Mineralogist*, **46**, 901 (1961).
25. Simons, E. L., A. E. Newkirk, and I. Aliferis, *Anal. Chem.*, **29**, 48 (1957).
26. Mielenz, R. C., N. C. Schieltz, and M. E. King, *Clays and Clay Minerals*, National Academy of Sciences–National Research Council, Washington, D. C., Publ. **327**, 1954, pp. 289–296.
27. Wendlandt, W. W., *J. Chem. Educ.*, **38**, 571 (1961).
28. Newkirk, A. E., and I. Aliferis, *Anal. Chem.*, **30**, 982 (1958).
29. De Keyser, W. L., *Nature*, **172**, 364 (1953).
30. De Keyser, W. L., *Bull. Soc. France Ceram.*, **20**, 1 (1953).
31. Erdey, L., F. Paulik, and J. Paulik, *Nature*, **174**, 885 (1954).
32. Waters, P. L., *Nature*, **178**, 324 (1956).
33. Erdey, L., *Periodica Polytech.*, **1**, 35, 91 (1957).
34. Erdey, L., *Chem. Zvesti*, **12**, 352 (1958).
35. Paulik, F., J. Paulik, and L. Erdey, *Z. Anal. Chem.*, **160**, 241, 321 (1958).
36. Waddams, J. A., and P. S. Gray, *Nature*, **183**, 1729 (1958).
37. Waters, P. L., *J. Sci. Instr.*, **35**, 41 (1958).
38. Campbell, C., S. Gordon, and C. L. Smith, *Anal. Chem.*, **31**, 1188 (1959).
39. Erdey, L., B. Liptay, G. Svehla, and F. Paulik, *Talanta*, **9**, 489 (1962).
40. Garner, W. E., *The Chemistry of the Solid State*, Butterworths, London, 1955.
41. Lukaszewski, G. M., and J. P. Redfern, *Lab. Pract.*, **10**, 721 (1961).
42. Prout, E. G., and F. C. Tompkins, *Trans. Faraday Soc.*, **40**, 488 (1944).
43. Dhar, S. K., and F. Basolo, *J. Inorg. Nucl. Chem.*, **25**, 37 (1963).
44. Nathans, M. W., and W. W. Wendlandt, *J. Inorg. Nucl. Chem.*, **24**, 869 (1962).
45. Campbell, C., and G. Weingarten, *Trans. Faraday Soc.*, **55**, 2221 (1959).
46. Berlin, A., and R. J. Robinson, *Anal. Chim. Acta*, **27**, 50 (1962).
47. Jacobs, P. W. M., and F. C. Tompkins, in *The Chemistry of the Solid State*, W. E. Garner, ed., Butterworths, London, 1955, pp. 198–212.
48. Freeman, E. S., and B. Carroll, *J. Phys. Chem.*, **62**, 394 (1958).
49. Van Tassel, J. H., and W. W. Wendlandt, *J. Am. Chem. Soc.*, **81**, 813 (1959).
50. Jacobs, T., *Nature*, **182**, 1086 (1958).

51. Padmanabhan, V. M., S. C. Saraiya, and A. K. Sundaram, *J. Inorg. Nucl. Chem.*, **12**, 356 (1960).
52. Lukaszewski, G. M., and J. P. Redfern, *Nature*, **190**, 805 (1961).
53. Lukaszewski, G. M., and J. P. Redfern, *J. Chem. Soc.*, **1962**, 4802.
54. Lumme, P., *Suomen Kemistilchti*, **32B**, 198, 237, 241, 253, 261 (1959).
55. Bear, J. L., and W. W. Wendlandt, *J. Inorg. Nucl. Chem.*, **17**, 286 (1961).
56. Wendlandt, W. W., W. R. Robinson, and W. Y. Yang, *J. Inorg. Nucl. Chem.*, **25**, 1495 (1963).
57. Markowitz, M. M., and D. A. Boryta, *Anal. Chem.*, **33**, 949 (1961).
58. Doyle, C. D., *J. Appl. Polymer Sci.*, **5**, 285 (1961).
59. Soulen, J. R., *Anal. Chem.*, **34**, 136 (1962).
60. Waters, P. L., *Anal. Chem.*, **32**, 852 (1960).
61. Doyle, C. D., *Anal. Chem.*, **33**, 77 (1961).

CHAPTER III

AUTOMATIC RECORDING BALANCES AND THERMOBALANCES

A. Introduction

The principles of thermogravimetric analysis (TGA) require that the sample be continuously weighed as a function of temperature. To do this, a thermobalance is employed, whether it be a manually operated or an automatic recording instrument. For practical reasons, the latter type of instrument is preferred in that not only does it involve a saving of time on behalf of the operator, but that it can be made inherently more accurate.

A thermobalance is basically an instrument used to continuously weigh a sample as a function of temperature or time. A modern instrument consists generally of the following components: (a) recording balance, (b) furnace, (c) furnace temperature programmer or controller, and (d) recorder, either of the strip-chart or X-Y function types. The specific details of each component depend on the particular application that is required of the instrument. For example, furnaces can be obtained that operate up to 2500°C or more, and employ atmospheres of air, inert gases, hydrogen, nitrogen, vacuum, etc. Likewise for the recording balance, sensitivities as low as 0.02 mg full scale deflection to 100 g. or more are available.

Some factors that must be considered in the construction or purchase of an automatic thermobalance have been given by Lukaszewski and Redfern (1). They are:

(1) The instrument should be capable of recording the weight loss or gain of the sample as a function of temperature and time.

(2) The thermobalance furnace should have a wide range of operation, such as from ambient temperature to 1500°C.

(3) The weight loss of the sample should be recorded to an accuracy of better than ±0.01%, while the temperature should be recorded to an accuracy of ±1%.

(4) The physical effects due to the normal functioning of the instrument should not affect the accuracy of the balance, e.g., radia-

tion and convection currents, and the magnetic effects due to the furnace heaters. Also, that the latter effect does not interact with any conducting or magnetic materials that may be studied.

(5) The position of the crucible within the furnace of the thermobalance should always be the same, so that the temperature recorded corresponds to the sample temperature.

(6) The furnace should be equipped to allow for the heating of samples in various atmospheres.

(7) The instrument should be as versatile as possible providing for easy change in heating rates together with automatic control of temperature programming.

(8) The balance should be adequately protected from the furnace and care should also be taken to keep the wear of the knife edges and other moving parts to a minimum to assure accuracy of weighing.

(9) The balance should be capable of simple, periodic calibration to insure accuracy of operation.

(10) The chart used to record weight loss and temperature rise should be capable of various speeds and that there is provision for accurate recording of a suitable time interval.

Obviously, each of these requirements cannot be met in every thermobalance. However, a number of commercially available instruments do incorporate these features.

Perhaps the most important component of the thermobalance is the recording balance. The requirements of a suitable recording balance are essentially those for a good quality analytical balance, namely, accuracy, reproducibility, sensitivity, capacity, rugged construction, and insensitivity to ambient temperature changes. In addition (2), the balance should have an adjustable range of weight change, a high degree of electronic and mechanical stability, be able to respond rapidly to changes in weight, be relatively unaffected by vibration, and be of sufficiently simple construction to minimize the initial cost and need for maintenance. From a practical viewpoint, the balance should be simple to operate and versatile in that it can be used for varied applications.

A number of excellent reviews have been written describing the various commercial and noncommercial recording balances, especially those by Gordon and Campbell (2), Duval (3), Lewin (4), Jacque et al. (5), and a book by Duval (6). Because of the vast number of recording balances and thermobalances of similar design that have

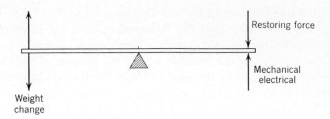

Fig. III.1. Null-type balance (2).

been described in the literature, only representative types of these instruments will be discussed here. It should be noted that in the review by Gordon and Campbell (2) in 1960, some 165 references to the literature were cited, indicating a large number of instruments.

Recording balances can be divided basically into two general classifications, based on their mode of operation. They are (a) deflection-type instruments, and (b) null-type instruments (2).

The automatic null-type instrument is based upon the principle given in Figure III.1. The balance incorporates a sensing element which detects a deviation of the balance beam from its null position; horizontal for beam balances and vertical for electromagnetic suspension types. A restoring force, of either electrical or mechanical weight loading, is then applied to the beam through the appropriate electronic or mechanical linkages, restoring it to the null position. This restoring force, proportional to the change in weight, is recorded directly or through an electromechanical transducer of some type.

The various deflection type balances are shown in Figure III.2. These instruments involve the conversion of the balance beam deflections about the fulcrum into the appropriate weight change curves by (a) photographically recording, (b) recorded electrical signals generated by an appropriate displacement measurement transducer, and (c) an electromechanical device. The type of deflection balances are

(a) The helical spring in which changes of weight are detected by contraction or elongation of the spring and which may be recorded by suitable transducers.

(b) The cantilevered beam, constructed so that one end of it is fixed and the other end, from which the sample is suspended, is free to undergo deflection.

(c) The suspension of a sample by an appropriately mounted strain gage that stretches and contracts in proportion to weight changes.

(d) The attachment of a beam to a taut wire which serves as the fulcrum and is rigidly fixed at one or both ends so that deflections are proportional to the changes in weight and the torsional characteristics of the wire.

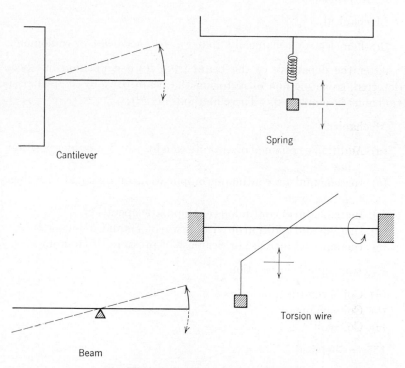

Fig. III.2. Deflection-type balances (2).

Gordon and Campbell (2) have summarized the various methods that have been employed to detect the deviation of a balance beam from its horizontal or vertical position in the null-point balances. They are:
Optical

(a) Light source–mirror–photographic paper
(b) Light source–shutter–photocell

Electronic

(*a*) Capacitance bridge
(*b*) Mutual inductance: coil–plate, coil–coil
(*c*) Differential transformer or variable permeance transducer
(*d*) Radiation detector (Geiger tube)
(*e*) Strain gage

Mechanical

(*a*) Pen electromechanically linked to balance beam or coulometer

After the departure of the beam from its rest position has been
detected, some method of restoring the beam back to the rest position must be employed.   These methods are (2):

Mechanical

(*a*) Addition or removal of discrete weights; or beam rider position-
       ing
(*b*) Incremental or continuous application of torsional or helical
       spring force
(*c*) Incremental or continuous chainomatic operation
(*d*) Incremental addition or withdrawal of a liquid (buoyancy)
(*e*) Incremental increase or decrease of pressure (hydraulic)

Electromagnetic interaction

(*a*) Coil–armature
(*b*) Coil–magnet
(*c*) Coil–coil

Electrochemical

(*a*) Coulometric dissolution or deposition of metal at electrode
       suspended from balance beam or coulometer

The manner in which the weight changes of the balance are recorded are summarized below (2):

Mechanical

(*a*) Pen linked to potentiometer slider
(*b*) Pen linked to chain-restoring drum
(*c*) Pen or electric arcing-point on end of beam

(*d*) Pen(s) linked to servo-driven photoelectric beam-deflection follower

Photographic

(*a*) Light source–mirror–photographic paper using either a drum, time base, or flat bed; temperature base–mirror galvanometer

Electronic

(*a*) Current generated in a transducing circuit such as photocell, differential transformer, strain gage, bridge, radiation detector, capacitor, or inductor
(*b*) Current passing through the coil of an electromagnet

In general, electronic recording is more versatile and convenient than a mechanically linked system because of the many transducers that can be used to obtain the electrical signal proportional to the change in weight as determined by either the deflection or null-type balance. The continuously recorded analog data from the primary curve can be simultaneously translated into other useful forms such as derivatives, integrals, logarithms, or any desired function, many of which lend themselves to the digital operations associated with automatic computation and automatic processes (2).

B. Commercial Instruments

1. Fisher Recording Balance Accessory

A schematic illustration of the Fisher Recording Balance Accessory (Fisher Scientific Co., 711 Forbes Avenue, Pittsburgh, Pennsylvania) is given in Figure III.3. The accessory can be installed on practically any beam-type analytical balance. It consists of a null-type instrument in which any deflection of the balance beam moves the core in the linear variable differential transformer thus producing an ac signal directly proportional to the deflection. The relative phase of the ac signal depends on the direction in which the core moves, and hence shows whether the sample is gaining or losing weight. The ac signal from the linear variable differential transformer is amplified, rectified, and used to apply a dc voltage across the restoring coil, producing a magnetic field which, in turn, acts on the suspended

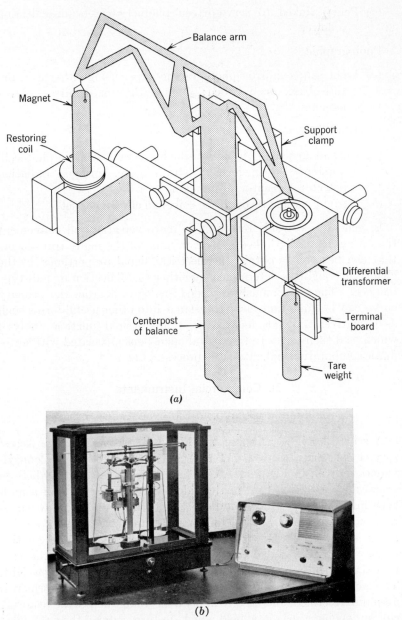

(a)

(b)

Fig. III.3. Fisher Recording Balance Accessory.

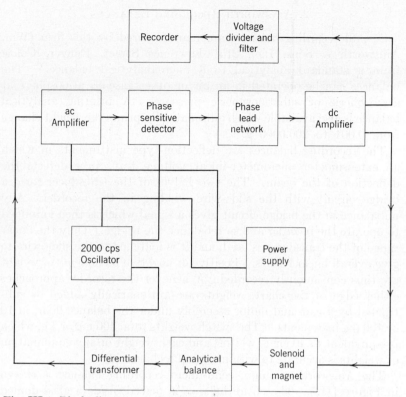

Fig. III.4. Block diagram of electronic circuitry for Fisher Recording Balance Accessory.

permanent magnet. A block diagram of the electronic circuitry is given in Figure III.4. Any deflection of the balance beam thus produces an opposing force that restores the original rest point of the balance. The current necessary to restore the balance beam to the null position is directly proportional to the gain or loss in weight. Part of this voltage producing the balancing current is applied to a millivolt recorder. If there are no disturbing magnetic fields present, the pen response is linear to better than ±1% of full scale, over the entire weight range. The capacity of the accessory is 200 mg to 5 g full scale on the high range, and 10–200 mg full scale on the low range. This range can be altered slightly by choice of a more or less sensitive recorder

2. Ainsworth Recording Balances

Several recording balances are manufactured by this firm (Wm. Ainsworth & Sons, Inc., 2151 Lawrence Street, Denver, Colo.) from a standard analytical to a microanalytical balance. The balances can be operated in an air or other gaseous atmosphere at atmospheric or subatmospheric pressures. A printing analytical balance is also available which automatically prints the weight change from 0.001 to 200.0000 g.

The recording balances are deflection-type instruments in which an extensometer micrometer-linear voltage transducer detects the deflection of the beam. The two halves of the transducer form a bridge circuit with the slide-wire winding in the recorder. Any unbalance in the bridge circuit gives a signal which is then amplified to operate the recorder and so rebalance the bridge. Only the linear range of the transducer is used, and it is matched to the slide wire to give overall linear results. Positive or negative increments of weight are thus continuously recorded. Whenever the recorder approaches either edge of the chart, weights are automatically added or subtracted by a cam and motor assembly under the balance floor, in 10 or 100 mg increments. The switch weights total 400 mg or 4 g, which is equivalent to 40 chart widths, and each weight or any combination of weights is accurate to within $^1/_{1000}$ of a chart width.

The Ainsworth vacuum, semi-micro recording balance is shown in Figure III.5. The entire balance is placed inside a glass-domed enclosure with ports in the bottom of the balance table for vacuum line or other connections. A two-pen recorder is available in which one pen records the weight change of the sample, the other pen the sample or furnace temperature; both are recorded as a function of time.

Waterbury et al. (7) have described the construction of a thermobalance, using the Ainsworth recording balance, which is enclosed in a glove box. The furnace employed was a Kanthal resistance element type capable of operation up to a maximum temperature of 1250°C. The furnace assembly was enclosed in a large stainless-steel glove box, while the balance was in a second glove box attached to the top of the furnace box.

Garn et al. (8) have also described a furnace mounting and control system for an Ainsworth vacuum recording balance.

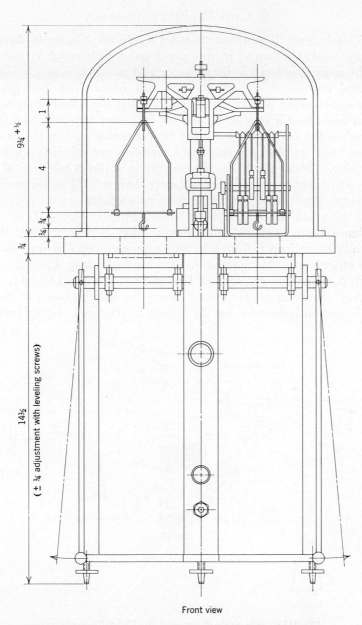

Front view

Fig. III.5. Ainsworth vacuum, semi-micro recording balance.

3. CAHN RG ELECTROBALANCE

This balance (Cahn Instrument Co., 15505 Minnesota Avenue, Paramount, California) is also a null-point instrument in which a light source photocell is the detector and an electromagnetic D'Arsonval movement supplies the restoring force. The loop gain of the servo system is in excess of 1000, so that the actual beam deflection under load is very small, and the balancing torque is essentially equal to the sample torque. The torque motor used in the balance is as linear as precise weights and precision potentiometers can determine. Thus, the balancing current is a direct measure of the sample weight to an accuracy of better than $\pm 0.1\%$ and a precision of better than $\pm 0.01\%$ of full scale sample weight.

A schematic diagram of the balance is given in Figure III.6. The balance beam contains three loops: loop A has a range from 0 to 200 mg; loop B from 5 to 1000 mg; and loop C is used to tare the other loops. Maximum capacities are 1 g for loop A and 2.5 g for loop B. The time constant for the balance is from 0.01 to 0.6 s.

Any change in sample weight causes the balance beam to move. This motion is detected by the change in photocell voltage because

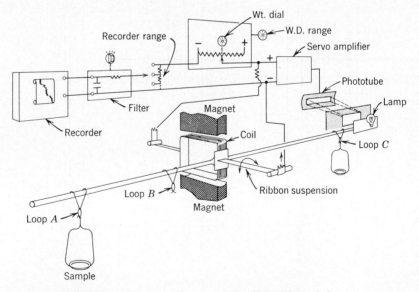

Fig. III.6. Schematic diagram of the Cahn Electrobalance.

of the movement of the shutter attached to the beam and which interrupts a light source.   The photocell voltage is amplified and then applied to the coil attached to the beam.   The coil is in a magnetic field, and current passing through it exerts a movement on the beam, instantaneously restoring it to a null position.   The coil current is thus a measure of sample weight.

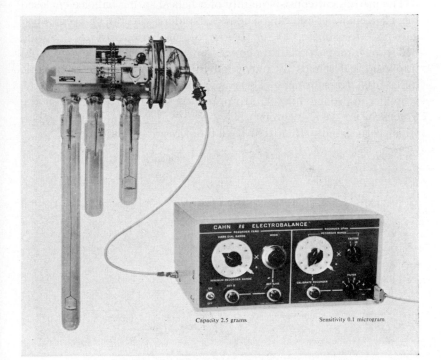

Fig. III.7.   Glass enclosure for Cahn RG Electrobalance.

The glass enclosure for the balance is shown in Figure III.7. Pressures as low as 10^{-8} Torr have been reported.   It is claimed that a vacuum atmosphere improves the balance performance somewhat.

Conversion of the Cahn Electrobalance to a thermobalance has been made by the Technical Equipment Corporation, Denver, Colorado, and is used in conjunction with the Deltatherm differential thermal analysis apparatus.

4. Thermo-Grav

This balance is of the deflection type in which the extension of a helical spring is measured by a linear variable differential transformer (American Instrument Co., 8030 Georgia Avenue, Silver Spring, Maryland). A schematic illustration of the balance is given in Figure III.8.

The instrument consists mainly of a helical spring balance enclosed in a glass chamber and can be operated under a vacuum or a controlled gaseous atmosphere, at or below atmospheric pressure. Spring deflections, proportional to changes in sample weight, are converted into electrical signals by movement of the core in a linear variable differential transformer. These signals, after passing through the amplifier and demodulator, are presented as weight changes on the Y-axis of an X–Y recorder. The X-axis records an input signal, which corresponds either to furnace temperature or elapsed time.

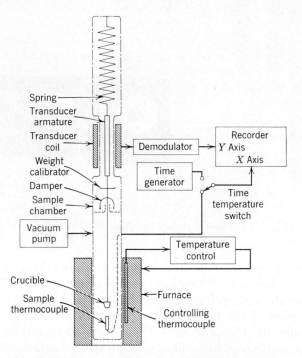

Fig. III.8. Schematic illustration of the Thermo-Grav.

The suspension system carries a weight calibrator pan, an oil-dashpot damper, and at the bottom, fused quartz rings to hold the sample and tare crucibles. Two furnaces are contained in the cabinet to allow consecutive runs to be made. Changes from 0 to 200 mg in weight can be measured with an accuracy of ±1% of full scale with sample weights up to 10 g. Furnace heating rates of 5–1000°C/h are provided while X-axis spans are adjustable for temperature increments of 200, 500, and 1000°C.

5. MAUER RECORDING BALANCE

This is a null-type balance which contains a light source–mirror–photocell detector and a electromagnetic coil acting upon a permanent magnet as the force restorer (Niagara Electron Laboratories, Andover, New York).

The balance consists of a conventional two-pan analytical balance. By means of an attached light source, photocell bridge, and beam mounted mirror, a signal is obtained which is related to the beam position, and to the rate of change of this position. This signal is amplified and impressed upon the coil of a solenoid that is mounted in a fixed position under the right-hand pan hanger. The solenoid coil magnetic field interacts with a permanent magnet that is suspended from the balance beam into the solenoid. The force on the suspended magnet is equal to the weight change of the sample, plus or minus a small error signal. This error signal amounts to a very slight off-balance residual required to operate the amplifier, and is less than the equivalent weight of $1/20$ of a mg. The range of the instrument for a full scale recorder deflection is 0–50, 100, 500, or 1000 mg with a readable accuracy of about ±0.15% of full scale.

6. HARROP THERMOBALANCE

The balance is a null-point-type instrument equipped with a linear variable differential transformer to detect the beam displacement and an electromagnetic restoring force system (Harrop Precision Furnace Co., 3470 East Fifth Avenue, Columbus, Ohio). The balance has a nominal sensitivity of ±0.002 g and a working capacity of 100 g. The furnace is capable of operation to 1050°C in any atmosphere compatible with Nichrome wire.

7. Sharples Recording Balance

The balance contains a torsion beam suspension with an inductive position-sensing detector and a restoring force obtained by a current

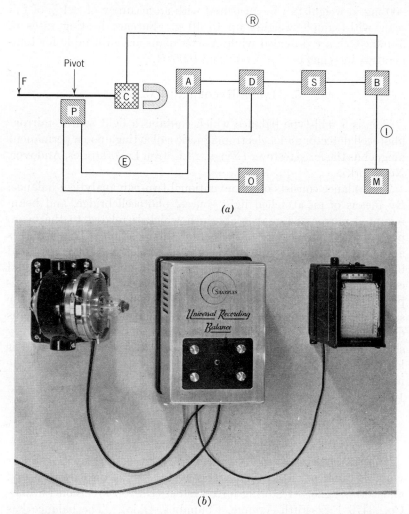

Fig. III.9. Sharples recording balance. (*a*) Schematic: F, force; P, sensing element; C, restoring force coil; E, error voltage; A, band pass amplifier; D, phase-sensitive detector; S, stabilizing network; B, dc amplifier; O, oscillator; R, correcting signal; M, continuous recorder. (*b*) Specific components.

flow through a wire coil in the field of a permanent magnet (Sharples Corporation Research Laboratories, 424 West 4th Street, Bridgeport, Connecticut).

A schematic diagram and a photograph of the balance are given in Figure III.9.

The operation of the balance is as follows: A force F, either positive or negative, acts upon the torsion suspension, causing it to pivot on a fulcrum. This movement is detected by the inductive position sensing element, P, which delivers an error voltage E, derived from the local 5 kc oscillator, O. The error voltage E is amplified by the band pass amplifier A and rectified by the phase sensitive detector D, through comparison with a reference voltage from the oscillator. The amplified and rectified error signal is passed through the stabilizing network S to provide proper retardation of the high-frequency components that would otherwise lead to instability. The stabilized signal, after passing through dc amplifier B, is applied as an error-correcting signal R to the restoring force coil C and to recorder M. Restoring force coil C is in the field of a permanent magnet and connected so that a current in it tends to oppose the movement of the balance beam due to force F.

The range of the balance is 0–25, 50, 100, and 250 mg full scale with an accuracy of better than ±1% of the full scale value. The response time varies with the range; 10 ms at 25 and 50 mg to 30 ms at the 250 mg range.

8. CHEVENARD THERMOBALANCE

More studies have been conducted on the Chevenard automatic thermobalance than perhaps all of the other instruments combined. The instrument was first described by Chevenard et al. (9) in 1944, and was used by them for studying the corrosion of metals at elevated temperatures with great success. The balance was adopted by Duval (6) for his classical studies in thermogravimetric analysis.

The balance has been modified in recent years; the model now available is the TH-59, which can be used to study samples in a high vacuum to temperatures of 1500°C. Provision has been made for automatic pen recording of the weight vs. time or weight vs. temperature curves, using a spot-follower photocell system.

The basic principles of the balance have not been changed very much. The balance is a deflection-type instrument containing a

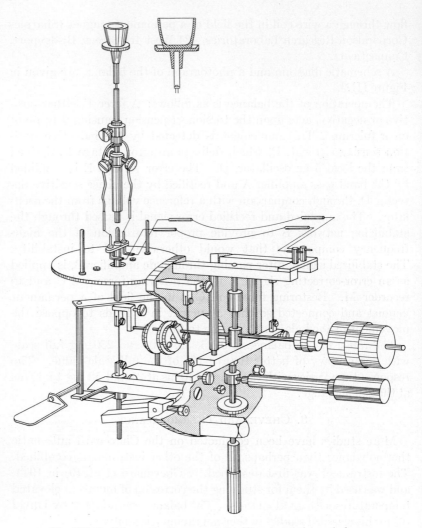

Fig. III.10. Schematic diagram of the Chevenard thermobalance.

wire-supported beam.   Deflections may be recorded photographically, as was done originally, or by some type of phototransducer.   The basic design is illustrated in Figure III.10.   The sample is placed at the end of a rod, which is suspended from one arm of a sensitive suspension balance; a movable counterpoise on the other arm is used for

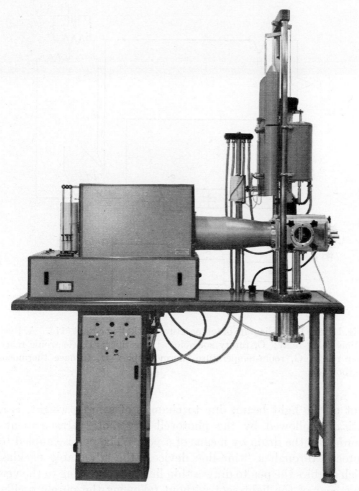

Fig. III.11. Chevenard thermobalance, basic components.

adjustment of the balance at the beginning of the run. Parasitic oscillations of the beam are magnetically damped. The rod and sample holder are inserted into a bifilarly wound furnace, which is mounted above the balance. The recording unit consists of a resistance-type photocell mounted on a motor-driven carriage and a revolving drum. A beam of light, reflected from a mirror on the balance beam, is allowed to impinge on the photocell. Any move-

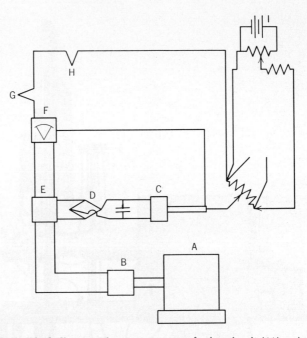

Fig. III.12. Block diagram of temperature-marketing circuit (11). A, Recorder B, time-delay relay; C, rotary solenoid; D, rectifier; E, electronic relay; F, meter relay; G, room-temperature thermocouple; H, furnace thermocouple; I, carbon cell.

ment of the light beam, due to changes of sample weight, is automatically followed by the photocell–servomoter arrangement and recorded on the drum by means of a pen. The pen is coupled to the photocell through a "thin-line device," the adjustable backlash of which enables the pen to draw a thin line corresponding to the vertical movement of the light spot without following the purely oscillatory movements of the photocell. The rotation of the drum is either a function of time or a function of temperature. The maximum range of the balance is about 50 g and on the lower ranges it is possible to have a sensitivity of 1 mg per each 5 mm of chart distance.

A photograph of the basic components of the balance is given in Figure III.11. The balance is manufactured by Societe A.D.A.M. E.L., Paris, France, and sold in the U.S.A. by Cooke, Troughton & Simms, Inc., 91 Waite Street, Malden 48, Massachusetts.

A number of modifications have been described for the Chevenard thermobalance. Gordon and Campbell (10) converted a photographic recording instrument into an electronic recording instrument by use of a linear variable differential transformer to convert balance beam displacements into linear electrical signals. After demodulation, the signal was recorded on a strip-chart potentiometric recorder. The range of weight change that could be linearly recorded was about 400 mg with an accuracy over a range of 200 mg of about ±0.25%. The response time for a 200 mg weight change was about 2 s.

A recorder temperature-marking system has been described by Griffith (11). The temperature detection and marking circuit are shown in Figure III.12. The furnace temperature was measured with a platinum–platinum–rhodium thermocouple whose output electromotive force (emf) was bucked by the emf generated by a second thermocouple maintained at room temperature. The difference in potential of the two thermocouples was fed into a milli-voltmeter relay, which, when the relay made contact, activated an electronic relay which simultaneously activated a time-delay relay and rotary solenoid. The time-delay relay was normally open and shorted the recorder for 30 s when activated, causing the pen of the recorder to move down scale. The rotary solenoid was fitted with seventeen 1-Ω resistors which, when activated, removed one resistor from the circuit of the bucking potential, thus causing the meter relay to return to zero. Thus, with a knowledge of the room temperature and the potentials at which the meter relay would make contact, 16 temperatures could be marked on each weight-loss curve and the temperature range could be varied as desired. The precision of the temperature measurements was about ±3°C in most instances, but varied with the temperature range employed.

Other changes to the balance have been mainly to the sample holders and to the furnace enclosure to allow better control of the furnace atmosphere (12,13).

9. UGINE-EYRAUD THERMOBALANCE

This balance consists of a shutter–light, source–photocell null detector and an electromagnetic coil–armature force restorer (manufactured by D.A.M., 6 Avenue Sidoine-Apollinaire, Lyon, France, and sold in the U.S.A. by Schueler & Co., 250 West 18th Street, New York, New York).

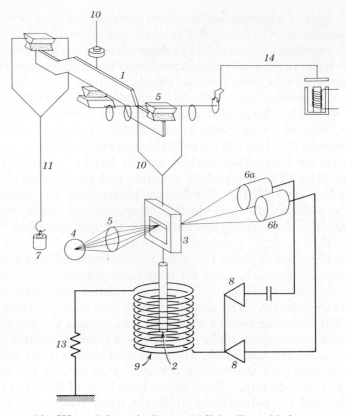

Fig. III.13. Schematic diagram of Ugine-Eyraud balance.

A schematic illustration of the balance is given in Figure III.13 and a photograph of the balance in Figure III.14.

The balance consists of an aluminum alloy balance beam, suspended on agate knife edges, enclosed inside a metal case. The beam (*1*) has a mass of soft iron (*2*) and a shutter (*3*) suspended from the left knife edge. This shutter regulates the light beam from lamp (*4*) focused by lens (*5*) striking the photocell (*6*). Current generated by the photocell is amplified by amplifier (*8*) and applied to the coil (*9*) within which the soft iron mass is located. The variation of this current is a measure of the weight change of the sample located in container (*7*) and can be recorded on an electronic potentio-

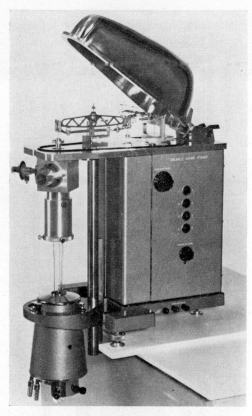

Fig. III.14. Ugine-Eyraud thermobalance.

metric recorder. The capacity of the balance is 200 g with a sensitivity and accuracy of better than ±0.1 mg.

The balance can be operated in a vacuum as well as at atmospheric pressure, and provision can be made for the collection and analysis of evolved gaseous decomposition products. The furnace has a maximum temperature of 1000°C.

10. STANTON THERMOBALANCE

The balance consists of a capacitor detection system with the restoring force applied by an incremental servomotor-operated electric weight loading device (manufactured by Stanton Instruments Ltd.,

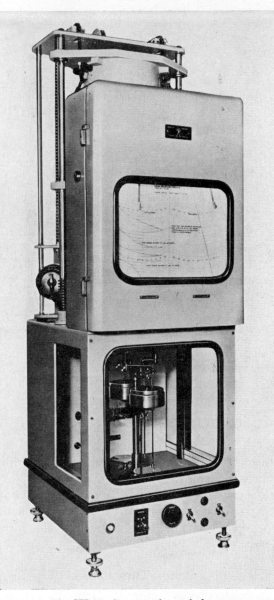

Fig. III.15. Stanton thermobalance.

London, England, and sold in the U.S.A. by the Burrell Corporation, 2223 Fifth Avenue, Pittsburgh, Pennsylvania).

One of the Stanton thermobalances, Model No. AD-2, is shown in Figure III.15. Furnace temperature and weight change are recorded on a two-pen electronic recorder mounted above the balance and in front of the furnace. The weight-change recorder has a sensitivity of 1 or 0.1 mg, the latter for a 1 g full-scale deflection, the former for a 0.1 g full-scale deflection of the recorder. The furnace normally has a limit of 1000°C.

Modifications of the balance to record both weight change and rate of weight change as functions of temperature have been described by Wilburn and Hesford (14). The sample crucible and support assembly have been modified by Lukaszewski (15).

11. BRABENDER THERMOBALANCE

This thermobalance was developed at the Steinkohlenbergbauverein Essen laboratories and consists of a stylus attached to one end of the balance beam which is periodically pressed against pressure sensitive recorder chart paper (C. W. Brabender Instruments, Inc., 50 East Wesley Street, South Hackensack, New Jersey). The thermobalance has a weight range of 1 g and is equipped with a furnace usable in the 200–1200°C temperature range.

12. SARTORIUS RECORDING BALANCES

Any of the Sartorius Series 2500 single-pan balances can be converted into an automatic recording balance by use of an electro-optical attachment which is mounted on top of the balance case (manufactured by Sartorius-Werke, A.G., Gottingen, Germany, and sold in the U.S.A. by Brinkmann Instruments, Inc., 115 Cutter Mill Road, Great Neck, New York). The attachment consists of a light source–shutter–photocell detector in which the shutter is mounted on the balance beam. Weight changes from 10–1000 mg can be recorded, depending on the type of balance employed. Output from the attachment is 10 mV full scale.

Another Sartorius recording balance is the microgram balance, designated as the ELMIC balance. A change in weight produces a torque moment which is equalized by a compensating current in a coil that moves in the magnetic field of an outer coil. The voltage generated in this coil is fed into an amplifier and the compensating current from the amplifier serves simultaneously for restoring the null point of the balance and for damping purposes. The balance has three ranges: 0–0.5, 0–0.2, and 0–0.1 mg. Maximum load is 500 mg with an accuracy of ±1%.

13. The Derivatograph

An automatic instrument which will simultaneously record the weight change, the rate of weight change, and the differential thermal

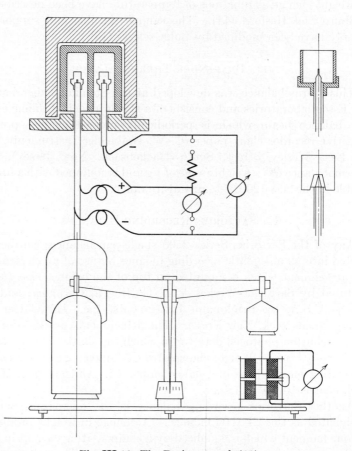

Fig. III.16. The Derivatograph (16).

analysis curves of a sample has been described by Paulik et al. (16) and is manufactured by Metrimpex, Budapest, Hungary.

The apparatus is illustrated in Figure III.16. The instrument uses a photographic recording technique in which all three curves are recorded simultaneously on the same time base. The balance consists of a permanent magnet attached to the beam of an analytical balance and suspended inside of a wire coil. Sample weight changes cause a movement of the magnet, inducing a current in the coil which is proportional to the change in weight. The change in weight and the rate of weight change are detected by sensitive galvanometers. Not only has a sample holder for solids been described, but also a novel liquid holder (17).

C. Noncommercial Instruments

Since the development of the first crude thermobalance by Honda (18) in 1915, a large number of manual and automatic recording balances and thermobalances have been reported in the literature. Duval (3) commented on the fact that since thermogravimetry was so simple in practice many investigators thought that it could be carried out with a more or less worn analytical balance. Modification of the instrument by drilling a hole in the base of the balance, replacement of one of the pans by a rod and sample holder, and installation of a simple furnace constituted a simple thermobalance. These easy solutions had numerous defects, such as the rod which extended below the balance rubbed on the balance case if the hole was too small and was subject to convection currents if the opening was too large (the effect became particularly detrimental above 600°C). Moreover, the traditional knife edge and agate plate of a balance could no longer be recommended if there was continuous contact between them, instead of the intermittent contact employed in ordinary weighing procedures. The vibrations, so often unavoidable in the laboratory, dulled the knife edges.

This last problem does not appear as serious as Duval envisioned, judging from the vast number of "converted" analytical balances described in the literature and also from experiences gained in the author's laboratory. Indeed, even commercial instruments that employ agate plates and knife-edge suspension of the balance beam are available. It is true that the bifunicular suspension has some advantages over the knife-edge construction, but it also has its problems.

The overhead, bell-shaped furnace is certainly advantageous over the under-the-balance design from the standpoint of convection currents, especially if the instrument is used at atmospheric pressure.

Since so many recording balances and thermobalances have been described, only the most novel, representative, or convenient types of

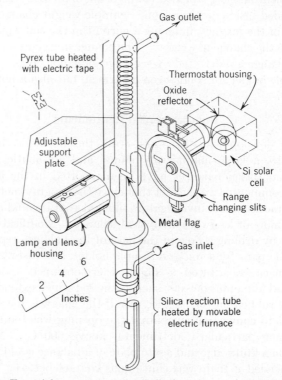

Fig. III.17. Essential components of helical spring recording balance (24).

recent description will be discussed here.   For a more complete coverage, especially from a historical view point, the book by Duval (6) and the review by Gordon and Campbell (2) are recommended.

Various types of helical spring recording balances have been described by Hooley (19), Izvekov (20), Van Nordstrand (21), Rabatin and Gale (22), Stephenson et al. (23), Fujii et al. (24), and Satava (25).

The helical-spring-type recording balance described by Fujii et al.

(24) is shown in Figure III.17.   The balance consists of a sensitive helical spring, the weighing mechanism; a metal flag attached to the spring which interrupts part of the light beam, the spring position indicator; and a light beam-photosensitive element, the position detector.   The light source was a 6 V tungsten filament lamp powered by a constant voltage power supply.   The photosensitive element was a silicon solar cell which measured the intensity of the light beam passing the spring position indicator and slit system.   Since all portions of the cell surface did not show the same energy conversion efficiency, the light beam was reflected from an aluminum oxide surface set 45° to the axis of the light path and the solar cell.   Thus, the entire area of the cell was uniformly illuminated at all times.   Different slit widths were used to adjust the range of the balance, i.e., by employing a narrow slit, a small weight change would produce a relatively large decrease in the voltage generated by the cell.   A microswitch and solenoid system allowed the range changes to be made automatically, covering a weight-change range of about 200 mg; maximum sample weight was 1.5 g while the sensitivity was 0.5 mg.

Torsion-type balances and thermobalances have been described by Waters (26,27), Wendlandt (28), Cueilleron and Hartmanshenn (29), Bostock (30), Eadie and Payne (31), Vieweg and Gast (32), Kraus et al. (33), and Rabatin and Card (34).

The torsion thermobalance described by Rabatin and Card (34) is illustrated in Figure III.18.   The instrument is rather novel in that it can be used in a vacuum or up to a pressure of 40 atm (600 lb in.^{2}).

The thermobalance consists of a torsion balance modified with a photocell–light source–shutter transducer system and enclosed in a metal chamber.   Any change in sample weight caused a change in position of the metal shutter attached to the balance beam, thus intercepting more or less parallel light, depending on whether weight loss or gain occurs.   This resulted in a proportional change in the photocell current which was recorded on a recorder.   A linear variable differential transformer was also used in place of the photocell with similar results being obtained.

The furnace consisted of Kanthal wire wound on a ceramic tube and was capable of operation to a maximum temperature of 1200°C. Gaseous atmospheres of nitrogen, oxygen, hydrogen, carbon monoxide, hydrogen sulfide, carbon dioxide, and ammonia were employed, some

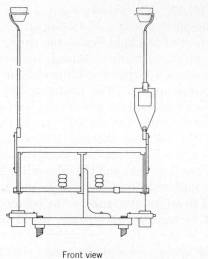

Front view   Side view

(a)

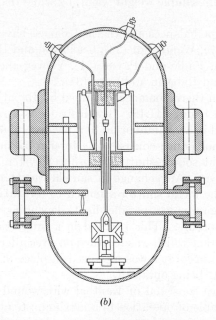

(b)

Fig. III.18. Torsion thermobalance. (a) Schematic diagram of balance assembly; (b) cross section of thermobalance pressure chamber (34).

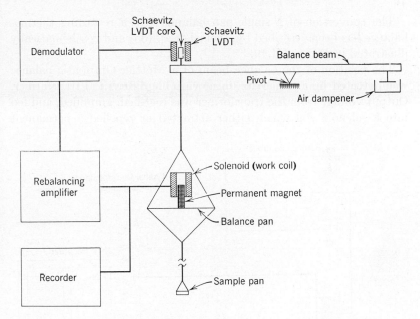

Fig. III.19. Schematic diagram of recording thermobalance (35).

only at moderate pressures, however, because of their reactivities at high temperatures.

Comparison between this balance and the Chevenard thermobalance showed that for most runs the results were almost identical. However, there were considerable variations for rapidly occurring reactions due to the slower response of the Chevenard balance.

By far the most common types of recording balances and thermobalances have been built starting with a standard analytical balance of the knife edge–agate plate type. By use of a suitable transducer detector and a force restoring mechanism, the balance was converted to a recording instrument. The addition of a suitable furnace and furnace temperature programmer completed the conversion to a thermobalance. Instruments have been described by Teetzel et al. (35), Campbell and Gordon (36), Eyraud and Eyraud (37), Reisman (38), Burriel Marti and Barcia Goyanes (39), Kinjyo and Iwata (40), Tamas (41), Zagorski (42), Garn (43), Erdey (44), Scholten et al. (45), Groot and Troutner (46), Markowitz and Boryta (47), and Splitek (48).

The conversion of a single-pan balance into a recording thermobalance has been described by Teetzel et al. (35) and is schematically illustrated in Figure III.19.

The position of the balance beam of a Mettler Gram-atic balance was detected by a Schaevitz linear variable differential transformer. Output voltage from the transformer was rectified, amplified, and fed into a solenoid coil which either attracted or repelled a permanent

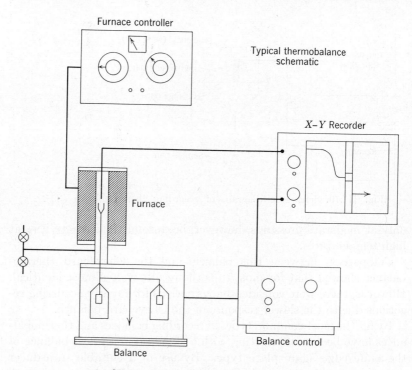

Fig. III.20. Automatic recording thermobalance.

magnet attached to the balance beam. The current through the solenoid is proportional to the weight change of the sample.

A similar arrangement was used by Campbell and Gordon (36) on a two-pan analytical balance except that the transformer output was not fed back into a work coil. Instead, the weight change was proportional to the displacement of a liquid by a rod suspended from the other end of the balance beam. This hydrostatic principle has pre-

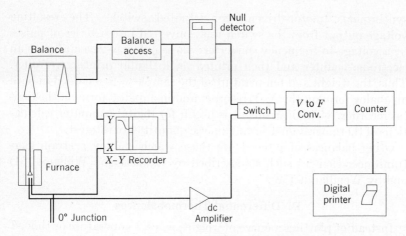

Fig. III.21. Schematic representation of digital recording thermobalance (50).

viously been applied to an analytical balance by Tryhorn and Wyatt (49).

One of the thermobalances presently used by the author is illustrated schematically in Figure III.20. The recording balance consisted of a conventional chain-o-matic instrument equipped with a Fisher Recording Balance Accessory, previously described on p. 53. The sample pan suspension system was similar to that described by Groot and Troutner (46) and Reisman (38). An over the balance type of furnace arrangement was employed in which a Hevi-Duty-type furnace, capable of opening in the long axis direction, was used. The opening of the furnace allowed it to cool down rapidly between consecutive runs. The temperature, as detected by a thermocouple located in the furnace chamber, was recorded on the X-axis, while the sample weight, as determined by the output from the recording balance accessory, was recorded on the Y-axis of an X–Y recorder. Each inch on the Y-axis normally corresponded to 10 mg of weight change while each inch on the X-axis normally corresponded to 100°C.

Conversion of the above thermobalance into a digital recording instrument has been described by Wendlandt (50) and is illustrated in Figure III.21. The instrument consists of the above thermobalance with provision for recording the weight change vs. furnace temperature on an X–Y recorder. The voltage outputs from the recording balance accessory and the furnace thermocouple were connected to a synchronous, motor-driven, cam-actuated switch. The resulting voltage output from the switch was converted into a series of pulses by a voltage-to-frequency converter; these pulses were counted on an electronic counter and then printed on a digital printing recorder. Thus, the weight and temperature of the sample were recorded in both an analog form on the $X-Y$ recorder and in a digital form on the digital recorder. The instrument is useful for digital computer calculations of thermogravimetric and kinetic quantities of interest.

Other balances of interest are those which employ a strain gage transducer element such as described by Bartlett and Williams (51) and by Wendlandt (52).

D. Differential Thermobalances

Instead of plotting a curve of weight, w, vs. temperature or time, T or t, thermobalances that plot the differential with respect to time, dw/dt, vs. temperature or time have been described. These differential thermobalances have been described by De Keyser (53,54), Erdey et al. (16,55), Waters (56), and Campbell et al. (57).

The Erdey et al. (16) instrument, the Derivatograph, has previously been described (see p. 72) and is commercially available. The De Keyser (53) instrument is illustrated schematically in Figure III.22 and is also available commercially as the Sartorius-De Keyser differential thermobalance.

The balance has provision for the suspension of two identical samples into two identical furnaces. The furnaces are heated at the same linear rate but one is kept approximately 5° hotter than the other. As the reactions involving changes in weight in the two samples occur consecutively, there is a weight differential, the magnitude of which is proportional to the heating rate of the furnace. The resulting differential curve is recorded photographically using a light beam reflected off from a mirror attached to the balance beam. Weight-change ranges of 5, 10, and 20 mg can be obtained.

Waters (56) described two types of differential thermobalances. Both balances employ essentially the same type of balance system in that they both have a photocell relay for converting the displacement of the beam from its null position into an electrical signal. An electromechanical device converts the electrical signal into a proportional mechanical force necessary to restore the balance to the null position. The method of electromechanical linkage differs in the

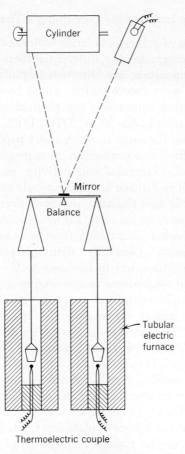

Fig. III.22. De Keyser differential thermobalance, schematic diagram (53).

two types of balances.   In the first type, the sample was counter-
balanced by the suspended electrode of a silver coulometer, the null
position of the balance being maintained by the continuous change in
weight of the silver electrode due to a control current passing through
the cell.   In the second type, which uses a torsion balance, the coun-
terbalancing torque was provided by a servomotor rotating the
torsion head.

Campbell et al. (57) have described a simple resistance–capacitance
circuit for differentiation of the output signal from a conventional
thermobalance.   "These circuits are discussed in the text."

E. Multiple Instruments Containing a Thermobalance

The combination of a thermobalance with another technique such as differential thermogravimetry, differential thermal analysis (DTA), gas evolution, gas analysis, gas chromatograph, infrared absorption spectroscopy, and mass spectrometry, would be expected to yield a wealth of information concerning the thermal dissociation process. By use of a single sample, the TGA, DTG, DTA, etc., curves can be obtained, usually on the same recorder chart paper. Conditions are therefore standardized concerning the gross properties of the sample such as particle sizes, thermal conductivity, sample packing, and sample size, as well as furnace heating rate, atmosphere, and furnace geometry. There is also the time-saving convenience of obtaining several different curves on the same sample simultaneously.

By far the most convenient to construct have been the TGA–DTA combined instruments. Generally, with this combination of techniques, little modification has to be made to the recording balance, except for electrical connections to the sample and reference thermocouples. The sample containers must be altered somewhat, and another container added to contain the reference thermocouple. Combined TGA–DTA instruments have been described by Reisman (38), Papailhau (58), Powell (59), Blazek (60), Kruger and Bryden (61), and Paulik et al. (16).

Powell (59) has modified the Chevenard thermobalance sample container as shown in Figure III.23. Sample holder A consisted of a ceramic crucible, $^7/_8$ in. in diameter and $^5/_8$ in. high, divided into two halves by means of a piece of platinum foil held in a groove in the sides and bottom of the crucible. Differential temperatures were measured by means of thermocouple B which was constructed of Pt–Pt, 13% Rh alloy wire. The differential thermocouples were passed through small holes in the side of the sample holder until the thermocouple junctions were at the center of each compartment. The sample holder was seated in a crucible holder, C, which was made from a silica rod. Small insulator spacers for the thermocouple wires were fixed at the two extremes of the silica rod. A flexible connection between the balance and a terminal block was made by means of fine-spiraled platinum wire, D, 0.005 in. in diameter welded to the heavier gage platinum wire on the silica rod and held in by spring-loaded clamp at the terminal block E. The weighed sample was

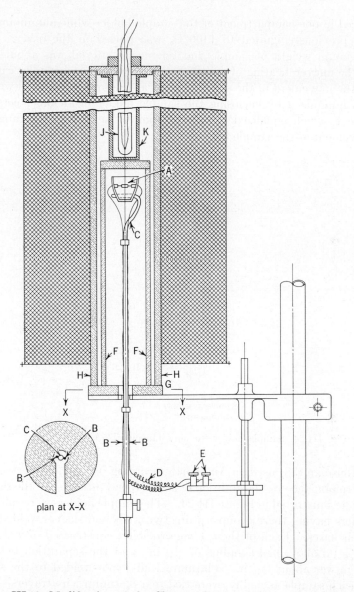

Fig. III.23. Modification of the Chevenard thermobalance for simultaneous TGA–DTA (59). A, sample holder; B, 0.02 in. platinum thermocouple leads; C, crucible holder of the thermobalance; D, 0.005 in. spiralled platinum leads; E, terminal block; F, inner ceramic tube; G, lower furnace stop cover; H, furnace tube; J, silica sheath; K, stainless steel sheath.

placed in one compartment of the sample holder while aluminum oxide, previously ignited to 1400°C, was placed in the other. The maximum weight of sample and reference material was about 5 g.

The uneven heating of sample and reference thermocouples caused by the movement of the sample holder as the sample changed weight was minimized by enclosing the sample holder in an inner ceramic tube F which equalized the distribution of heat over the range of movement of the sample holder.

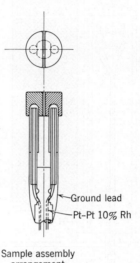

Sample assembly
arrangement

Fig. III.24. Sample holder for simultaneous TGA–DTA studies (38).

Reisman (38) used an Ainsworth recording balance, converted to a thermobalance by the addition of an overhead furnace and the sample holder illustrated in Figure III.24.   The sample holders were split cylinders having thermocouple protective wells and sleeves welded into their bases.   Each of these 1 mg crucibles, constructed of a Pt–Au, 20% Pd alloy, had a radius of $5/16$ in., and the separation between them was about $1/16$ in.   Platinum leads, spot-welded to the sleeve of each sample assembly, were tied to a platinum wire traversing the length of the main support rod.   Connection from the sample and reference thermocouples to a connection block outside of the balance was made by coils of 0.001 in. diameter copper wire.

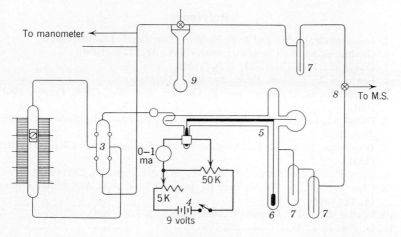

Fig. III.25. Gas circulating system and balance (62). (*1*) pump electric coils; (*2*) teflon-covered iron piston; (*3*) value system; (*4*) electric circuit; (*5*) balance assembly; (*6*) platinum sample holder; (*7*) cold traps; (*8*) needle valve; (*9*) flowmeter.

The apparatus described by Blazek (60) permitted not only the simultaneous determination of the TGA–DTA curves but also permitted the analysis of the gaseous decomposition products as well. The apparatus previously described by Paulik et al. (16) gave the TGA, DTG, and DTA curves simultaneously, and is discussed on p. 82.

A gas circulating system, in which a sample undergoing thermal dissociation can be weighed continuously, by means of a magnetic balance, and the gas analyzed simultaneously, has been described by Scala et al. (62). The system is schematically illustrated in Figure III.25.

The circulating system consists basically of a magnetic pump in which a Teflon-encased soft iron core is free to move inside a precision molded tube, surrounded by four solenoids. The balance consists of a Pyrex glass beam suspended on a stainless steel cradle by means of jewel bearings and pivots, an Alnico magnet is suspended on one end of the beam, and a sample holder suspended on the other end of the beam. A thin metal pointer was attached to the sample holder end of the beam. A solenoid on the outside of the glass system was used to restore the null position of the balance.

References

1. Lukaszewski, G. M., and J. P. Redfern, *Lab. Pract.*, **10**, 469 (1961).
2. Gordon, S., and C. Campbell, *Anal. Chem.*, **32**, 271R (1960).
3. Duval, C., *Anal. Chem.*, **23**, 1271 (1951).
4. Lewin, S. Z., *J. Chem. Educ.*, **39**, A575 (1962).
5. Jacque, L., G. Guiochon, and P. Gendrel, *Bull. Soc. Chim. France*, **1961**, 1061.
6. Duval, C., *Inorganic Thermogravimetric Analysis*, 2nd ed., Elsevier, Amsterdam, 1963.
7. Waterbury, G. R., R. M. Douglass, and D. F. Metz, *Anal. Chem.*, **33**, 1019 (1961).
8. Garn, P., C. R. Geith, and S. De Bala, *Rev. Sci. Instr.*, **33**, 293 (1962).
9. Chevenard, P., S. Wache, and R. de la Tullaye, *Bull. Soc. Chim. France*, **11**, 41 (1944).
10. Gordon, S., and C. Campbell, *Anal. Chem.*, **28**, 124 (1956).
11. Griffith, E. J., *Anal. Chem.*, **29**, 198 (1957).
12. Newkirk, A. E., *Anal. Chem.*, **32**, 1558 (1960).
13. Soulen, J. R., and I. Mockrin, *Anal. Chem.*, **33**, 1909 (1961).
14. Wilburn, F. W., and J. R. Hesford, *J. Sci. Instr.*, **40**, 91 (1963).
15. Lukaszewski, G. M., *Nature*, **194**, 959 (1962).
16. Paulik, F., J. Paulik, and L. Erdey, *Z. Anal. Chem.*, **160**, 241 (1958).
17. Paulik, F., J. Paulik, and L. Erdey, *Z. Anal. Chem.*, **160**, 321 (1958).
18. Honda, K., *Sci. Rept. Tohoku Univ.*, **4**, 97 (1915).
19. Hooley, J. G., *Can. J. Chem.*, **35**, 374 (1957).
20. Izvekov, I. V., *Trudy Krymsk. Filiala, Akad. Nauk. S.S.S.R.*, **4**, 81 (1953).
21. Van Nordstrand, R. A., U. S. Patent 2,692,497, Oct. 26, 1954.
22. Rabatin, J. G., and R. H. Gale, *Anal. Chem.*, **28**, 1314 (1956).
23. Stephenson, J. L., G. W. Smith, and H. V. Trantham, *Rev. Sci. Instr.*, **28**, 380 (1957).
24. Fujii, C. T., C. D. Carpenter, and R. A. Meussner, *Rev. Sci. Instr.*, **33**, 362 (1962).
25. Satava, V., *Collection Czech. Chem. Commun.*, **24**, 2172 (1959).
26. Waters, P. L., *J. Sci. Instr.*, **35**, 41 (1958).
27. Waters, P. L., *Coke Gas*, **20**, 252 (1958).
28. Wendlandt, W. W., *Anal. Chem.*, **30**, 56 (1958).
29. Cueilleron, J., and O. Hartmanshenn, *Bull. Soc. Chim. France*, **1959**, 164.
30. Bostock, W., *J. Sci. Instr.*, **29**, 209 (1952).
31. Eadie, F. S., and R. E. Payne, *Iron Age*, **172**, 99 (1954).
32. Vieweg, R., and T. Gast, *Kunststoffe*, **34**, 117 (1944).
33. Kraus, D. L., A. W. Petrocelli, and J. C. Price, *Anal. Chem.*, **33**, 479 (1961).
34. Rabatin, J. G., and C. S. Card, *Anal. Chem.*, **31**, 1689 (1959).
35. Teetzel, F. M., M. A. Munroe, J. A. Williamson, A. E. Abbott, and D. J. Stoneking, Publ. **NLCO-713,** Office of Technical Services, Washington, D. C., January 24, 1958.
36. Campbell, C., and S. Gordon, *Anal. Chem.*, **29**, 298 (1957).
37. Eyraud, C., and I. Eyraud, *Laboratory*, **12**, 13 (1955).

38. Reisman, A., *Anal. Chem.*, **32**, 1566 (1960).
39. F. Burriel Marti and C. Barcia Goyanes, *Anales Real Soc. Espan. Fis. Quim. (Madrid)*, **47B**, 73 (1951).
40. Kinjyo, K., and S. Iwata, *J. Chem. Soc. Japan, Pure Chem. Sect.*, **74**, 642 (1953).
41. Tamas, D., *Magy. Kem. Folyoirat*, **62**, 383 (1956).
42. Zagorski, Z., *Przemysl Chem.*, **8**, 326 (1952).
43. Garn, P., *Anal. Chem.*, **29**, 839 (1957).
44. Erdey, L., *Chem. Zvesti*, **12**, 352 (1958).
45. Scholten, P. C., W. M. Smit, and M. D. Wijner, *Rec. Trav. Chim.*, **77**, 305 (1958).
46. Groot, C., and V. H. Troutner, *Anal. Chem.*, **29**, 835 (1957).
47. Markowitz, M. M., and D. A. Boryta, *Anal. Chem.*, **32**, 1588 (1960).
48. Splitek, R., *Hutnicke Listy*, **13**, 697 (1958).
49. Tryhorn, F. G., and W. F. Wyatt, *Trans. Faraday Soc.*, **23**, 238 (1927).
50. Wendlandt, W. W., *Anal. Chem.*, **34**, 1726 (1962).
51. Bartlett, E. S., and D. N. Williams, *Rev. Sci. Instr.*, **28**, 919 (1957).
52. Wendlandt, W. W., *J. Chem. Educ.*, **38**, 566 (1961).
53. De Keyser, W. L., *Bull. Soc. Ceram. France*, **20**, 1 (1953).
54. De Keyser, W. L., *Nature*, **172**, 364 (1953).
55. Erdey, L., F. Paulik, and J. Paulik, *Nature*, **174**, 885 (1954).
56. Waters, P. L., *J. Sci. Instr.*, **35**, 41 (1958).
57. Campbell, C., S. Gordon, and C. L. Smith, *Anal. Chem.*, **31**, 1188 (1959).
58. Papailhau, J., *Bull. Soc. Franc. Mineral. Crist.*, **82**, 367 (1959).
59. Powell, D. A., *J. Sci. Instr.*, **34**, 225 (1957).
60. Blazek, A., *Hutnicke Listy*, **12**, 1096 (1957).
61. Kruger, J. E., and J. G. Bryden, *J. Sci. Instr.*, **40**, 178 (1963).
62. Scala, L. C., W. M. Hickam, and A. Langer, *Rev. Sci. Instr.*, **29**, 988 (1958)

CHAPTER IV

APPLICATIONS OF THERMOGRAVIMETRY

A. Introduction

With all its limitations and sources of error, the technique of thermogravimetry is a useful one. The data obtained by different thermobalances may not agree in detail with each other, but data obtained on the same instrument are generally reproducible and accurate enough for most purposes. If the instrument is used for, say, quality control purposes, it can accurately and quickly monitor a large number of samples. Other applications can also be cited, such as the remarkable revolution it has nurtured in inorganic and organic gravimetric analysis. Indeed, the phrase, "ignite sample at a red-heat," has little meaning in the modern chemical laboratory. With the thermobalance, the ignition and drying temperatures for an analytical precipitate can be obtained in a very short period of time.

The many applications of the thermobalance are summarized below (1–3):

    (*1*) Thermal decomposition of inorganic and organic substances

    (*2*) Corrosion of metals in various atmospheres at elevated temperatures

    (*3*) Solid-state reactions

    (*4*) Roasting and calcining of minerals

    (*5*) Distillation and evaporation of liquids

    (*6*) Pyrolysis of coal, petroleum, and wood

    (*7*) Determination of moisture, volatiles, and ash contents

    (*8*) Rates of evaporation and sublimation; latent heats

    (*9*) Dehydration and hygroscopicity studies

    (*10*) Automatic thermogravimetric analysis

    (*11*) Thermal oxidative degradation of polymeric substances

    (*12*) Decomposition of explosive materials

    (*13*) Development of gravimetric analytical procedures

    (*14*) Reaction kinetics studies

    (*15*) Discovery of new chemical compounds

Indeed, the technique has wide application in the fields of metallurgy, paints and ink chemistry, ceramics, mineralogy, organic chemistry, physical chemistry, biochemistry, polymer chemistry, analytical chemistry, geochemistry, inorganic chemistry, etc. The applications in each of the four basic fields of chemistry have been summarized by Lukaszewski and Redfern (4) and in analytical chemistry by Duval and others (3,5–7).

1. Applications to Analytical Chemistry

Palei et al. (6) have summarized the application of thermogravimetry to problems in analytical chemistry as follows:

(*1*) New weighing compositions in gravimetric analysis and the determination of their temperature stability ranges.

(*2*) For weighing substances which are unstable at ambient temperatures, such as those which absorb CO_2 and H_2O from the air.

(*3*) For studying the behavior of materials in atmospheres of various gases.

(*4*) For determination of the purity and thermal stability of analytical reagents, including primary and secondary standards.

(*5*) For determination of the composition of complex mixtures.

(*6*) For the systematic study of the properties of materials in relation to the methods used for their preparation.

(*7*) For automatic gravimetric analysis.

Duval (3) has also discussed the above topics in addition to others, such as:

(*1*) Various filtration techniques such as the ignition of filter paper.

(*2*) Should a precipitate be dried or ignited?

(*3*) Use of the thermobalance for discovery of new methods of separation and in gasometry.

(*4*) The study of the sublimation of various substances.

(*5*) Correction of errors in analytical chemistry.

(*6*) Use of thermogravimetry in functional organic analysis.

This list will probably be extended as new uses are made of readily available commercial thermobalances.

B. Automatic Thermogravimetric Analysis

One of the main contributions that the thermobalance has made to analytical chemistry has been the technique of automatic thermo-

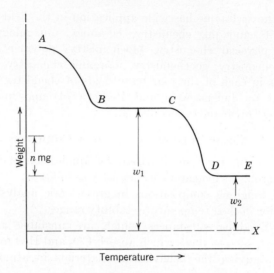

Fig. IV.1. Automatic thermogravimetric analysis for a single component system.

gravimetric analysis. Using the weight-loss curve, as illustrated in Figure IV.1, the principle upon which the technique is based, for a single component system, will be discussed.

Using a clean and dry crucible, the base line of the thermobalance is determined as indicated by the dashed line X. The crucible is removed from the balance, loaded with the wet precipitate, and then replaced on the balance. The precipitate is heated and the weight-loss curve recorded in the usual manner. From the horizontal weight plateau, BC, the weight w_1 can be obtained and from DE the weight w_2 is taken. Since the weight levels indicate that a definite stoichiometry of the precipitate has been attained, multiplication of w_1 or w_2 by the appropriate gravimetric factor gives the weight of metal ion present. The metal ion content obtained by calculation from w_1 will probably be the most accurate because of the greater accuracy in weight measurement and the smaller gravimetric factor of the precipitate.

For certain precipitates, the entire operation, filtration, drying, and recording on the thermobalance takes only 12 min (3).

In the case of a binary mixture, the procedure is similar. Take the case of the mixture as illustrated in Figure IV.2.

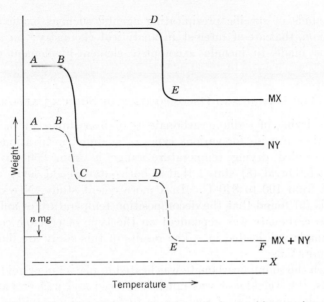

Fig. IV.2. Automatic thermogravimetric analysis of a binary mixture.

The weight-loss curves for the pure individual components, MX and NY, are given, as well as for a mixture of MX + NY. Component MX decomposes from D to E while NY decomposes from B to C. In the mixture curve, horizontal weight levels are formed at the same temperatures as were present on the two initial component curves. Thus, from the mixture curve, the amount of NY can be obtained by determining the value of BC; the amount of MX from the value of DE. Thus, in one simple operation, the analysis of certain binary or ternary mixtures can be obtained with reasonable accuracy.

C. Applications to Analytical Chemistry

A comprehensive discussion of the weight-loss curves for a large number of compounds of analytical interest has recently been made by Duval (3). It is not the intention of this discussion to include these; indeed, the reader is invited to use this comprehensive reference book whenever possible. Rather, this discussion will attempt to include only representative examples of thermogravimetry, preferably the most recent work if possible. It will be limited to compounds of specific precipitating agents, such as oxalic acid or cupferron, that are of interest in analytical chemistry; no attempt will be made to include a complete element-by-element description.

1. THE DRYING AND DECOMPOSITION OF SODIUM CARBONATE

The drying of sodium carbonate is of importance in the standardization of acids for various types of acidimetric titrations. The recommended drying temperature range is from 250 to 300°C, although Duval (8) stated that a horizontal weight level was obtained from 100 to 840°C. In a more recent study, Newkirk and Aliferis (9) found that the decomposition temperature of anhydrous sodium carbonate was dependent on the type of crucible container the sample was heated in. The results of this study are illustrated in Figure IV.3.

When the sodium carbonate was heated in platinum or gold sample holders, the weight loss was much less rapid and was probably due to the decomposition of the sample to form sodium oxide and carbon dioxide. As seen in curve 6, the presence of a nitrogen gas stream resulted in a faster rate of weight loss, while when water was present (curve 7) the observed weight loss rate was less. A sample of sodium carbonate dried at 350°C showed no further weight change on further heating for 12 h at 600°C and 4 h at 650°C in a platinum crucible in air. The reaction of sodium carbonate with coarse silica sand occurred rapidly at 800–850°C as shown by curve 9. On grinding the silica mixture, the first evidence of weight loss was at about 500°C (curve 10) or somewhat less than the temperature in curve 9.

It was recommended that sodium carbonate for analytical use be dried by heating in dry air or carbon dioxide using a platinum or other inert sample container in the temperature range of 250 to at least 700°C.

2. IGNITION TEMPERATURES OF ALUMINUM OXIDE

Although in 1949 Dupuis and Duval (10) studied the pyrolysis of hydrous alumina, $Al_2O_3 \cdot nH_2O$, prepared by using some 25 precipitating agents, more recent works by Erdey and Paulik (11) and Milner and Gordon (12) have raised questions concerning the

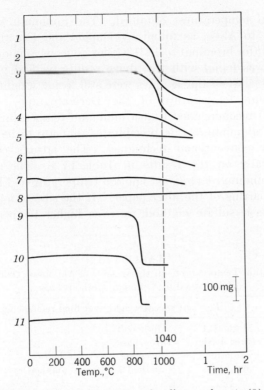

Fig. IV.3. Weight-loss curves of sodium carbonate (9).

Curve[a]	Crucible	Atmosphere	Sample
1	Porcelain	Air	Na_2CO_3
2	Porcelain	Air	Na_2CO_3[b]
3	Porcelain	Dry N_2[c]	Na_2CO_3
4	Alumina	Air	Na_2CO_3
5	Platinum	Air	Na_2CO_3
6	Platinum	Dry N_2[c]	Na_2CO_3
7	Platinum	Wet N_2[c]	Na_2CO_3
8	Platinum	CO_2[c]	Na_2CO_3
9	Platinum	Dry N_2[c]	$Na_2CO_3 + SiO_2$
10	Platinum	Dry N_2[c]	$Na_2CO_3 + SiO_2$[d]
11	Gold	Dry N_2[c]	Na_2CO_3[e]

[a] Heating rate 300°C/h, except runs 9 and 10.
[b] Crucible covered.
[c] Gas flow rate 250 ml/min.
[d] Heating rate 300°C/h to 520°C, then 50°C/h.
[e] Maximum temperature 922°C, but sample cooled and held 1 h at 915°C after reaching 922°C.

low ignition temperatures obtained. The minimum temperatures for ignition to Al_2O_3, as found by Dupius and Duval (10), were from 280°C (for bromine) to 1031°C (for aqueous ammonia). Little agreement was found with the above results by Erdey and Paulik (11) in that most of the samples were still losing weight at 1000°C, the maximum temperature of the Derivatograph. Milner and Gordon (12) recommended that a minimum temperature of 1200°C be used for aluminum oxide precipitates that are to be ignited and weighed by conventional techniques. The latter's conclusion is based partially on the results in Table IV.1. The results show that the minimum *conventional* ignition temperature is 1 h at 1100°C, following charring of the filter paper. If the sulfate ion is present, as in the basic sulfate method, an even higher temperature is indicated.

TABLE IV.1

Effect of Ignition Temperatures on the Weights of Aluminum Oxide Precipitates Obtained by Different Methods (12)

Temp.,[a] °C	Per cent excess weight over final reference value			
	Method A (urea–basic sulfate method), %	Method B (urea–basic succinate method), %	Method C (urea method),[b] %	Method D (ammonium hydroxide method), %
650	19.2	3.9	3.1	4.5
800	9.8	2.3	1.7	2.4
950	3.4	1.0	1.0	1.2
1100	0.6	0.0	0.0	0.2
1200	0.2	0.0	0.0	0.1
1200 (2nd hour)	Ref. value	Ref. value	Ref. value	Ref. value

[a] After charring of the filter paper, the precipitates were ignited at 500°C for 8 h before being ignited for 1 h at each of the stated temperatures.

[b] Chloride, but not sulfate or succinate, was present.

Duval (13) maintains that if the sample is to be heated, cooled, and weighed outside of the thermobalance, it is necessary to ignite the aluminum oxide to a higher temperature such that it will not be hygroscopic while it is being cooled and weighed on an analytical balance. Using automatic thermogravimetric analysis, it was stated, this source of error was eliminated and that the lower temperatures can be employed. Duval (13), however, coes not comment on the different curves presented by Erdey and Paulik (11). The latter concluded that the internal structure of the hydrous aluminum oxide is determined by such variables as the rate and temperature of precipitation, and only to a small extent by the nature of the precipitant. They also stated that the lower temperatures reported by Dupuis and Duval (10) were due to the variable precipitation conditions employed, since these are difficult to reproduce. Even small variations would have a marked effect on the ignition temperatures.

3. COMPLEX MIXTURES OF HYDRATES

Griffith (14) has applied thermogravimetry to the determination of the water content of mixtures of hydrated and anhydrous salts up to six phases. The method is based upon the fact that when a proper rate of heating is employed, a selected decomposition of the phase with the highest dissociation pressure takes place. When the phase of the highest dissociation pressure is completely decomposed, the compound with the second highest dissociation pressure begins to decompose, and so on. Thus, the water content in two different phases of a mixture of hydrates may be observed by the rate of loss of water from the mixture.

The thermal decomposition curve of a mixture of sodium carbonate 1-hydrate and sodium pyrophosphate 10-hydrate at a constant temperature of 100°C is given in Figure IV.4a. There is no indication from the curve as to where the $Na_4P_2O_7 \cdot 10H_2O$ was completely dehydrated or where the $Na_2CO_3 \cdot H_2O$ began to dehydrate. The dissociation pressures of these two compounds are very nearly the same at higher temperatures, but at lower temperatures (~ 60°C) the differences in dissociation pressures become appreciable. If this mixture is decomposed at 60°C, there is a distinct change of slope at the stoichiometric end point of the curve. In Figure IV.4b the same mixture heated at a slow rate, 8.7°C/h, of temperature rise from 30 to 100°C is illustrated. A pronounced curve break was observed in the curve, which demonstrates the need for a proper choice of rate of temperature rise program.

Other examples presented by Griffith (14) were $Na_5P_3O_{10} \cdot 6H_2O$ and mixtures of $Na_5P_3O_{10}$, $Na_5P_3O_{10} \cdot 6H_2O$, $Na_4P_2O_7$, $Na_4P_2O_7 \cdot 10H_2O$,

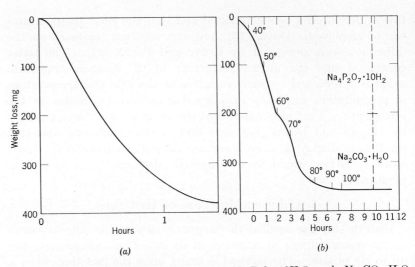

Fig. IV.4. (a) Decomposition curve of $Na_4P_2O_7 \cdot 10H_2O$ and $Na_2CO_3 \cdot H_2O$ at 100°C; (b) same mixture with slowly rising temperature (14).

Na_2CO_3, and $Na_2CO_3 \cdot H_2O$; $Na_2B_4O_7 \cdot 10H_2O$ and $Na_4P_2O_7 \cdot 10H_2O$; $MgSO_4 \cdot 7H_2O$, and $CoCl_2 \cdot 6H_2O$; and a mixture of $Na_2CO_3 \cdot H_2O$ and $K_2CO_3 \cdot 1.5H_2O$. The average error found in the analysis of the above mixtures was ±1.2%.

4. ANALYSIS OF CLAYS AND SOILS

Hoffman et al. (15,16) studied the thermogravimetry of soils, relatively pure clays, crystalline carbonates, and soils to which known amounts of clays and carbonates were added. Sharp breaks were observed in the decomposition curves of relatively pure clay minerals at elevated temperatures, which suggested the use of thermogravimetry for the determination of pure clays and simple clay mixtures. The quantities that could be determined by this technique were water content, organic matter content, and inorganic carbonates.

The decomposition curves of most soils showed horizontal weight levels starting at 150–180°C and extending to 210–240°C, indicative of either hygroscopic moisture, or hygroscopic moisture plus easily volatile organic compounds. In general, the weight-loss values fell between those obtained by the Karl Fischer method and oven-drying at 105°C. The organic matter started to burn off between 210 and 240°C and was usually completed at 500°C. In organic soils and those containing less than 15% clay, a relatively close estimate of the organic matter could be made from the weight-loss curve. When the clay content varied from 15 to 40%, the loss in weight at 500°C usually gave an estimate of the organic matter, which was in satisfactory agreement with dry combustion and wet oxidation data. When the clays contained more than 40% clay, it was not possible to distinguish between weight losses due to decomposition of organic matter and those due to the elimination of the lattice water of clays. This work also suggests that the lattice water in the pure clay samples can be quantitatively determined. Because the lattice water came off at different temperatures with different clays, it may be possible to use these temperatures as an additional means of identification and characterization.

5. Analysis of Fission Product Oxides and Nitrates

The DTA and thermogravimetry of cesium nitrate, strontium nitrate, cerium(III) nitrate 6-hydrate, zirconyl nitrate 2-hydrate, and ruthenium dioxide, up to a temperature of 1500°C, were studied by Campbell et al. (17).

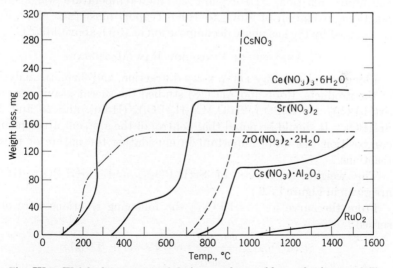

Fig. IV.5. Weight-loss curves of fission product oxides and nitrates (17).

The weight-loss curves of the above compounds are given in Figure IV.5.

Pure $CsNO_3$ began to decompose with the evolution of brown fumes at 710°C and continued to decompose up to 970°C, the temperature at which the sample had completely volatilized. When $CsNO_3$ was mixed with aluminum oxide, the decomposition began at about 750°C and continued to 940°C, at which temperature some 50% of the sample had volatilized. From 940 to 1100°C, however, a plateau in the curve was observed, which indicated the formation of a stable compound which then slowly decomposed from 1100 to 1525°C, the highest temperature attainable. Analysis of the compound formed in the 940–1100°C region indicated the formation of $CsAlO_2$. However, x-ray diffraction analysis failed to confirm this stoichiometry.

The compounds, $Ce(NO_3)_3 \cdot 6H_2O$, $Sr(NO_3)_2$, and $ZrO(NO_3)_2 \cdot 2H_2O$ all decomposed to give the metal oxides, CeO_2, SrO, and ZrO_2, respectively. The weight-loss curve of RuO_2 indicated a slow weight loss from 1025 to 1400°C, and a more rapid loss from 1400 to 1515°C. The first weight loss was probably due to the reaction

$$RuO_2(s) \xrightarrow{>600°C} Ru(s,\alpha) + O_2(g)$$

however, the weight loss found was greater than that calculated for the above reaction. To explain the high-temperature weight-loss reactions, oxidation of RuO_2 to RuO_4 (vapor) must take place, accompanied by the gas phase decomposition of RuO_4 above 1425°C.

6. Analysis of Phosphor Raw Materials

Using complementary DTA, x-ray diffraction, and chemical analysis of the products, Ropp and Aia (18) studied the thermogravimetry of $Sr(H_2PO_4)_2$, $Cd(H_2PO_4)_2 \cdot 2H_2O$, $Cd_5H_2(PO_4)_4 \cdot (H_2O)_4$, and α- and β-$SrHPO_4$. It should be noted that control of the ambient atmosphere composition was quite important in elucidating the nature of these reactions.

The weight-loss curves of $Sr(H_2PO_4)_2$, and $Cd(H_2PO_4)_2 \cdot 2H_2O$ are given in Figure IV.6.

From the curve for $Sr(H_2PO_4)_2$, the following reactions were observed:

$$Sr(H_2PO_4)_2(s) \xrightarrow{190-210°C} SrH_2P_2O_7(s) + H_2O(g)$$

$$SrH_2P_2O_7(s) \xrightarrow{320-330°C} \gamma\text{-}Sr(PO_3)_2(s) + H_2O(g)$$

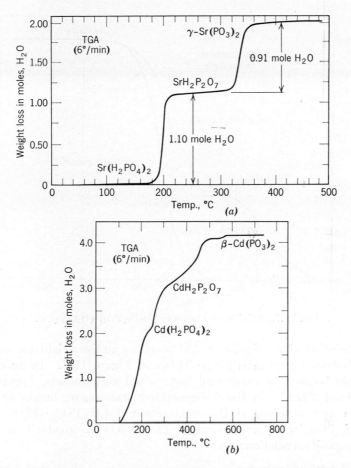

Fig. IV.6. Weight-loss curves of: (a) $Sr(H_2PO_4)_2$; (b) $Cd(H_2PO_4)2 \cdot 2H_2O$ (18).

For $Cd(H_2PO_4)_2 \cdot 2H_2O$, the reactions were similar except for the dehydration reaction. The reactions observed were:

$$Cd(H_2PO_4)_2 \cdot 2H_2O(s) \xrightarrow{130°C} Cd(H_2PO_4)_2(g) + 2H_2O(g)$$

$$Cd(H_2PO_4)_2(s) \xrightarrow{210°C} CdH_2P_2O_7(s) + H_2O(g)$$

$$CdH_2P_2O_7(s) \xrightarrow{410°C} \beta\text{-}Cd(PO_3)_2(s) + H_2O(g)$$

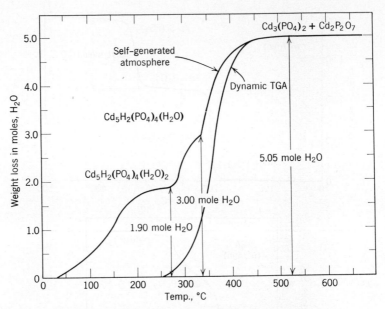

Fig. IV.7. Weight-loss curves of $Cd_5H_2(PO_4) \cdot (H_2O)_4$ (18).

The effect of a self-generated atmosphere on the weight-loss curve is illustrated for $Cd_5H_2(PO_4)_4 \cdot (H_2O)_4$ in Figure IV.7. In an open sample holder, the compound lost weight continuously, beginning at about 250°C. In the self-generated atmosphere, breaks in the curve were observed at the composition, $Cd_5H_2(PO_4)_4 \cdot (H_2O)_2$ and $Cd_5H_2(PO_4)_4(H_2O)$, respectively. The reactions involved in the decomposition reaction were:

$$Cd_5H_2(PO_4)_4 \cdot (H_2O)_4(s) \xrightarrow{150°C} Cd_5H_2(PO_4)_4(H_2O)_2(s) + 2H_2O(g)$$

$$Cd_5H_2(PO_4)_4 \cdot (H_2O)_2(s) \xrightarrow{290C} Cd_5H_2(PO_4)_4(H_2O)(s) + H_2O(g)$$

$$Cd_5H_2(PO_4)_4 \cdot (H_2O)(s) \xrightarrow{340°C} Cd_3(PO_4)_2 \cdot Cd_2P_2O_7(s) + 2H_2O(g)$$

The use of DTA and thermogravimetry data is an extremely useful combination for defining the reaction temperatures and products of formation of solid-state reactions. The successful use of the above methods depend to a great extent on the manner in which the data were obtained, and in many cases, on the thermal behavior of the compound being analyzed.

7. ANALYSIS OF CALCIUM SILICATE HYDRATES FOR FREE LIME AND CARBONATE

The free lime [$Ca(OH)_2$] and carbonate ($CaCO_3$) contents of calcium silicate hydrates, ranging from 1.0 to 20%, were determined by a thermogravimetric method by Biffen (19). The weight-loss curves for a series of calcium silicate hydrates, calcium silicate hydrates plus varying amounts of calcium hydroxide, and calcium silicate hydrates plus varying amounts of calcium carbonate, are given in Figure IV.8.

The curves for the calcium silicate hydrates are all quite similar, show no sharp breaks, and exhibit a gradual slope for a straight line between 375 and 650°C. The curve breaks above 600°C are due to the decomposition of carbonate content in the sample.

Using synthetic mixtures of calcium silicate hydrate and calcium hydroxide, the series of curves obtained all indicated curve breaks, at about 500°C, which were caused by calcium hydroxide decomposition as was shown by authentic weight-loss curves for the pure compounds. By taking the vertical distance from the point at which the straight-line curve starts to change, due to evolution of the combined water from the calcium silicate hydrate, to the point where it resumes the calcium silicate decomposition drop, and calculating the calcium hydroxide from the loss in weight of water equivalent to this vertical distance, a good estimate of the amount of calcium hydroxide was obtained in all cases.

The decomposition of calcium silicate hydrate samples containing added amounts of calcium carbonate, and in some cases calcium hydroxide, is given in Figure IV.4c. The presence of calcium carbonate is indicated by the curve break, due to the evolution of carbon dioxide, in the temperature range 700–900°C. If a vertical distance is measured between the points where this straight line begins to drop and then becomes horizontal, the carbon dioxide content of the sample can be easily obtained.

Good agreement with other accepted methods was reported for the determination of water, free lime, and carbonate in calcium silicate hydrates by the thermogravimetric method.

8. DETERMINATION OF MAGNESIUM, CALCIUM, STRONTIUM, AND BARIUM

The determination of calcium, strontium, and barium ions in the presence of one another has been carried out by thermogravimetry

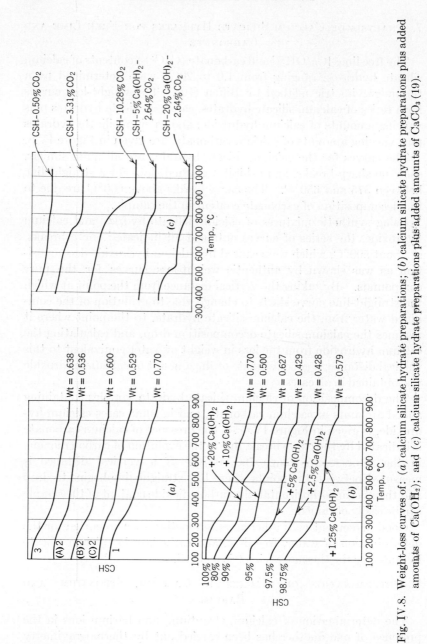

Fig. IV.8. Weight-loss curves of: (a) calcium silicate hydrate preparations; (b) calcium silicate hydrate preparations plus added amounts of Ca(OH)₂; and (c) calcium silicate hydrate preparations plus added amounts of CaCO₃ (19).

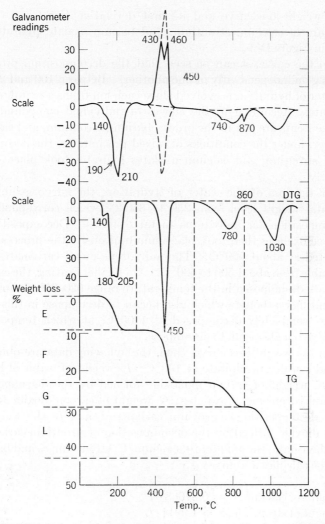

Fig. IV.9. Weight-loss curves of calcium, strontium, and barium oxalate hydrates (21).

by Erdey et al. (20,21). The ions are precipitated in the form of mixed metal oxalate hydrates and decomposed on the thermobalance. From the resulting weight-loss curves, the amount of calcium, strontium, and barium can be determined.

The weight-loss curve and its first derivative (see Chap. II) of a mixture of calcium, strontium, and barium oxalate hydrates are shown in Figure IV.9.

From the curve, it can be seen that the decomposition processes are going on independently of one another. Between 100 and 250°C. the water of hydration is evolved since each ion froms a metal oxalate 1-hydrate. According to the curves of individual compounds, the water contents are lost in the order: barium, strontium, and calcium. However, under the conditions of mixed precipitates, the decomposition of strontium and calcium oxalates hydrates took place simultaneously.

After the loss of the water of hydration, the curve exhibited a horizontal weight level from 250 to 360°C, which corresponded to the composition for anhydrous metal oxalates. Decomposition of the three oxalates then took place simultaneously, the process being completed at about 500°C. The anhydrous metal carbonates were then stable from about 500 to 620°C. On further heating, the calcium carbonate decomposed in the temperature range 620–860°C, followed by strontium carbonate which also began to decompose in this range and was completely decomposed at 1100°C, at which temperature barium carbonate began to decompose.

From the weight-loss curve, then, the following data are obtained: D, weight of dry precipitate at 100°C; E, weight of water of hydration; F, weight of carbon monoxide formed by the decomposition of the anhydrous metal oxalates; G, weight of carbon dioxide formed by the decomposition of calcium carbonate; and L, the weight of carbon dioxide formed by the decomposition of strontium carbonate. From these data, the amounts of calcium, C, strontium, S, and barium, B, can be calculated from:

Amount of calcium, $C = 0.91068 \cdot G$
Amount of strontium, $S = 1.9911 \cdot L$
Amount of barium, $B = 0.58603 \cdot D - 1.9457 \cdot G - 2.5788 \cdot L$

Assuming that the amounts of C, S, and B are unity, the error of the determination was calculated as

$$\frac{\Delta D}{D} = \frac{\Delta E}{E} = \frac{\Delta F}{F} = \frac{\Delta G}{G} = \frac{\Delta L}{L} = 0.1\%$$

The simultaneous determination of calcium and magnesium by thermogravimetry has been described by Dupuis and Dupuis (22). Using the weight-loss curve of a typical dolomite sample, as illustrated in Figure IV.10, the amounts of calcium and magnesium can be calculated. Using the principles previously discussed under automatic thermogravimetric analysis (see p. 89), EF corresponds

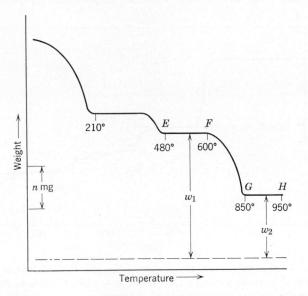

Fig. IV.10. Weight-loss curve of a mixture of a calcium and magnesium carbonate precipitate (wet).

to a mixture of MgO and $CaCO_3$ and GH corresponds to a mixture of MgO and CaO. The difference, $w_1 - w_2$ is equal to the weight of carbon dioxide evolved between 500 and 900°C by the decomposition of calcium carbonate. The amount of calcium oxide is then

$$w(\text{CaO}) = (w_1 - w_2) \cdot \frac{56}{44} = (w_1 - w_2) \cdot 1.272$$

and the amount of magnesium oxide by the difference,

$$w(\text{MgO}) = w_2 - w(\text{CaO})$$

The method illustrates very nicely the principles of automatic analysis developed by Duval.

9. Potassium Hydrogen Phthalate

Although the use of the thermobalance was supposed to eliminate the confusion concerning drying and decomposition temperatures of analytical precipitates and reagents, in many cases, it has only contributed to this confusion. In comparing four different investigations concerning the drying and decomposition temperatures of

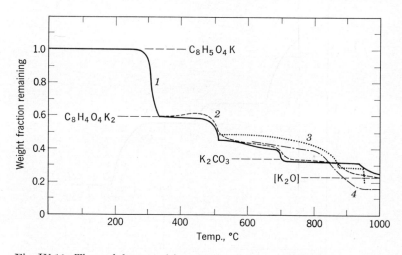

Fig. IV.11. Thermal decomposition of 0.1 g samples of $KHC_8H_4O_4$ at a heating rate of 300°C/h, under various conditions. (——) air atmosphere, Pt crucible; (- - - -) air atmosphere, porcelain crucible, without protective sleeve on crucible support rod; (. . . .) nitrogen atmosphere, porcelain crucible; (—·—·) nitrogen atmosphere, preheated sample to 300°C (26).

potassium hydrogen phthalate, four different results were obtained, not to mention the drying temperatures recommended by nonthermogravimetric methods. Dupuis and Duval (23) first reported that the decomposition of $KHC_8H_4O_4$ began at 172°C; Duval (24), in a later study, found a decomposition temperature of 240°C at a 150°C/h heating rate, and 236°C at a 300°C/h heating rate. Belcher et al. (25) reported that the compound began to decompose at 200°C and recommended a drying temperature of 100–150°C. Lastly, Newkirk and Laware (26) reported a procedural decomposition temperature of about 260°C. In view of the previous discussion on the limitations of thermogravimetry, these conclusions are perhaps not very unusual. It is believed (26) that these studies have little value in determining the safe, long-term drying temperature for a primary standard substance.

The weight-loss curves of $KHC_8H_4O_4$, under various atmospheric conditions, are given in Figure IV.11.

There are four major decomposition reactions that take place during the pyrolysis: (1) the volatilization of water and phthalic anhydride and the formation of a residue of dipotassium phthalate, $K_2C_8H_4O_4$; (2) decomposition of the latter compound to form potassium carbonate and carbonaceous material; (3) the carbonaceous material loses weight slowly and finally burns giving a residue of K_2CO_3; and (4) the potassium carbonate decomposes with the evolution of carbon dioxide, while the K_2O formed reacts with the porcelain crucible sample holder.

The various conditions under which the thermal decomposition takes place are illustrated by the curves in Figure IV.11.   The slight weight increase between 425 and 450°C, noted on the dashed curve, was caused by the evaporation of phthalic anhydride from the furnace walls with increasing temperature and its condensation on the crucible support rod.

Newkirk and Laware (26) found that the initial isothermal rate of decomposition of $KHC_8H_4O_4$ in carbon dioxide at 235°C was about 15 mg/g/h.   This compares with an extrapolated value of 7 mg/g/h previously reported by Caley and Brundin (27). However, Duval (24) found no observable weight loss from isothermal runs at 150, 160, and 170°C, respectively.   If a sample weight of 0.5 g is assumed for his experiments, Newkirk and Laware (26) calculated that the weight changes expected would be 0.004, 0.011, and 0.030, respectively.   Since these changes are too small to be detected by the Chevenard thermobalance, it is therefore not surprising that Duval observed no weight changes and that his observations do not conflict with those of Caley and Brundin.

10. RARE-EARTH CUPFERRATES AND NEOCUPFERRATES

The cupferron (ammonium salt of N-nitrosophenylhydroxylamine) and neocupferron (α-naphthyl-N-nitrosohydroxylamine) metal chelates of the trivalent rare-earth elements have been studied by thermogravimetry by Wendlandt (27,28) and Wendlandt and Bryant (29).

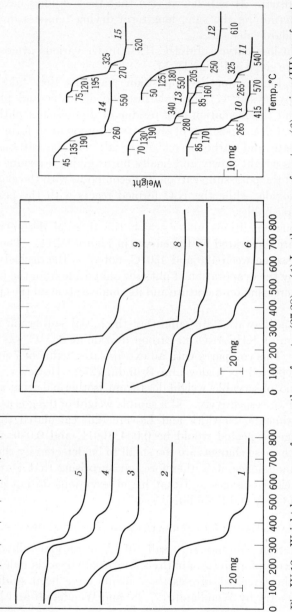
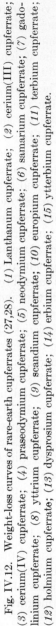

Fig. IV.12. Weight-loss curves of rare-earth cupferrates (27,28). (1) Lanthanum cupferrate; (2) cerium(III) cupferrate; (3) cerium(IV) cupferrate; (4) praseodymium cupferrate; (5) neodymium cupferrate; (6) samarium cupferrate; (7) gadolinium cupferrate; (8) yttrium cupferrate; (9) scandium cupferrate; (10) europium cupferrate; (11) terbium cupferrate; (12) holmium cupferrate; (13) dysprosium cupferrate; (14) erbium cupferrate; (15) ytterbium cupferrate.

The weight-loss curves for the metal cupferrates are given in Figure IV.12. The curves of the lanthanum, praseodymium, neodymium, samarium, and scandium complexes were all quite similar in appearance. The thermal stabilities of these compounds were remarkably higher than those of any other metal cupferrates so far determined. The first weight losses began at about 150–180°C, giving a small break in the curve, then a plateau extending to about

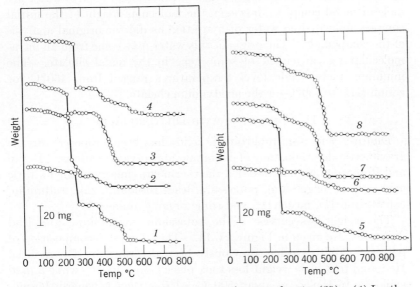

Fig. IV.13. Weight-loss curves of rare-earth neocupferrates (29). (1) Lanthanum neocupferrate; (2) cerium(III) neocupferrate; (3) cerium(IV) neocupferrate; (4) praseodymium neocupferrate; (5) neodymium neocupferrate; (6) samarium neocupferrate; (7) gadolinium neocupferrate; (8) yttrium neocupferrate.

280–290°C. Further weight loss then took place, giving the metal oxide weight levels beginning at 450–600°C.

In general, the heavier rare-earth metal cupferrates were less stable thermally than the corresponding lighter rare-earth complexes. However, the minimum oxide level temperatures were in the same general temperature range. The thermograms indicated that except for several of the lighter element compounds, it is not possible to dry the precipitated complexes to constant weight and then weigh as the stoichiometric metal chelates. In several cases, the amount of metal oxide found for the ignited complexes was less than the theoretical amount, indicating coprecipitation of chelating agent.

The weight-loss curves of the lighter rare-earth metal neocupferrates are given in Figure IV.13. The neocupferrates of the lighter rare-earth metal ions were less stable than the corresponding iron-(III) and Cu(II) chelates. The first weight losses, in which gaseous substance with an apparent molecular weight of 18 was evolved, began at about 80°C. This strongly suggests the loss of a mole of water per mole of metal complex; however, the molecular weight of the initial complex indicated no water of hydration as did the original analysis of the compounds. The origin of this water may come from an intramolecular rearrangement of some type in the metal chelate. The minimum metal oxide level temperatures ranged from 460°C for cerium(III) to 750°C for the neodymium chelate.

11. COMPOUNDS WITH DILITURIC ACID

Dilituric acid (5-nitrobarbituric acid) has been proposed for the gravimetric determination of inorganic and organic cations. Berlin and Robinson (30) have studied the thermogravimetry of the dilituric acid salts of magnesium, potassium, lead, rubidium, zinc, cadmium, cobalt, iron(II), nickel(II), and some organic amines.

The weight-loss curves of the potassium, magnesium, and lead diliturates are given in Figure IV.14. The thermal decomposition of potassium diliturate has previously been described by Duval (31). He found that little weight loss took place before 400°C, while a mild explosion took place at about 500°C. Using the Chevenard thermobalance, Berlin and Robinson (30) found that anhydrous potassium diliturate was stable up to 250°C, but decomposed rapidly between 250 and 355°C. Above 355°C there was a slow decomposition terminating at 1040°C with the production of K_2O. At 770°C, there was an inflection point corresponding to the decomposition of K_2CO_3. A sample prepared by the same method as above but not dried previously in an oven gave the same type of weight-loss curve.

The dehydration of magnesium diliturate 8-hydrate began at 100°C and proceeded in two steps. An intermediate semistable hydrate was formed at 140°C, after the loss of four molecules of water. After the loss of four additional molecules of water, the anhydrous compound was obtained, which was stable between 220 and 260°C. Above 260°C there was a rapid but nonexplosive decomposition.

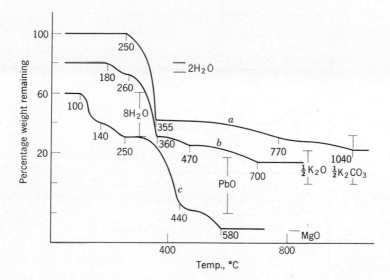

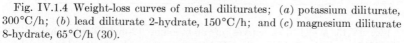

Fig. IV.1.4 Weight-loss curves of metal diliturates; (a) potassium diliturate, 300°C/h; (b) lead diliturate 2-hydrate, 150°C/h; and (c) magnesium diliturate 8-hydrate, 65°C/h (30).

An inflection point found at 440°C corresponded to a weight 8% larger than would be expected for the weight of $MgCO_3$. At 580°C, constant weight was obtained which was 11% of the original weight and corresponded to slightly more than the calculated percentage weight of magnesium oxide.

Lead diliturate 2-hydrate was stable up to 180°C. From 180 to 260°C it lost two molecules of water, followed by a more rapid decomposition to 360°C. The inflection point at 470°C corresponded to the composition for $PbCO_3$, and at 700°C to PbO.

12. SOME AMINE MOLYBDOPHOSPHATES

The thermal decomposition of the oxine (8-quinolinol), ammonium, and quinolinium phosphomolybdates have been studied by thermogravimetry. Much controversy has existed in the literature concerning the drying or ignition temperature of ammonium 12-molybdophosphate. Dupuis and Duval (32) stated that the precipitate, using Treadwell's method, has the composition $(NH_4)_3PO_4(MoO_3)_{12}$·-$2HNO_3$·H_2O. The precipitate loses water and nitric acid on heating

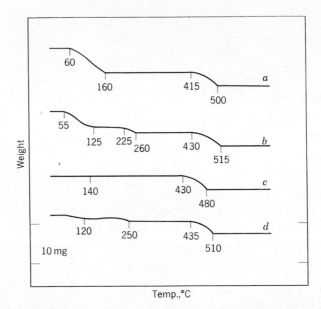

Fig. IV.15. Weight-loss curves of ammonium 12-molybdophosphate (33).
(a) HNO_3 washed air dried; (b) NH_4NO_3 washed, air dried; (c) HNO_3 washed
oven dried; (d) NH_4NO_3 washed, oven dried.

to 180°C and then gives a plateau to 410°C. However, if the precipitate is first dried in air, the weight loss up to 180°C corresponds
only to the loss of the 2 moles of nitric acid and not $2HNO_3 + H_2O$,
the water apparently being lost on air drying. The horizontal weight
level from 180 to 410°C corresponds to the formula $(NH_3)_3PO_4$-
$(MoO_3)_{12}$.

Wendlandt (33), using Stockdale's method of precipitation, obtained the weight-loss curves as shown in Figure IV.15. The air-
dried precipitate began to evolve loosely held water at 60°C, giving
a horizontal weight level from 160 to 415°C, which corresponded to
the composition $(NH_4)_2HP(Mo_3O_{10})_4 \cdot H_2O$. Above 415°C, additional weight loss occurred to give the oxide level, $P_2O_5 \cdot 24MoO_3$,
beginning at 500°C. The 160°C oven-dried sample gave a similar
thermogram except for the evolution of the loosely held water. The
ammonium-nitrate-washed precipitate, after being air-dried, began
to evolve loosely held water at 55°C. From 225 to 260°C, NH_4NO_3
was evolved giving a horizontal weight level from 260 to 430°C,

which corresponded to the composition $(NH_4)_3[P(Mo_3O_{10})_4]$. Total decomposition began at 435°C, resulting in the $P_2O_5 \cdot 24MoO_3$ weight level at 510°C.

Undoubtedly, the disagreement between various workers is due to the nature of the precipitation reaction, and not to the instrumentation involved. The drying temperatures for the nitric-acid-washed precipitate found by Wendlandt (33), 160–415°C, were similar to the 180–410°C temperatures reported by Dupuis and Duval (32),

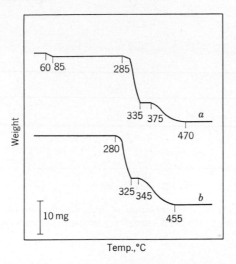

Fig. IV.16. Thermal decomposition curves of oxine molybdophosphate (a) Air-dried; (b) oven-dried at 140°C (36).

although the compositions were different. Even with the somewhat different compositions, the molecular weights of the two compounds would be almost identical so that little error would result in whichever gravimetric factor was employed.

The same problems were encountered with the oxine phosphomolybdate as were found for the corresponding ammonium compound. Duval (34) first reported that the composition corresponding to that of the 2-hydrate was stable in the temperature range of 176–225°C; he later reported (35) that the 2-hydrate was stable in the temperature range 236–268°C. Beyond 341°C, the compound began to decompose, giving the $P_2O_5 \cdot 24MoO_3$ level beginning at 765°C. No reference

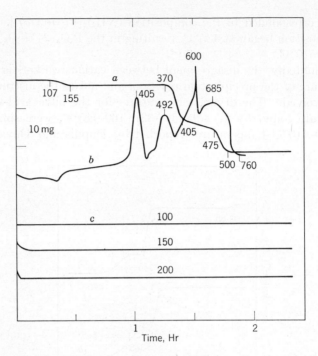

Fig. IV.17. Thermal decomposition of quinolinium phosphomolybdate. (a)
Thermobalance curve; (b) DTA curve; (c) isotherm curves: all temperatures in
°C (38).

was made, nor were supporting data given, for the apparent change in
drying temperature ranges.

Wendlandt and Brabson (36) studied the thermal decomposition
of oxine molybdophosphate prepared by the method of Brabson and
Edwards (37). The thermograms of this compound are given in
Figure IV.16. The air-dried precipitate began to lose weight at
60°C, giving a horizontal weight level from 85 to 285°C, which corresponded to the composition for the anhydrous compound, $3C_9H_7$
$ON \cdot H_3(PMo_{12}O_{40})$. This compound began to decompose at 375°C,
resulting in the oxide level, $P_2O_5 \cdot 24MoO_3$, beginning at 470°C. The
oven-dried sample decomposed in a manner similar to that of the
above compound.

The thermal decomposition of quinolinium phosphomolybdate
has been studied by Wendlandt and Hoffman (38) using thermo-

gravimetry and DTA. According to the weight-loss curve in Figure IV.17, the quinolinium phosphomolybdate precipitate began to lose weight starting at 107°C. A horizontal weight level was then observed from 155 to 370°C, which corresponded to the composition of the anhydrous compound $(C_9H_7N)_3 \cdot H_2PO_4 \cdot 12MoO_3$. Beyond 370°C, rapid decomposition took place, giving the $P_2O_5 \cdot 24MoO_3$ level at 500°C.

To determine the optimum drying time for the precipitated compound, samples were studied at constant temperatures on the thermobalance. At 100°C, a horizontal curve was obtained, indicating that the compound did not lose the hydrate water nor decompose in any other manner. At 150°C, the hydrate water was lost in a very short time, giving a horizontal weight level on further heating. At a still higher temperature, 200°C, the hydrate water was lost almost immediately, and there was no evidence of any decomposition. From the isotherm curves, it can be concluded that quinolinium phosphomolybdate can be rendered anhydrous by drying at 150 or 200°C for less than 15 min.

13. (Ethylenedinitrilo)tetraacetic Acid and its Derivatives

Because of the importance of (ethylenedinitrilo)tetraacetic acid (EDTA) and its derivatives in analytical chemistry, their thermal properties were studied by Wendlandt (39). The compounds studied and their suppliers included disodium calcium (ethylenedinitrilo)tetraacetate 2,3-hydrate ($Na_2CaEDTA \cdot 2,3H_2O$, Sequestrene Na2Ca); hydroxyethyl(ethylenedinitrilo)triacetic acid (HEDTA, Chel DM Acid); trans-o-diaminocyclohexanetetraacetic acid (DCHTA, Chel 600); EDTA, J. T. Baker Chemical Co.; Sequestrene AA, Geigy Chemical Co.; $Na_2EDTA \cdot 2H_2O$, Eastman Organic Chemicals and J. T. Baker Chemical Co.; Sequestrene Na2, Geigy Chemical Co.; nitrilotriacetic acid (Chel 300), Geigy Chemical Co.; and diethylenetriaminepentaacetic acid (DTPA, Chel 330 Acid), Geigy Chemical Co.

The thermal decomposition curves are given in Figure IV.18, while the corresponding transition temperatures, and weight-loss data are given in Tables IV.2 and IV.3.

The free acid, EDTA, and its derivatives all decomposed at relatively high temperatures; the lowest was recorded for HEDTA at 153°C and the highest for EDTA (Sequestrene AA) at 265°C. The salts, however, exhibited weight losses at lower temperatures because

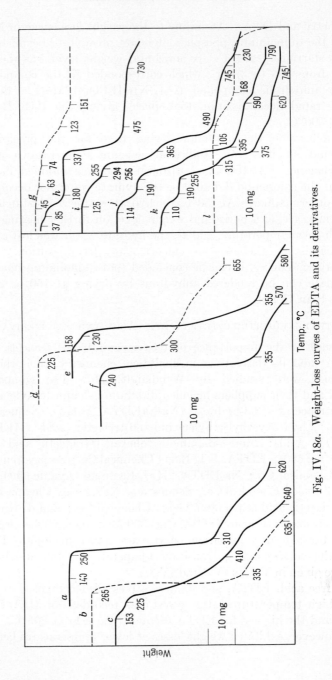

Fig. IV.18a. Weight-loss curves of EDTA and its derivatives.

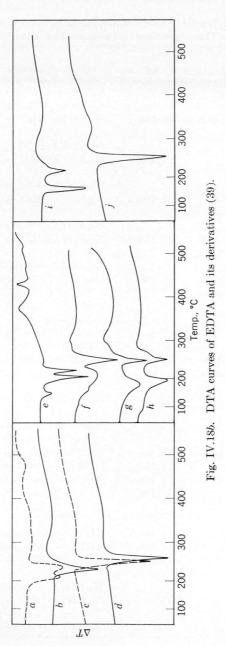

Fig. IV.18b. DTA curves of EDTA and its derivatives (39).

TABLE IV.2. Results of Thermal Analysis of EDTA and its Derivatives
(Minimum Thermogravimetric Decomposition Temperatures (39)

Compound	Figure ref.	Transition	Temp., °C
EDTA (J. T. Baker)	IV.18a, a	EDTA → decomposition	250
EDTA (Sequestrene AA)	IV.18a, b	EDTA → decomposition	265
$Na_2EDTA \cdot 2H_2O$ (Sequestrene Na2)	IV.18a, i	$Na_2EDTA \cdot 2H_2O \rightarrow Na_2EDTA$	125
		$Na_2EDTA \rightarrow Na_2CO_3$	294
$Na_2EDTA \cdot 2H_2O$ (Eastman)	IV.18a, j	$Na_2EDTA \cdot 2H_2O \rightarrow Na_2EDTA$	114
		$Na_2EDTA \rightarrow Na_2CO_3$	256
$Na_2EDTA \cdot 2H_2O$ (J. T. Baker)	IV.18a, k	$Na_2EDTA \cdot 2H_2O \rightarrow Na_2EDTA$	110
		$Na_2EDTA \rightarrow Na_2CO_3$	255
$Na_2EDTA \cdot 2H_2O$ (J. T. Baker) (3°C per min)	IV.18a, l	$Na_2EDTA \cdot 2H_2O \rightarrow Na_2EDTA$	105
		$Na_2EDTA \rightarrow Na_2CO_3$	230
$Na_2CaEDTA \cdot 2\text{-}3H_2O$ (Sequestrene Na2Ca)	IV.18a, h	$Na_2CaEDTA \cdot xH_2O \rightarrow$ $Na_2CaEDTA \cdot 3H_2O$	37
		$Na_2CaEDTA \cdot 3H_2O \rightarrow$ $Na_2CaEDTA$	85
		$Na_2CaEDTA \rightarrow Na_2CO_3 +$ $CaCO_3$	337
$Na_2CaEDTA \cdot 2\text{-}3H_2O$ (Sequestrene Na2Ca) (3°C per min)	IV.18a, g	$Na_2CaEDTA \cdot xH_2O \rightarrow$ $Na_2CaEDTA \cdot 3H_2O$	45
		$Na_2CaEDTA \cdot 3H_2O \rightarrow$ $NaCaEDTA \cdot 1H_2O$	63
		$Na_2CaEDTA \cdot 1H_2O \rightarrow$ $Na_2CaEDTA$	123
HEDTA (Chel DM Acid)	IV.18a, c	HEDTA → decomposition	153
DCHTA (Chel 600)	IV.18a, e	DCHTA → decomposition	158
DTPA (Chel 330 Acid)	IV.18a, d	DTPA → decomposition	225
NTA (Chel 300)	IV.18a, f	NTA → decomposition	240
	Endotherm peak maxima		
EDTA (J. T. Baker)	IV.18b, d	EDTA → decomposition	265
EDTA (Sequestrene AA)	IV.18b, c	EDTA → decomposition	257
$Na_2EDTA \cdot 2H_2O$ (J. T. Baker)	IV.18b, h	$Na_2EDTA \cdot 2H_2O \rightarrow Na_2EDTA$	195
		$Na_2EDTA \rightarrow$ decomposition	255
$Na_2EDTA \cdot 2H_2O$ (Eastman)	IV.18b, g	$Na_2EDTA \cdot 2H_2O \rightarrow Na_2EDTA$	185
		$Na_2EDTA \rightarrow$ decomposition	253

(continued)

TABLE IV.2 (*continued*)

Compound	Figure ref.	Transition	Temp., °C
$Na_2EDTA \cdot 2H_2O$ (Sequestrene Na2)	IV.18b, f	$Na_2EDTA \cdot 2H_2O \rightarrow Na_2EDTA$	212
		$Na_2EDTA \rightarrow$ decomposition	255
$Na_2CaEDTA \cdot 2\text{-}3H_2O$ (Sequestrene Na2Ca)	IV.18b, e	$Na_2CaEDTA \cdot xH_2O \rightarrow$ $Na_2CaEDTA \cdot 3H_2O$	107
		$Na_2CaEDTA \cdot 3H_2O \rightarrow$ $Na_2CaEDTA \cdot 1H_2O$	168
		$Na_2CaEDTA \cdot 1H_2O \rightarrow$ $Na_2CaEDTA$	190
		$NaCaEDTA \rightarrow$ decomposition	348 403
HEDTA (Chel DM Acid)	IV.18b, i	$HEDTA \rightarrow$ decomposition	168 223
DCHTA (Chel 600)	IV.18b, a	$DCHTA \rightarrow$ decomposition	214 237
DTPA (Chel 330 Acid)	IV.18b, b	$DTPA \rightarrow$ decomposition	235
NTA (Chel 300)	IV.18b, j	$NTA \rightarrow$ decomposition	260

TABLE IV.3. Weight-Loss Data for EDTA and its Derivatives (39)

Compound	Water, %	
	Experimental	Theoretical
$Na_2EDTA \cdot 2H_2O$ (J. T. Baker)	10.5 10.2 9.7 10.1	9.68
$Na_2EDTA \cdot 2H_2O$ (Eastman)	10.1 10.0	9.68
$Na_2EDTA \cdot 2H_2O$ (Sequestrene Na2)	9.3 9.5	9.68
$Na_2CaEDTA \cdot 2\text{-}3H_2O$ (Sequestrene Na2Ca)	1.72 (residual water) 1.93 1.81	
	11.7 (3-hydrate) 11.8 12.6	12.62
	4.34 (1-hydrate) 4.29 5.00	4.59

of the evolution of hydrate-bound water. Of the three samples of
Na₂EDTA·2H₂O studied, the J. T. Baker sample decomposed at
the lowest temperature, 110°C, followed by the Eastman sample
at 114°C, and then Sequestrene Na2 at 125°C. Horizontal weight
levels corresponding to the anhydrous salt were poorly defined, perhaps as a result of the rapid heating rate employed. The lower

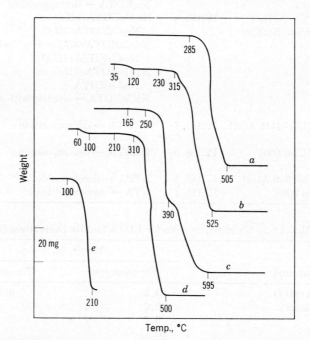

Fig. IV.19. The weight-loss curves of some metal 2-(o-hydroxyphenyl)benzoxa-
zole chelates (43). (a) Cadmium HPB chelate; (b) nickel HPB chelates; (c)
copper(II) HPB chelate; (d) cobalt(II) HPB chelate; (e) HPB.

heating rate, 3°C/min, gave a good horizontal weight level from 168
to 230°C for the J. T. Baker Na₂EDTA sample. The amount of
water evolved was greater than that required by theory on all of
the samples except the Sequestrene Na2. The J. T. Baker sample
had the largest amount of water, the source of which is unknown
unless it is loosely retained water. If it were the latter, the first weight
loss would probably occur at lower temperatures. After the loss of
the hydrate water, the anhydrous salt decomposed to yield a residue

of sodium carbonate. The thermal stability of the anhydrous compound compared favorably with that for the free acid.

These results are not in agreement with the previous work of Duval (40) in which dehydration was completed in the temperature range 100–120°C, while the anhydrous compound began to decompose at 135°C. The results above indicate that the anhydrous compound is far more stable than previously reported.

The thermal decomposition of NTA is in fair agreement with Duval (41), although the above value for the first weight loss is 40° lower. The EDTA and DTPA minimum decomposition temperatures are in excellent agreement with those previously reported (42). However, it is not known just how these previous values were determined.

The thermal decomposition of $Na_2CaEDTA \cdot 2,3H_2O$ revealed that perhaps the water of hydration corresponded to 1- and 3-hydrates instead of 2- and 3-hydrates. The weight-loss data at the 3°C/min heating rate gave breaks in the curve at compositions corresponding to the 3- and 1-hydrates but not the 2-hydrate. Another break was observed at 74°C, but it did not correspond to a composition having the formula for the 2-hydrate. Because definite weight levels were not obtained, this is not conclusive enough to designate them as true hydrates. Anhydrous $Na_2CaEDTA$ possessed excellent thermal properties; no weight losses were observed up to 337°C.

14. SOME 2-(o-HYDROXYPHENYL)BENZOXAZOLE METAL CHELATES

The thermogravimetry of the Cd, Cu(II), Co(II), and Ni(II) chelates of 2-(o-hydroxyphenyl)benzoxazole (HPB) was studied by Wendlandt (43). The weight-loss curves, as shown in Figure IV.19, revealed that the first weight losses for the chelates took place in the 165–285°C temperature range. The cadmium HPB chelate was the most stable, while the cobalt complex was the least stable. All of the metal chelates decomposed to yield the metal oxide levels in the temperature range from 500 to 595°C.

15. AMINE AND METAL TETRAPHENYLBORON COMPOUNDS

The thermogravimetry of the metal and amine tetraphenylboron compounds has been studied by Wendlandt and co-workers. Compounds of analytical interest that were studied include: NH_4, K, Rb, and Cs (44); Tl (45); Na, Li, Hg(I,II), and Ag (46); some primary, secondary, and tertiary amines (47); and 8-quinolinol and its derivatives (48).

The weight-loss curves of several of the tetraphenylboron compounds are given in Figure IV.20. All of the compounds began to decompose in the 130–265°C temperature range; ammonium TPB (TPB is tetraphenylboron) was the least stable, potassium TPB was the most stable.

After the initial decomposition of the precipitate the organic ma-

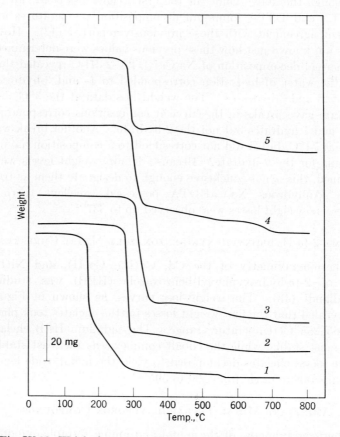

Fig. IV.20. Weight-loss curves of some tetraphenylboron compounds (44). (*1*) Ammonium tetraphenylborate; (*2*) mixture of ammonium and potassium tetraphenylborates; (*3*) potassium tetraphenylborate; (*4*) rubidium tetraphenylborate; (*5*) cesium tetraphenylborate.

terial of the tetraphenylboron ion is slowly oxidized until the level corresponding to the metal metaborate (MBO_2) is reached in the temperature range 715–825°C. The pyrolysis of the metal tetraphenylboron compound proceeds according to the general equation.

$$M[B(C_6H_5)_4] + 3O_2 \rightarrow MBO_2 + 24CO_2 + 10H_2O$$

where M is K, Rb, or Cs. The behavior of the ammonium precipitate was different from that of the other three compounds. This precipitate began to sublime at about 130°C. After about two-thirds of the material had sublimed, the remaining amount decomposed slowly, until at 625°C a small quantity of boric oxide (B_2O_3) remained in the thermobalance pan.

The drying temperatures previously described in the literature for the ammonium precipitate are correct. Care should be taken that the temperature does not exceed 130°C, where sublimation of the compound begins. Because there was such a great difference in the stability temperatures for the ammonium and potassium precipitates, it was thought that perhaps this could be the basis for an automatic determination of the two ions. Curve 2 of Figure IV.20 shows the pyrolysis of a mixture of 20.35% ammonium and 59.65% potassium tetraphenylboron. As the curve did not show two separate levels, the method cannot be used for the automatic determination of these two ions.

An interesting fact is also revealed by the pyrolysis curves. There seems to be a linear relationship between the size of the alkali metal ion and the temperature at which decomposition begins. The ammonium ion, which has a radius about equal to that of the potassium ion (1.48 Å), does not fall on the curve. This is perhaps due to the different type of behavior which the ammonium precipitate undergoes on pyrolysis. The other three compounds all decompose in the same general manner.

16. THORIUM AND ZIRCONIUM SALTS OF SOME ORGANIC ACIDS

The thermogravimetry of a number of organic acid salts of thorium and zirconium has been studied by Wendlandt (49–52). A representative group of weight-loss curves for several of the thorium salts is given in Figure IV.21, while the corresponding weight-loss and composition data are given in Table IV.4 (49).

In general, the first weight losses took place below 150°C, which,

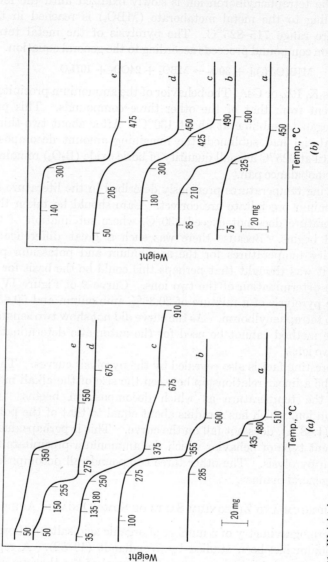

Fig. IV.21. Weight-loss curves of some thorium salts of organic acids (49). A: (a) Benzoate; (b) phenylacetate; (c) mercaptobenzothiazole; (d) pyrogallate; (e) m-hydroxybenzoate. B: (a) o-aminobenzoate; (b) cresoxyacetate; (c) cinnamate; (d) stearate; (e) 2,4-dichlorophenoxyacetate.

after various stages of decomposition and oxidation, gave thorium oxide weight levels in the 450–675°C temperature range. The oxide level appeared only above 675°C except in the case of thorium mercaptobenzothiazole, where it was not obtained even at 910°C, the upper limit of the thermobalance.

TABLE IV.4

Minimum Oxide Level Temperature Limits and Composition Data for Some Thorium Salts of Organic Acids (49)

Precipitate	Temp., °C[a]	Sample weight, mg	Oxide weight, mg Found	Oxide weight, mg Theor.	Formula found
1. Thorium benzoate	510	93.8	34.9	34.6	$Th(C_6H_5CO_2)_4$
2. Thorium phenylacetate	500	99.3	33.3	33.9	$Th(C_6H_5CH_2CO_2)_4$
3. Thorium mercaptobenzothiazole	>910	96.3	28.4	28.4	$Th(C_7H_4NS_2)_4$
4. Thorium pyrogallate	675	94.9	49.4	48.9	$Th(OH)_2(C_6H_3O_3)_2$
5. Thorium stearate	450	96.8	31.6	30.7	$Th(OH)_2(HOC_6H_4CO_2)_2$
6. Thorium m-hydroxybenzoate	550	99.8	53.8	52.3	$Th(OH)_2(HOC_6H_4CO_2)_2$
7. Thorium cinnamate	490	88.7	32.6	33.9	$Th(OH)(C_6H_5C_2H_2CO_3)_3$
8. Thorium m-cresoxyacetate	500	85.4	40.8	37.9	$Th(OH)_2(CH_3C_6H_4OCH_2-CO_2)_2$
9. Thorium o-aminobenzoate	450	93.1	52.9	58.6	$Th(OH)_3(NH_2C_6H_4CO_2)$
10. Thorium 2,4-dichlorophenoxyacetate	475	88.9	27.9	25.8	$Th(OH)(Cl_2C_6H_3OCH_3-CO_2)_3$

[a] Heating rate 4.5°/min.

17. SOME METAL OXALATES

The metal oxalates have been the subject for a number of thermogravimetry studies, both from a practical and theoretical viewpoint. Since many metal oxalates have been recommended for gravimetric determination procedures, the drying and ignition temperatures of these compounds have been of great interest. Many kinetics studies

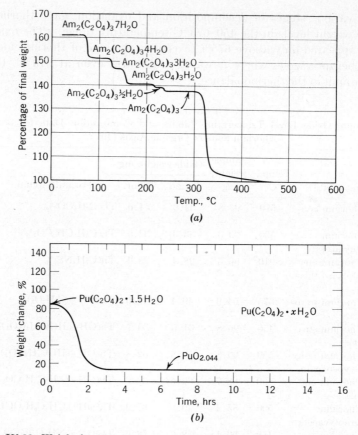

Fig. IV.22. Weight-loss curves of: (a) americium(III) oxalate hydrate in air; (b) plutonium oxalate hydrate (53,54).

have been carried out using metal oxalates in order to test various theories on the nature of the thermal dissociation process.

Duval (3) has summarized the thermogravimetry data for the drying and ignition temperatures of a large number of metal oxalates. Some of the more recent studies are reported here.

The weight-loss curves of americium(III) and plutonium(IV) oxalate hydrates are given in Figure IV.22.

Because of the highly toxic nature of these two materials, rather elaborate precautions were taken during the thermogravimetry of

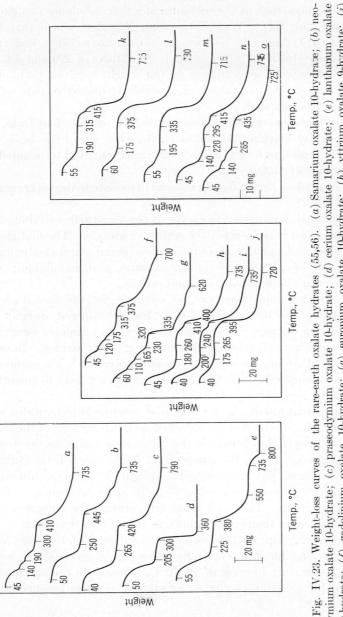

Fig. IV.23. Weight-loss curves of the rare-earth oxalate hydrates (55,56). (a) Samarium oxalate 10-hydrate; (b) neodymium oxalate 10-hydrate; (c) praseodymium oxalate 10-hydrate; (d) cerium oxalate 10-hydrate; (e) lanthanum oxalate 10-hydrate; (f) gadolinium oxalate 10-hydrate; (g) europium oxalate 10-hydrate; (h) yttrium oxalate 9-hydrate· (i) holmium oxalate 10-hydrate; (j) erbium oxalate 6-hydrate; (k) lutetium; (l) ytterbium; (m) thulium; (n) dysprosium; (o) terbium.

these substances, such as the enclosure of a thermobalance in a glove-box (see Chap. III).   Waterbury et al. (53) determined that Pu-$(C_2O_4)_2 \cdot 1 \cdot 5H_2O$ began to lose weight slowly above 50°C and very rapidly above 150°C.   Between the temperatures of 290 and 330°C, the rate of weight loss decreased as the weight level for plutonium dioxide began.   No indication of a stable hydrated oxalate or of carbonate was indicated.

The weight-loss curve for americium(III) oxalate 7-hydrate, as determined by Markin (54), indicated the existence of the 4-, 3-, 1-, and 0.5-hydrates, as well as anhydrous $Am_2(C_2O_4)_3$ and terminated in the formation of AmO_2.

The weight-loss curves for the rare-earth oxalate hydrates are given in Figure IV.23.

The thermal decomposition curves of the rare-earth metal oxalate hydrates can be roughly classified into three groups.   The first group includes the oxalates of lanthanum, praseodymium, and neodymium; the second consists of samarium, europium, and gadolinium; the third contains yttrium, holmium, and erbium.

In the first group, there was no evidence for the formation of intermediate hydrates.   The 10-hydrates decomposed directly to the anhydrous oxalates.   However, the anhydrous oxalates were very unstable and immediately decomposed to give the oxides.   In only one case, lanthanum, was a basic carbonate observed.   The minimum oxide level temperatures in this group were higher than in the other two groups.

In the second group, the formation of intermediate hydrates was first observed.   No levels were obtained, perhaps because of the heating rate employed, but breaks in the curve were found for the 6- and the 2-hydrates.   Again, the composition for the anhydrous oxalates was approached, but no horizontal weight levels were obtained. The oxide levels were obtained at slightly lower temperatures than in the first group.   The oxide level temperature for europium was anomalously lower than for the other two elements in this group.

In the third group, the first stable intermediate hydrate levels were observed.   The 2-hydrates appeared to be stable, giving stable levels over a temperature interval of 40–90°C.   Breaks in the curve were noted for the anhydrous oxalates, which immediately decomposed to give the oxides.

Dysprosium and terbium can be placed in Group II, with samarium,

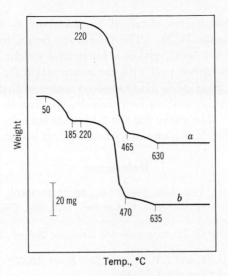

Fig. IV.24. Weight-loss curves of: (a) scandium oxalate 2-hydrate; (b) scandium oxalate 6-hydrate (55).

europium, and gadolinium, because the formation of intermediate hydrates was indicated but definite weight levels were not obtained. Ytterbium, thulium, and lutetium can be placed in Group III, with yttrium, holmium, and erbium, because stable hydrate weight levels were obtained.

As in the decomposition of the other metal oxalates, the 2-hydrates appear to be surprisingly stable. The anhydrous metal oxalates are apparently too unstable to exist, and decompose with the evolution of carbon monoxide and carbon dioxide. It may be possible to determine the mixture with a Group I metal oxalate because of the stability of the Group III metal oxalate 2-hydrate.

Contrary to the results of Duval (57), it was found that scandium precipitated as scandium oxalate 6-hydrate, in agreement with the careful study by Riley (58) but in disagreement with Duval's 10-hydrate. It is difficult to understand the apparent discrepancy in composition of the original precipitate and also the widely divergent weight-loss curves obtained. Duval reported a curve inflection which approximated the composition for the 5-hydrate; it was not isolated however. No horizontal plateau was obtained for a composition corresponding to an anhydrous compound.

The weight-loss curves obtained for scandium 6- and 2-hydrates are given in Figure IV.24. The 6-hydrate began to lose water of hydration at about 50°C, giving a horizontal weight level from 185 to 220°C, which agreed well with the composition for the 2-hydrate. Beyond 220°C, $Sc_2(C_2O_4)_3 \cdot 2H_2O$ evolved water of hydration, as well as carbon monoxide and carbon dioxide, to give the Sc_2O_3 weight level at 635°C. The curve for the 2-hydrate was similar, except for the loss of the first four moles of hydrate-bound water.

References

1. Gordon, S., and C. Campbell, *Anal. Chem.*, **32**, 271R (1960).
2. Jacque, L., G. Guiochon, and P. Gendrel, *Bull. Soc. Chim. France*, **1961**, 1061.
3. Duval, C., *Inorganic Thermogravimetric Analysis*, 2nd ed., Elsevier, Amsterdam, 1963.
4. Lukaszewski, G. M., and J. P. Redfern, *Lab. Pract.*, **10**, 552 (1961).
5. Duval, C., *Anal. Chem.*, **23**, 1271 (1951).
6. Palei, P. N., I. G. Sentyurin, and I. S. Sklyarenko, *Zh. Anal. Khim.*, **12**, 329 (1957).
7. Zagorski, Z., *Przemysl Chem.*, **8**, 326 (1952).
8. Duval, C., *Anal. Chim. Acta*, **13**, 32 (1955).
9. Newkirk, A. E., and I. Aliferis, *Anal. Chem.*, **30**, 982 (1958).
10. Dupuis, T., and C. Duval, *Anal. Chim. Acta*, **3**, 191 (1949).
11. Erdey, L., and F. Paulik, *Acta Chim. Acad. Sci. Hung.*, **7**, 45 (1955).
12. Milner, O. I., and L. Gordon, *Talanta*, **4**, 115 (1960).
13. Duval, C., ref. 3, pp. 227–228.
14. Griffith, E. J., *Anal. Chem.*, **29**, 198 (1957).
15. Hoffman, I., M. Schnitzer, and J. R. Wright, *Chem. Ind.* (*London*), **1958**, 261.
16. Schnitzer, M., J. R. Wright, and I. Hoffman, *Anal. Chem.*, **31**, 440 (1959).
17. Campbell, P. F., M. H. Ortner, and C. J. Anderson, *Anal. Chem.*, **33**, 58 (1961).
18. Ropp, R. C., and M. A. Aia, *Anal. Chem.*, **34**, 1288 (1962).
19. Biffen, F. M., *Anal. Chem.*, **28**, 1133 (1956).
20. Erdey, L., F. Paulik, G. Svehla, and G. Liptay, *Z. Anal. Chem.*, **182**, 329 (1961).
21. Erdey, L., G. Liptay, G. Svehla, and F. Paulik, *Talanta*, **9**, 489 (1962).
22. Dupuis, T., and J. Dupuis, *Microchim. Acta*, **1958**, 186.
23. Dupuis, T., and C. Duval, *Chim. Anal.*, **33**, 189 (1951).
24. Duval, C., *Anal. Chim. Acta*, **13**, 32 (1955).
25. Belcher, R., L. Erdey, F. Paulik, and G. Liptay, *Talanta*, **5**, 53 (1960).
26. Newkirk, A. E., and R. Laware, *Talanta*, **9**, 169 (1962).
27. Wendlandt, W. W., *Anal. Chem.*, **27**, 1277 (1955).
28. Wendlandt, W. W., *Anal. Chim. Acta*, **21**, 116 (1959).

29. Wendlandt, W. W., and J. M. Bryant, *Anal. Chim. Acta*, **13**, 550 (1955).
30. Berlin, A., and R. J. Robinson. *Anal. Chim. Acta*, **24**, 224, 319, 432 (1961).
31. Duval, C., *Anal. Chim. Acta*, **4**, 159 (1950).
32. Dupuis, T., and C. Duval, *Anal. Chim. Acta*, **4**, 256 (1950).
33. Wendlandt, W. W., *Anal. Chim. Acta*, **20**, 267 (1959).
34. Duval, C., *Inorganic Thermogravimetric Analysis*, 1st ed., Elsevier, Amsterdam, 1953, pp. 130, 132.
35. Duval, C., ref. 3, pp. 245–246.
36. Wendlandt, W. W., and J. A. Brabson, *Anal. Chem.*, **30**, 61 (1958).
37. Brabson, J. A., and O. W. Edwards, *Anal. Chem.*, **28**, 1485 (1956).
38. Wendlandt, W. W., and W. M. Hoffman, *Anal. Chem.*, **32**, 1011 (1960).
39. Wendlandt, W. W., *Anal. Chem.*, **32**, 848 (1960).
40. Duval, C., *Anal. Chim. Acta*, **16**, 545 (1959).
41. Duval, C., *Anal. Chim. Acta*, **20**, 20 (1959).
42. *Keys to Chelation*, Dow Chemical Co. Bull., 1959, p. 4.
43. Wendlandt, W. W., *Anal. Chim. Acta*, **18**, 638 (1958).
44. Wendlandt, W. W., *Anal. Chem.*, **28**, 1001 (1956).
45. Wendlandt, W. W., *Anal. Chim. Acta*, **16**, 216 (1957.)
46. Wendlandt, W. W., *Chemist-Analyst*, **46**, 38 (1957.)
47. Wendlandt, W. W., *Chemist-Analyst*, **47**, 6 (1958).
48. Wendlandt, W. W., J. H. Van Tassel, and G. R. Horton, *Anal. Chim. Acta*, **23**, 332 (1960).
49. Wendlandt, W. W., *Anal. Chem.*, **29**, 800 (1957).
50. Wendlandt, W. W., *Anal. Chim. Acta*, **17**, 295 (1957).
51. Wendlandt, W. W., *Anal. Chim. Acta*, **18**, 316 (1958).
52. Wendlandt, W. W., *Anal. Chim. Acta*, **16**, 129 (1957).
53. Waterbury, G. R., R. M. Douglass, and C. F. Metz, *Anal. Chem.*, **33**, 1018 (1961).
54. Markin, T. L., *J. Inorg. Nucl. Chem.*, **7**, 290 (1958).
55. Wendlandt, W. W., *Anal. Chem.*, **30**, 58 (1958).
56. Wendlandt, W. W., *Anal. Chem.*, **31**, 408 (1959).
57. Duval, C., ref. 3, p. 287.
58. Riley, R. F., Ph.D. Thesis, Michigan State University, 1954.

CHAPTER V

DIFFERENTIAL THERMAL ANALYSIS

A. Introduction

Differential thermal analysis (DTA) is a thermal technique in which the heat effects, associated with physical or chemical changes, are recorded as a function of temperature or time as the substance is heated at a uniform rate. Heat or enthalpic changes, either exothermic or endothermic, are caused by phase transitions—such as fusion, crystalline structure inversions, boiling, sublimation, and vaporization; dehydration reactions; dissociation reactions or decomposition reactions; oxidation and reduction reactions; destruction of crystalline lattice structure; and chemical reactions. Generally speaking, phase transitions, dehydration, reduction, and some decomposition reactions produce endothermic effects, whereas crystallization, oxidation, and some decomposition reactions produce exothermic effects.

The heat effects occurring during these chemical and physical changes are measured by a *differential* method, hence the name, *differential thermal analysis*. In thermal analysis (see Chap. XI), the temperature of the sample is measured as a function of time, and a heating or cooling curve is recorded. In this technique, the sample temperature is continuously compared with a reference material temperature, the difference in temperature being recorded as a function of furnace temperature or time (assuming that the furnace temperature rise is linear with respect to time). Experimentally, this is accomplished by employing a furnace that contains a sample holder or block and containing two symmetrically located and identical chambers. Each chamber contains an identical thermocouple or other temperature detection device (thermistor, resistance thermometer, etc.). The sample to be investigated is placed in one chamber and a thermally inert substance, having a similar heat capacity such as α-alumina (Al_2O_3), is placed in the other. The sample and α-alumina are then heated at a uniform rate by the furnace and the temperature difference (ΔT) between them, as detected by

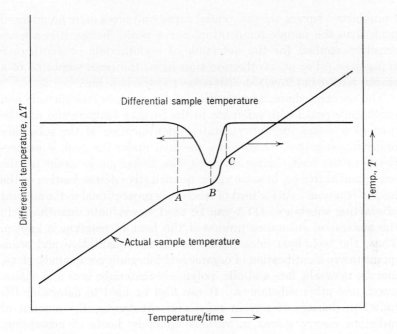

Fig. V.1. Comparison between sample temperature and differential sample temperature.

temperature detection devices, is recorded as a function of time or temperature of the furnace.

A comparison between the actual sample temperature and the differential sample temperature for an endothermic reaction is illustrated in Figure V.1.

The sample began to undergo an endothermic transition at point A on the curves. As can be seen on the sample temperature curve, the sample temperature is no longer linear with respect to time, but lags the furnace temperature due to the absorption of heat. At about B, the reaction is completed and the sample temperature increases, attaining the furnace temperature again at C. In the case of the differential temperature curve, the sample and reference temperature differ only during the actual transition which began at A. This results in a peak in the curve, the maximum of which occurs at about B. Above B, the curve returns to the base line, due to the equalization of sample and reference temperatures. As can be seen from the two curves, the differential curve contains a more pronounced peak than the sample temperature curve peak; hence, it is a more sensitive method for the detection of endothermic or exothermic transitions. For an exothermic transition, the peak would be of a similar nature but inverted with respect to the base line.

The number, shape, and position of the various endothermic and exothermic peaks with reference to the furnace temperature may be used as a means for the qualitative identification of the substance under investigation. Also, since the area under the peak is proportional to the heat change involved, the technique is useful for the semiquantitative or, in some cases, quantitative determination of the heat of reaction. As the heat of reaction is proportional to the amount of reacting substance, DTA can be used to evaluate quantitatively the amount of substance present if the heat of reaction is known. Thus, the technique finds much use in the qualitative and semiquantitative identification of organic and inorganic compounds, clays, metals, minerals, fats and oils, polymeric materials, coal and shales, wood, and other substances. It can also be used to determine the radiation damage of certain polymeric substances, the amount of radiation energy stored in various minerals, heats of adsorption, effectiveness of catalytic materials, heats of polymerization, and others. Quantitatively, it can be used for the determination of a reactive component in a mixture, or the heat of reaction involved in a physical or chemical change.

Because of the renewed interest in DTA during the past ten years, the literature on this subject has grown exponentially. Excellent reviews on the subject have been written by Murphy (1–4), Pask and Warner (5), Norton (6), Grim (7), Ramachandran and Bhattacharyya (8), Lehmann et al. (9), Lukaszewski and Redfern (10), Garn (11), Redfern (12), and Bhattacharyya and Ganguly (13). Books and/or book chapters have been written by Smothers et al. (14), Mackenzie (15), Smothers and Chiang (16), Kissinger and Newman (17), Gordon (18), Gordon and Campbell (19), and Wendlandt (20). It is of interest to note that in ref. 16 a bibliography of over 1546 titles has been compiled.

Some mention should be made of the historical aspects of DTA, which represents an interesting example of a multiscientific discipline approach to the development of a new experimental technique. In the now-classic paper entitled "De l'action de la chaleur sur les argiles," Le Chatelier (21) described, in 1887, a method for studying clays and minerals which was to lead to the development of the technique now known as differential thermal analysis. Le Chatelier and other investigators, Ashley (22), Wholin (23), Rieke (24), Wallach (25), and Mellor and Holdcroft (26), studied the thermal changes which took place in a substance as it was heated by recording its temperature, as measured with a thermocouple, as a function of time. Breaks in the "heating curve" were thus obtained, indicative of dehydration, decomposition, phase transitions, and other reactions initiated by heating. This heating-curve method was not very sensitive to small heat effects and was adversely affected by changes in heating rate, recording equipment, etc.

In 1899, Roberts-Austen (27) suggested that a two- (instead of a one-) thermocouple system be employed. One of the thermocouples was placed in the sample and the other in a reference block in the furnace. Thus, the differential temperature reading, which was more sensitive to small temperature changes in the sample than the single-thermocouple method, was recorded or plotted as a function of time or temperature. In a much neglected paper, Burgess (28), in 1908, discussed the merits of the single- and double-thermocouple system, as applied to cooling curve data. This paper should be required reading for all serious investigators in the field of DTA so that the principles discussed will not be "discovered" again, as has been done so often in the past by other workers without giving credit to Burgess' prophetic investigations. Burgess (28) discussed the representation of cooling curve data by plots of sample temperature, T, vs. time, t, difference in temperature between T and the temperature of a neutral body, T', or $T - T' = \Delta T$, in which ΔT was plotted against t; T vs. dT/dt; and T vs. dt/dT. These various representations were interpreted for three kinds of transformations: (a) The substance remains at a constant temperature; (b) the substance cools at a reduced rate, which may or may not be constant over a portion of the transformation; and (c) the substance undergoes an increase in temperature during the first part of the transformation.

Burgess (28) also discussed the various types of experimental arrangements and recording systems known at that time. Equations were also presented for the calculation of the heats of transformation that were observed; this was done some 36 years before the work of Speil et al. (29).

The first application of the differential thermocouple method to the study of a chemical problem was made by Houldsworth and Cobb (30), although Fenner (31) had previously studied the phase transitions in silicate minerals. The former investigators studied the behavior of fire clays and bauxite on heating, a field of investigation in which DTA was to become an important tool. Since this first paper, numerous investigations on the thermal decomposition of various clays and minerals have appeared in the literature, included among them are studies by Norton (6), Grim (7), Berkelhamer (32), Kerr and Kulp (33), Kauffman and Dilling (34), Foldvari-Vogl (35), and Mackenzie (15). DTA is now accepted as a routine tool for the qualitative and semiquantitative determination of a large number of clays and minerals.

It has only been quite recently that DTA has been applied to basic chemical problems. Besides the study of inorganic and organic systems, the study of polymer systems by DTA has created a great amount of interest.

B. Theory

A great amount of work has been carried out concerning the theoretical interpretation of the DTA curve. All of the theories relate, in some manner, the area of the differential curve peak to the various parameters of the sample and apparatus. The equations representing these parameters were developed through the use of conventional heat transfer relationships and the geometry of the sample and sample holder. The derivation of each of these theories is beyond the scope of this discussion, so that only the final mathematical expressions will be presented.

In the theory developed by Speil et al. (29) and modified by Kerr and Kulp (33), the area enclosed by the differential curve is

$$\frac{M(\Delta H)}{gk} = \int_{a}^{c} \Delta T \, dt \qquad (V.1)$$

where M is the mass of reactive sample, ΔH is the heat of reaction, g is a geometrical shape constant for the apparatus, k is the thermal conductivity of the sample, ΔT is the differential temperature, and a and c are the integration limits of the differential curve. This expression is perhaps one of the simplest and relates the heat of reaction of the sample to the peak area through use of the proportionality constants or near constants, g and k. It neglects the differential terms and the temperature gradients in the sample and also considers the peak area to be independent of the specific heat of the sample. It is basically only an approximate relationship.

Vold (36) derived the expression:

$$\frac{\Delta H}{C_s}\left(\frac{df}{dt}\right) = \left(\frac{dy}{dt}\right) + A(y - y_s) \qquad (V.2)$$

where C_s is the heat capacity of the cell plus its contents, f is the fraction of the sample transformed at any time t, y is the differential temperature, y_s is the steady-state value of the differential temperature achieved at a sufficiently long time after the initial condition $y = y_1$ at $t = t_1$, and A is a constant.

At the beginning of the peak, $y_1 = 0$ at $t = t_1 = 0$. The differential temperature then rises to a value y_s, dependent primarily on the difference in heat capacity of the sample and reference materials, the heating rate, and the heat-transfer coefficients. After a transformation is completed, the differential temperature again approaches y_s according to the above equation.

A practical analysis of the DTA curve involves the plotting of $\log(y - y_s)$ vs. time, beginning at the top of a peak. The points should all lie on the curve which becomes linear at the end of the transformation and yields a value of the time at which the transformation is completed.

The inherent limitations of this theory, according to Vold (36), are: (a) the assumption of a constant value of the heat capacity of the sample; and (b) the assumption that the sample temperature is uniform throughout at each time instant. The heat capacity of the sample is that of the cell plus that of the transformed amount of the sample plus that of the untransformed amount. These amounts change during the course of the reaction. Thus, in practice, if the heat capacity of the cell is made large, this fluctuation is considered to be minor, although sensitivity is reduced. The non-uniformity of the sample temperature is not considered to be important enough to vitiate the method, although it does effect the transformation temperature rather than the calculation of the heat effects. Reduction of the heating rate, measurement of the sample temperature at its outside surface nearest the furnace wall, and various extrapolation procedures all reduce the error but do not eliminate it entirely (36).

Using a sample block constructed from an infinitely high thermal conductivity metal such as nickel, in which the sample holder geometry is a cylinder, Boersma (37) found that the peak area was equal to

$$\int_{t_1}^{t_2} \theta_0 dt = qa^2/4\lambda \qquad \text{(V.3)}$$

where t_1 and t_2 are the times at the beginning and end of the peak, q is the heat of transformation per unit volume, θ_0 is the differential temperature, a is the radius of cavity filled with sample, and λ is the thermal conductivity of the sample material.

For a spherical metal sample container

$$\int_{t_1}^{t_2} \theta_0 dt = qa^2/6\lambda \qquad \text{(V.4)}$$

and for a one-dimensional case of a flat plate

$$\int_{t_1}^{t_2} \theta_0 dt = qa^2/2\lambda \qquad \text{(V.5)}$$

Lastly, for an infinitely large ceramic block, there are no finite solutions for the one- and two-dimensional cases; there is a solution for a spherical holder, however, or

$$\int_{t_1}^{t_2} \theta_0 dt = \frac{qa^2}{6} \left(\frac{2}{\lambda_c} + \frac{1}{\lambda_s} \right) \qquad \text{(V.6)}$$

where λ_c is the thermal conductivity of the ceramic material and λ_s is the thermal conductivity of the sample.

In the above equations as applied to a conventional DTA apparatus, the sample is used for two entirely different purposes:

(a) a producer of heat

(b) heat measuring resistance in which the flow of heat develops a temperature difference to be measured.

To separate these two functions, Boersma (37) recommended the use of metal sample and reference cups in which the temperature difference was measured from outside the sample and reference materials. The peak area then depended on the heat of reaction and the calibration factor of the instrument and no longer contained any sample properties such as volume and thermal conductivity. The peak area is now related to the heat of reaction by

$$\int_{t_1}^{t_2} \theta dt = \frac{mq}{G} \tag{V.7}$$

where m is the mass of the sample, and G is the heat-transfer coefficient between the nickel cup and the surrounding nickel shield. Although no data were presented, Boersma (37) claimed that measurements on the dehydration of $CuSO_4 \cdot 5H_2O$ confirmed equation (V.7) quantitatively. The samples were said to differ widely in packing density.

The treatment of the heat-transfer process for a sample slab and a cylinder has also been presented by Tsang (38).

C. Factors Affecting Results

With much similarity to thermogravimetry, DTA curves are not very reproducible from one apparatus to another. Also as with weight-loss curves, various workers have expected too much of DTA curves. Since the data are quite empirical, a correlation cannot be made between, say, peak maximum temperature and thermal stability of the sample material. Not only are the peak temperatures dependent on the various instrumental and sample parameters, but so are the general shape of the curve and the magnitudes of the peaks and peak areas. Since the curves are so dependent on instrument factors, there has been much consideration given to the standardization of DTA units, especially their heating rates and sample holders (39–41). However, it is doubtful that these recommendations will be accepted.

The DTA curve is dependent on two general types of variables; they are: (a) instrumental factors; and (b) sample characteristics. The former includes:

(a) Instrumental factors

(1) Furnace atmosphere
(2) Furnace size and shape
(3) Sample holder material
(4) Sample holder geometry
(5) Wire and bead size of thermocouple junction
(6) Heating rate
(7) Speed and response of recording instrument
(8) Thermocouple location in sample

The latter consists of:

(b) Sample characteristics

   (1) Particle size
   (2) Thermal conductivity
   (3) Heat capacity
   (4) Packing density
   (5) Swelling or shrinkage of sample
   (6) Amount of sample
   (7) Effect of diluent
   (8) Degree of crystallinity

1. SAMPLE HOLDER MATERIAL

In general, a sample holder, either of the block or cup type, constructed of a low thermal conductivity material, will give better peak resolution for a endothermic reaction than one constructed of a high thermal conductivity material (42–44); for exothermic reactions, the resolution is worse for a low thermal conductivity material. Since most reactions studied by DTA are endothermic, it would appear that the low thermal conductivity sample holders would be preferred. In actual practice, however, the metal sample holders (high thermal conductivity) are more widely used, perhaps because of the ease of their fabrication and their durability and strength.

A comparison between ceramic and metal sample holders has been made by Webb (40), Mackenzie (46), Arens (42), and Gerard-Hirne and Lamy (43). Webb (40) found that for reactions involving the evolution of a gas, the ceramic sample holders gave peaks with maximas shifted to lower temperatures. However, for a crystalline phase transition such as the $\alpha \rightarrow \beta$ quartz transformation, the results were identical for metal and ceramic containers. Thus, it was concluded that the difference was due to the ceramic holder allowing the gaseous decomposition products to diffuse into the furnace atmosphere, lowering the concentration of the gas in the sample, and so leading to a more rapid completion of the reaction. By using silica liners in the ceramic holder, this gaseous diffusion did not take place and hence the results were identical for ceramic and metal containers.

A comparison of the two types of sample holders (40) for endothermic reactions, such as the decomposition of $Ca(OH)_2$, $CaCO_3$,

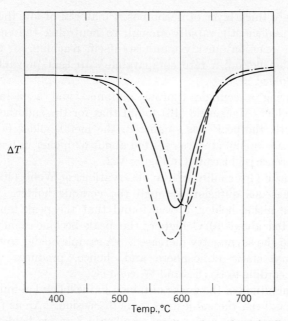

ΔT

400   500   600   700
Temp.,°C

Fig. V.2. Thermograms for the main endothermic peak of kaolinite; (- - -) porous alumina holder; (——) nickel holder; (·······) nickel holder with lid (46).

and $MgCO_3$, showed that the nickel block was only slightly less sensitive than a ceramic sample holder. At temperatures of about 500°C, it gave peak areas which were about 80% of those for the ceramic, and at about 900°C, about 70%. The metal holder yielded peaks which were sharper and also increased the resolution of adjacent peaks. Webb (40) explained this as follows: An endothermic reaction begins in the portion of the sample nearest the walls of the sample well and in case of the metal (nickel, in this case) holder, heat is readily available from the large mass of metal of high thermal conductivity in contact with the cooler decomposing material. Rapid heat flow into this superficial layer masks the early part of the reaction by neutralizing the endothermic effect before it can affect the thermocouple junction. It is for this reason that the endothermic reaction appears to start at a higher temperature. When the temperature reaches a value at which the rate of decomposition becomes so rapid that the heat from the metal can no longer penetrate the

increasingly thick layer of decomposed material of low thermal conductivity sufficiently rapidly enough to neutralize the endothermic
effect, the reaction quickly manifests itself, reaching, for the rest of
the reaction period, a rate comparable with that prevailing in the
ceramic holder.

Comparing a ceramic (porous alumina) and a metal (nickel)
sample holder, Mackenzie (46) found that for the endothermic peak
in kaolinite, the peak was smaller in the metal holder (about 75%
that of the ceramic) and was shifted about 6° higher in temperature.
This difference is illustrated in Figure V.2.

Mackenzie (46) confirmed the observations of Webb (40) concerning the gaseous diffusion through the ceramic holder. Placing a
lid on the nickel holder, it was found that the peak temperatures
were shifted about 10°C higher, the peak became somewhat narrower, and the asymmetry increased. A sample holder cover induces
an internal static atmosphere and, hence, produces deleterious
effects, according to Bayliss and Warne (44).

The magnitude of the peaks obtained in nickel and alumina sample
holders has been the subject of some discussion. Arens (42) stated
that the exothermic peaks were smaller in ceramic holders than in
nickel, while Gerard-Hirne and Lamy (43) reported the opposite
effect. Mackenzie (46) found that the exothermic peak in montmorillonite was smaller in a nickel sample holder than in alumina,
in agreement with the latter investigators.

Mackenzie (46), although citing the advantages of a nickel sample
holder, does not think that rigid standardization upon this type of
holder is desirable. He found that while the nickel holder was suitable for dolomite determinations, an alumina holder of low porosity
gave reasonable results. For some studies, the alumina holder may
be preferable since the loss of 25% in peak area with the metal holder
may be quite serious.

In comparing two different metal sample holders, nickel and platinum, Gruver (45) found that peak intensities were smaller for the
nickel holder than for the platinum. This difference was ascribed to
the difference in heat capacities of the two metals and the resulting
heat reservoir effect. Boersma (37) concluded that although ceramic
holders give the greater peak area, they are not usable because the
temperature fields of several samples in the same block can penetrate
each other, thus causing mutual interference.

2. GEOMETRY OF SAMPLE HOLDER

The geometry of the sample holder has a large effect on the intensity of the peak and the peak areas obtained.   In Boersma's (37) equations for peak area, the value of $qa^2/4\lambda$ was obtained for a cylindrical metal sample holder and $qa^2/6\lambda$ for a spherical holder.   Experi-

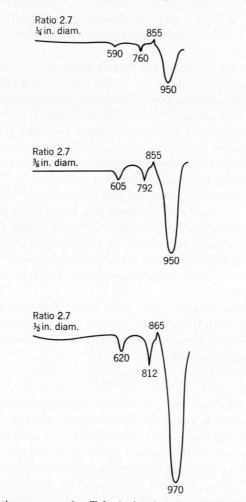

Fig. V.3. DTA thermograms for Talc A showing the effect of hole diameter on the shape of the peaks.   Bulk volume to volume of sample holder ratio of 2.7 (5).

mentally, the spherical holder is difficult to construct, although an approach to a sphere has been made by Lehmann et al. (9), who used a cylindrical holder with a rounded bottom. In a spherical arrangement, the thermal effects from all parts of the sample arrive "in phase" at the centrally located thermocouple junction (44).

Hauser (47) found, using platinum foil-lined cylindrical sample holders, that a $3/16$-in. diameter holder gave "sharper" peaks than the $1/8$- and $1/4$-in. diameter containers. All cylindrical holders were $3/4$ in. in height.

Using a nickel block having sample holes of $1/4$, $3/8$, and $1/2$ in. in diameter, Pask and Warner (5) found that, at a given heating rate, the sizes of the reaction peaks increased with an increase in size of the holes. This effect is illustrated in Figure V.3. Thus, because the thermal effects always start at about the same temperature, the peak temperature for a given reaction shifts to higher values, since a longer time is necessary for completion of the reaction. The degree of shift, however, is not constant; it is controlled by the rate of reaction and is dependent upon the test material. If it is desirable to increase the sensitivity to illustrate reactions accompanied by small heat effects, the size of the sample can be increased. However, if a number of reactions occur close to each other, the size of sample, i.e., the diameter, should be reduced in order to get maximum resolving power. As the samples get larger, the peaks begin to merge and lose identity.

No definitive studies have been made comparing a block-type sample holder with the sample cup type. The lack of a heat reservoir in the sample cup type should increase the intensity and the area of the curve peaks obtained.

3. THERMOCOUPLES

Boersma (37) has shown by theoretical considerations that the heat loss by conduction along the thermocouple wires is fairly large and can have a considerable effect on the area of the peak obtained. Since the temperature in the sample center is measured by means of a thermocouple, part of the heat produced in the sample is carried away by the thermocouple wires and therefore too low a sample temperature is measured.

In Figure V.4 is illustrated a spherical sample-filled cavity in a nickel block containing a thermocouple junction of radius r_0. During

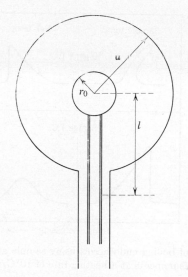

Fig. V.4. Heat leakage through thermocouple wires (37).

a reaction, a temperature gradient exists in the wires over length l. It is assumed that at the distance l, which is slightly larger than a, the radius of the sample cavity, the wires have attained the temperature of the nickel block. If the area of the thermocouple wires is A and θ_0 is the thermojunction temperature, the amount of heat carried away by the thermocouple leads is

$$Q = \int_{t_1}^{t_2} \frac{A\lambda p}{l} \, \theta_0 dt \qquad (V.8)$$

where λ_p is the thermal conductivity of the wires. By various mathematical manipulations, the peak area for a spherical sample holder becomes

$$\int_{t_1}^{t_2} \theta_0 dt = \frac{qa^2}{6\lambda} \cdot \frac{\alpha}{1 + (\Lambda/\lambda)} \qquad (V.9)$$

where α, which is very nearly unity, comes from the altered geometry of the holder and is equal to

$$\alpha = 1 - (r_0^2/a^2) [3 - 2(r_0/a)] \qquad (V.10)$$

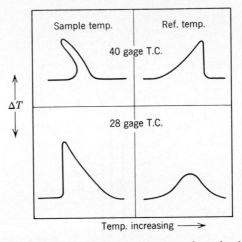

Fig. V.5. Character of boiling endotherms using sample and reference temperature measurements at a heating rate of 10°C/min (48).

and Λ is the heat leakage through the wires, or

$$\Lambda = \lambda_p(r_0/l)(A/4\pi r_0^2)[1 - (r_0/a)] \qquad (V.11)$$

For low thermal conductivity samples, $(\lambda/\Lambda) \ll 1$, the peak area
will become independent of the sample conductivity λ, whereas a
high sample conductivity will cause an inverse proportional relationship.

For cylindrical holders, the expression is

$$\int_{t_1}^{t_2} \theta dt = \frac{qa^2}{4\lambda} \cdot \frac{1 - \dfrac{r_0^2}{a^2}\left[1 + 2\ln\dfrac{a}{r_0}\right]}{1 + \dfrac{A}{l}\left(\dfrac{\lambda_p}{\lambda}\right)\dfrac{\ln(a/r_0)}{2\pi h}} \qquad (V.12)$$

For most samples, the thermal conductivities are about 0.3 J/ms
°C, which makes λ/Λ about equal to unity. Therefore, according
to equation (V.9), the heat leakage through the wires reduces the
peak area to less than 50% of its theoretical value.

Hauser (47) also studied the effect of wire and thermojunction
size on the peak shapes. He concluded that the larger wire size (No.
22 compared to No. 28 gage) and the larger bead size (1.43 mm
compared to 0.8 mm) gave the more pronounced peaks on the thermal

decomposition curves. In considering the electrical resistance characteristics of the thermocouple wires, he found that No. 28 gage wires have too high a resistance for proper electrical properties without too great a thermal conductivity. A 1.43 mm thermojunction diameter was much more efficient in maintaining the emf than the smaller junctions, but still the mass of the junction was not great enough to absorb an excessive amount of heat.

The effect of thermocouple wire size on the transition temperature of benzoic acid and toluene was studied by Vassallo and Harden (48). For No. 28 gage wire, at a heating rate of 10°C/min, the melting point (mp) of benzoic acid was 121.7°C. The effect was also observed for a heating rate of 40°C/min. For the No. 28 gage wire, the peak heights were about 15% less than those obtained for the larger wire. The difference in peak shapes and intensities for the sample and reference temperatures using the various wire gages is illustrated in Figure V.5. The shapes of the curves are entirely different for the different size wires.

4. THERMOCOUPLE LOCATION

The temperature distribution in reference and sample materials has been calculated by Smyth (49) and is illustrated in Figure V.6. The distribution curves for the reference material are at all instants of time identical parabolas, as would be deduced from the equation

$$T = T_c + \alpha t + \frac{1}{2}(1/a)\alpha x^2 \qquad (V.13)$$

where T is the temperature, t is the time, x is the distance in the direction of heat flow, α is the heating rate, a is the diffusivity of the material, and T_c is a constant having the dimensions of a temperature.

The sample material curve starts out as a parabola; as the outer layers reach the inversion temperature, so much heat is required to change them from the low to high form that the heat supply is interrupted. The rate of heating at the center of the sample material slows up before the material at the center has reached the inversion temperature. As soon as the rate of heating at the center starts decreasing, the differential temperature curve will start to deviate from its base line. At this point, neither the center of the sample material nor the center of the reference material is at the inversion temperature. Smyth (49) states that not too much importance can be attached to this point of initial deviation.

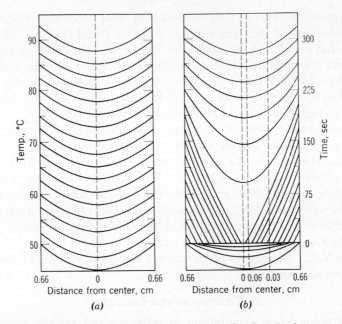

Fig. V.6. Temperature distribution, at 18.75 s intervals, of: (a) reference material; (b) sample material (49).

When the sample material inversion is completed, the distribution curve comes to a sharp point at its center. Since such a sharp point corresponds to a very high value of the second derivative of the equation

$$\frac{\partial^2 T}{\partial x^2} = \frac{1}{a} \frac{\partial T}{\partial t}$$ (V.14)

it would be expected that there would be a rapid rise in temperature at the center. This rapid rise gradually slows down, until after more than 300s, the sample material has caught up with the reference material causing the differential temperature to again become zero.

To illustrate more clearly the applications of Smyth's (49) calculations, the manner in which the differential temperature curve deviates as a function of reference temperature is presented. In DTA, the shape of the curve and also the peak maxima temperatures are variable depending upon the source of the reference temperature.

This is illustrated by the curves in Figure V.7 in which the differential temperature is plotted against the temperature of the center of the reference material, the surface of the sample material, and center of the sample material.

In curve (a), the curve departs from zero some distance below the 50°C inversion temperature and reaches its peak some 20°C above the inversion temperature. In curve (b), the sample material surface temperature would correspond to the temperature of the metal block in which the sample and reference cavities are located. This

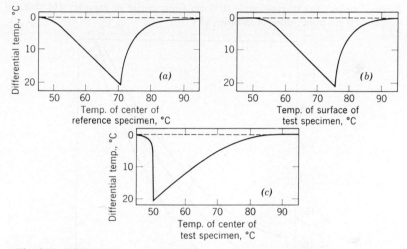

Fig. V.7. Differential temperature plotted against the temperature: (a) at the center of the reference material; (b) of the surface of the sample material; and (c) at the center of the sample material (49).

curve starts deviating from the base line at the inversion temperature, which, if this temperature could be accurately determined, would have useful significance on such a curve. If the differential temperature is plotted against the temperature at the center of the sample material, as shown in curve (c), the peak maximum temperature would be equal to the inversion temperature.

Smyth (49) very vividly illustrated the type of DTA curve obtained if the sample and reference thermocouples are not symmetrically located in their respective chambers. This asymmetry effect is shown in Figure V.8.

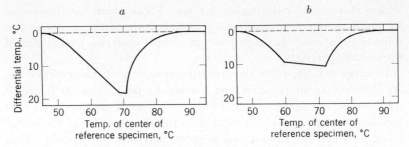

Fig. V.8. Effect of having an asymmetric arrangement of sample and reference thermocouples. (a) thermocouple 0.06 cm from center of sample; (b) thermocouple 0.30 cm from center of sample (49).

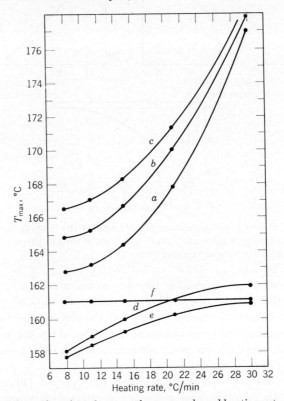

Fig. V.9. Effect of location of system thermocouple and heating rate on temperature at T_{max} using successive runs on different sample weights of 8.3% salicylic acid on carborundum (50).   Case 1: (a) 0.0952 g; (b) 0.1125 g; (c) 0.1555 g. Case 2: (d) 0.0952 g; (e) 0.0822 g.   Case 3: (f) 0.0952 g.

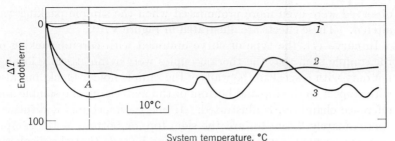

Fig. V.10. System temperature vs. $\Delta\,T$ for carborundum in both cells (50). Curve (1): symmetrically located thermocouples; curve (2): unsymmetrically located thermocouples in uniformly packed samples; curve (3): unsymmetrical thermocouples in a non-uniformly packed sample.

Curve (a) shows the differential temperature curve if the thermocouple is 0.06 cm from the center, instead of at the center, of the sample material. In curve (b), a rather extreme case is presented in which the sample thermocouple is 0.30 cm from the sample center. In both curves, the peak maxima temperatures are completely different from those of the symmetrically centered thermocouples.

Apparently, Barrall and Rogers (50) were unaware of the work of Smyth (49) in that they also studied the effect of thermocouple asymmetry and the deviation of the differential temperature base line. The effect of the location of the thermocouple whose output is recorded against the differential temperature is illustrated in Figure V.9.

In case (1), the system or x-axis thermocouple was located directly in the middle of the sample holder block. As can be seen from curves a, b, and c, the T_{max} temperature increases rapidly with an increase in the heating rate. For case (2), the thermocouple was located in the center of the reference sample, and the resulting curves, d and e, showed a less pronounced change of T_{max} with heating rate. In case (3), in contrast to the first two cases, there was no change in the T_{max} temperatures with change in heating rate. It was also stated that the endothermic peak was more symmetrical and the recorded melting range was narrower for case (3).

Barrall and Rogers (50) also determined the effect on the base line of the differential curve if the thermocouples were not located symmetrically in the sample and reference chambers. The irregularities observed were even more pronounced when the sample packing was altered. These effects are illustrated in Figure V.10.

In curve (*1*), the type of curve obtained with careful packing of the sample such that the thermocouples were symmetrically located not only with respect to the walls of the sample holder block, but also with respect to the top and bottom of the material in the sample and reference chambers, is illustrated. If one thermocouple is displaced approximately 2 mm toward the side, top, or bottom of the sample chamber, curve (*2*) was obtained. It can be seen that the displaced thermocouple heats up more quickly than the symmetrically located thermocouple, thus causing the deviation of the curve up to *A*. After the temperature difference has been established, the curve remains essentially constant for the remainder of the run. In curve (*3*), it is seen that loose packing leads not only to a displacement of the curve, but also to maxima and minima, presumably due to the shift of support particles as they expand during the heating process.

5. HEATING RATE

Although the effect of heating rate on the peak maxima temperatures and peak areas have been known for a number of years, only recently have these changes been explained in detail. In general, an increase in heating rate will shift the peak maxima temperatures to higher values and will slightly increase the peak area. The higher heating rate will decrease the resolution of two adjacent peaks, thereby masking one of the peaks. At very low heating rates, the peak areas become very small on certain types of instruments, depending on the heat-sink properties of the sample holder.

Speil et al. (29) first pointed out that the actual peak temperature is the point at which the differential heat input equals the rate of heat absorption and therefore

$$\Delta T_{max} = (dH/dt)_{max} \cdot M/gk \qquad (V.15)$$

as given in equation (V.1). A high rate of heating will cause dH/dt to increase because more of the reaction will take place in the same interval of time, and therefore the height or the apex or the differential temperature, ΔT_{max}, will be greater. As the return to the base line is a time function, as well as a temperature-difference function, the return will occur at a higher actual temperature with more rapid

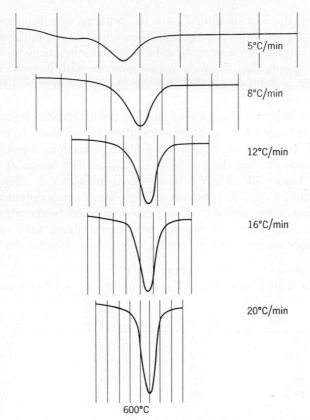

Fig. V.11. Variation of peak temperature of kaolin with rate of temperature increase (29).

heating. This is illustrated for kaolin in Figure V.11. The peak areas were reported to be equal to within ±3%, although there seemed to be a slight tendency toward smaller areas with low heating rates.

Kissinger (51,52) has shown that the peak maximum temperature is dependent on the heating rate and can be used to determine the kinetics of the reaction. This relationship is

$$\frac{d\left(\ln \dfrac{\phi}{T_{\max}{}^2}\right)}{d\left(\dfrac{1}{T}\right)} = -\frac{E^*}{R} \qquad (V.16$$

where ϕ is the heating rate, T_{max} is the peak maximum temperature, and E^* is the activation energy of the reaction.   The variations of T_{max} with heating rate for magnesite, calcite, and brucite are given in Table V.1.   It is seen that the T_{max} values increase with increase in heating rate;   a change of 9.5°C/min for the latter increases the T_{max} temperature by 62°C.

The variation in T_{max} is very small if the differential temperature is measured against the sample temperature rather than the reference material temperature.   In a careful investigation, Vassallo and Harden (48) studied the variation of T_{max} for the fusion of benzoic acid and Marlex 50.   The results are shown in Table V.2.   The sample temperature, C_{sample} (C_s), was essentially constant over the entire range of heating rates studied.   Using the reference temperature, A_{ref} (A_r), the T_{max} values for benzoic acid varied about 4.0°C over the heating rate ranges.   Similar results were obtained for Marlex 50.

TABLE V.1

Effect of Heating Rate on T_{max} Temperatures for Several Compounds (52)

°C ϕ, min	Magnesite	T_{max}, °C Calcite	Brucite
3	597	871	461
4.5	615	874	469
6	626	888	484
10	642	911	494
12.5	659	927	505

TABLE V.2

Variation of T_{max} for Some Fusion Reactions with Heating Rate (48)

°C ϕ, min	T_{max}, °C Benzoic acid A_{ref}[a]	C_{sample}[b]	Marlex 50 A_{ref}	C_{sample}
5	121.5	121.8	136.0	134.2
10	121.6	121.7	138.0	134.4
15	122.1	121.9	138.7	134.2
25	124.0	121.9	139.5	134.2
40	125.5	121.9		134.2
80		121.8		134.4

[a] $A_{ref} = \Delta T$ plotted against reference material temperature.

[b] $C_{sample} = \Delta T$ plotted against sample temperature.

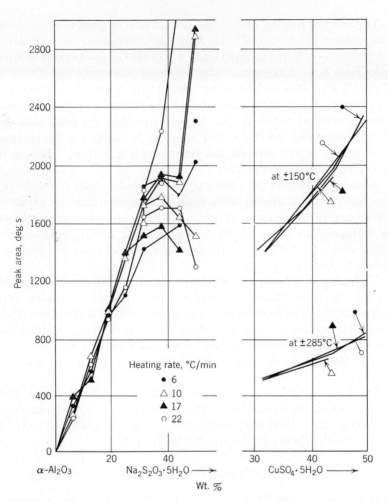

Fig. V.12. Effect of heating rate on peak areas for dilutions of $Na_2S_2O_3 \cdot 5H_2O$ and $CuSO_4 \cdot 5H_2O$ in α-Al_2O_3. Sample density is 1.1 g/cm³ with a total weight of 400 mg (59).

Murray and White (53), using kaolin and Wyoming bentonite, have also studied the effect of heating rate on the peak maxima temperatures. Other studies on this effect have been by Sewell (54), Kissinger et al. (55), Skinner (56), Stross and Abrams (57), Bayliss and Warne (44), Arens (42), and Grim and Rowland (58).

The effect of heating rate on the peak area is of great importance in quantitative DTA studies. De Jong (59) determined the peak areas for mixtures of $Na_2S_2O_3 \cdot 5H_2O$ and $CuSO_4 \cdot 5H_2O$ in α-Al_2O_3 at heating rates from 6 to 22°C/min. The results of this study are shown in Figure V.12. It is seen that the heating rate change has little effect on the peak areas, in the case of $Na_2S_2O_3 \cdot 5H_2O$, up to about a 30% concentration in α-Al_2O_3. For ratios above this, the peak areas do vary considerably but this is said to be due to changes in the thermal conductivity of the sample, not heating rate variation. This is in agreement with Speil et al. (29).

Barrall and Rogers (50), contrary to the above studies, found that the peak areas increased with heating rate for mixtures of silver nitrate and carborundum. The true area due to fusion was obtained by extrapolation of the curves to zero heating rate, calculating the extra area attributable to temperature lag between sample and reference materials.

Nathans and Wendlandt (60) found that the peak areas for a given sample size of lanthanum, europium, and ytterbium sulfates were independent of the heating rate, except for heating rates below 3°C/ min. The deviation at low heating rates can be explained by the condition that the heat absorbed by the reaction must be *measurably* greater than the heat supplied by the furnace and sample block assembly.

The heating rate of the furnace should be essentially linear with respect to time during the run. There should be no rapid fluctuations of heating rate as these will cause spurious peaks to appear in the DTA curve. Such effects have been noted by Vold (36).

6. Furnace Atmosphere

In the case of a reaction which involves the evolution or absorption of a gaseous component, the peak temperature and the shape of the peak will be affected by the gas pressure of the system. If the gaseous environment is identical to the evolved or absorbed gas, the changes will be more pronounced as can be shown thermodynamically by the expression

$$\left(\frac{d \ln K_p}{dT} \right) = \frac{\Delta H}{RT^2} \tag{V.17}$$

where K_p is the equilibrium constant for the reaction and ΔH is the heat of reaction. Thus, in an atmosphere containing a fixed partial pressure of the evolved gas, a substance will not begin to dissociate to an appreciable extent until the dissociation pressure of the decomposition reaction equals or exceeds the partial pressure of the gaseous component in the surrounding atmosphere. The higher the partial pressure of the surrounding gas, the higher the dissociation temperature of the substance. Thus, the surrounding gaseous environment has a pronounced effect on the DTA curves so obtained. Furthermore, the reaction of the gaseous atmosphere with the sample can also produce peaks in the curve, i.e., oxygen in the air causing an oxidation reaction and hence an exothermic peak.

Generally, two types of gaseous atmosphere techniques are employed: (a) a static gaseous atmosphere usually in an enclosed system; and (b) a dynamic gaseous atmosphere in which a gas flow is either maintained through the furnace or through the sample and reference materials. The first type is the most difficult to reproduce since the atmosphere surrounding the sample is continually changing in concentration due to gas evolution by the sample and by furnace convection currents. Under controlled conditions, the dynamic atmosphere is the simplest to maintain and reproduce.

The effect of gaseous atmosphere on the DTA curves has been studied by a number of investigators. Rowland and Lewis (61) studied the effect of air and nitrogen atmospheres on the decomposition of clays containing organic matter, oil shale, and pyrites, as well as the effect of carbon dioxide atmospheres on the decomposition of calcite, dolomite, and other carbonate minerals.

Lodding and Hammell (63) studied the dissociation of iron hydroxides in a reducing atmosphere of hydrogen. The apparatus was so constructed that the gaseous atmospheres could be changed at will from hydrogen to nitrogen to air. When goethite was heated in hydrogen, it dehydrated below 300°C forming amorphous Fe_3O_4 which recrystallized to magnetite between 300 and 360°C. The hydrogen was then flushed from the system with nitrogen, followed by air. The air caused the oxidation of magnetite to maghemite, $\gamma\text{-}Fe_2O_3$, at about 450°C, followed by a second exothermic peak from 775 to 836°C which was due to the $\gamma\text{-}Fe_2O_3 \rightarrow \alpha\text{-}Fe_2O_3$ transition. Similar studies were made on magnetite, hematite–alumina, and gibbsite–goethite mixtures.

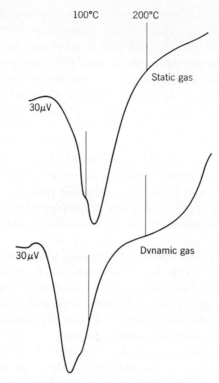

Fig. V.13. DTA curves of illitic shale showing difference in results between static gas and dynamic gas methods (64).

In a comprehensive study, Stone (64) compared the results obtained in static and dynamic gas atmospheres, as well as the effect of various gas atmospheres at different pressures, on certain decomposition reactions. A comparison between static and dynamic gas atmospheres on the thermal decomposition of illitic shale is given in Figure V.13. As can be seen, the peak maximum temperature, T_{max}, is shifted to lower temperatures in the dynamic gas technique. The shape of the curves is similar in both techniques.

The effect of two different gaseous atmospheres on the curve obtained for lignite is illustrated in Figure V.14. In the dynamic nitrogen atmosphere, the lignite pyrolyzes and distills off volatile matter; in oxygen, the lignite oxidizes, giving rise to exothermic instead of endothermic peaks.

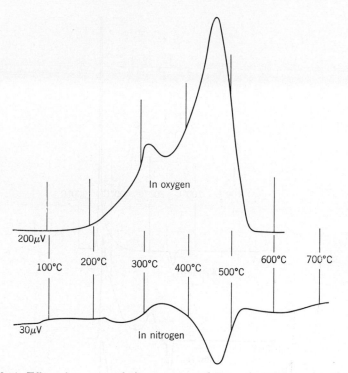

Fig. V.14. Effect of oxygen and nitrogen atmosphere on the DTA curves of a 2.5%
lignite–97.5% alumina mixture (64).

Still another effect is illustrated by use of the dynamic gas atmosphere, the Le Chatelier–Braun effect.   Stone (64) studied the thermal decomposition of ammonium perchlorate under the following conditions: (a) 4 atm ammonia; (b) 4 atm nitrogen; (c) 1 atm nitrogen; and (d) 10^{-2} mm vacuum.   The results obtained are shown in Figure V.15.

Since ammonia is one of decomposition products, it would be expected that the T_{max} for the decomposition reaction ($\sim$425°C) would be shifted to higher temperatures in the ammonia atmosphere. There was little effect of nitrogen pressure on the decomposition reaction, as shown by the curves for 1 and 4 atm of nitrogen pressure. However, in a vacuum, the exothermic peak became an endothermic one and also shifted the T_{max} to a lower temperature.   It is highly probable that NH_4ClO_4 decomposes by a different mechanism under

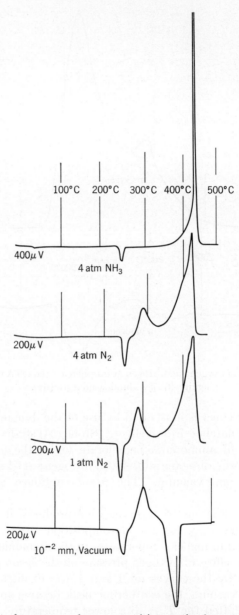

Fig. V.15. Effect of pressure and gas composition on the decomposition of a 50% NH_4ClO_4–50% alumina (64).

conditions of vacuum. It should be noted that various atmospheres have little effect on the crystalline phase transition, as represented by the endothermic peak with a T_{max} of about 250°C. Other studies on the effect of gaseous environment on the DTA curves obtained included Foldvari-Vogl (35), Bayliss and Warne (44), Hodgson (65), Crandall and West (66), Rowland and Jonas (67), and Rudin et al. (68).

7. Miscellaneous Instrumental Factors

Few studies have been made concerning the type, size, geometry, and position of the furnace in relation to the sample holder. Most of the investigations have been concerned with the sample holder rather than the furnace itself.

Hauser (47) found that the most desirable type of furnace contained a 1–1.5 in. diameter internal core rather than a larger 2 in. core. He stated that there was a smaller temperature gradient in the smaller diameter furnace. A vertical mounting position, rather than horizontal, gave a better temperature gradient also.

The sensitivity of the amplifier and recorder will effect the intensities and general shapes of the peaks obtained, although other factors, such as the quantity of sample, also effect the curve peaks. Gruver (45) illustrated this effect on the DTA curves of quartz mixtures as shown in Figure V.16. The first curve was run at low sensitivity and only the cristobalite inversion at 270°C and the quartz

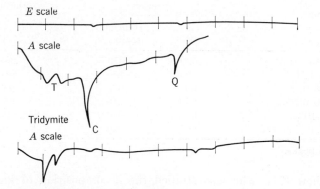

Fig. V.16. Effect of recorder sensitivity on a 40% tridymite–30% cristobalite-quartz; T, tridymite; C, cristobalite (45).

inversion at 573°C appear. In the second curve, the sensitivity was increased some 25 times and the tridymite inversions at 117° and 163°C can now be seen. A high sensitivity recording of the $Na_2CO_3 \cdot 10H_2O$ dehydration peaks has been made by Reisman (69). Small peaks which were not visible on the lower sensitivity recordings appeared.

8. Sample Particle Size

There are a number of conflicting studies concerning the effect of particle size and particle size distribution of the sample on the peak areas and T_{max} values. Speil et al. (29) found that the peak areas under the kaolin dehydration peak varied from 725 to 2080 mm^2 over the particle size range of 0.05–0.1 to 5–20μ. It was also found that the T_{max} values varied from 580° to 625°C. However, Norton (6) found that the T_{max} values remained essentially constant, but that the temperature at which the dehydration reaction was completed varied from 610 to 670°C over a particle size range of <0.1 to 20–44 μ. Grimshaw et al. (70) agreed with the latter study in that, with particle sizes down to 1 μ, the thermal characteristics of the kaolin samples were independent of particle size. This effect is illustrated in Table V.3.

TABLE V.3
Effect of Particle Size on the Thermal Characteristics of Kaolin (70)

Average particle size, μ	Endothermic reaction		Exothermic
	T_{max}, °C	Finishing temp., °C	T_{max}, °C
10–44	600	670	980
0.5–1.0	605	650	980
0.25–0.5	605	630	980
0.10–0.25	600	615	980
<0.10	600	610	945, 990[a]
<0.10 dialyzed	605	610	955, 986[a]

[a] Two peaks.

Carthew (71), who also studied the decomposition of kaolinite, in the particle size range of >2 to 0.25–0.1 μ, agreed with the work of Norton (6) and Grimshaw et al. (70). For particle sizes from 2–1 μ

to 0.25–0.1 μ, the peak areas were essentially constant as were the T_{max} values. The disagreement with Spiel et al. (29) was attributed to the fact that they obtained their particle size fractions by a grinding process, which could reduce the degree of crystallinity of the kaolin.

Other studies on the effect of particle size on the DTA curves obtained for chrysotile (72), talc (73), clays (45), dehydration of metal sulfate hydrates (74), and goethite (75) have been reported.

Barrall and Rogers (76) found that in a blank run of small glass beads against large beads, the base line displacement indicated that the large beads did not transmit heat as well as the small beads. The base line gradually decreased with increasing temperature and a large fraction of the displacement remained at 200°C.

9. AMOUNT OF SAMPLE

According to the various theories of DTA, the peak area should be directly proportional to the quantity of reactive sample. Within certain limits, this relationship is linear although deviations are indicated at the higher limit of sample weight. A number of studies have been made to elucidate this effect on the DTA curve. Wittels (77,78) studied the effect of sample size on peak area and the heat of reaction of tremolite and of calcite. For the former, a series of samples ranging in weight from 20 to 130 mg, at a heating rate of 30°C/min, were studied. The results are given in Table V.4 and Figure V.17.

TABLE V.4

Relationship Between Sample Weight and Peak Area for Tremolite (78)

Sample		Peak area, in.^{2}
No.	Weight, mg	
1	130	1.50
2	115	1.42
3	90	1.25
4	80	1.16
5	58	0.93
6	52	0.84
7	42	0.70
8	34	0.57
9	25	0.44
10	20	0.35

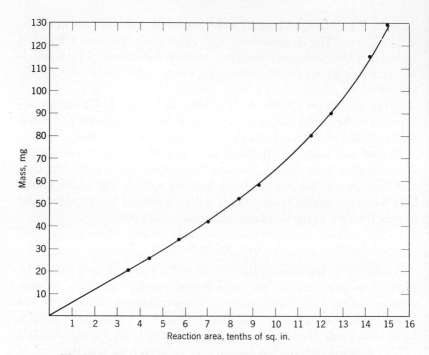

Fig. V.17. Plot of peak area vs. sample mass for tremolite (78).

The curve exhibited a marked departure from linearity when the mass of the sample exceeded approximately 60 mg. Wittels (78) explained this deviation as due to thermal gradients in the sample which became noticeable above this sample weight. This curve, of course, applied only to the specific apparatus described (77). In studying the thermal dissociation of calcite, Wittels (77) found that the peak area vs. heat of reaction curve, calculated from sample size, was linear from 0.30 (0.123 cal) to 3.00 mg (1.215 cal), the entire range studied.

Carthew (71), studying the thermal decomposition of kaolin in the 0.15–0.8 g sample-weight range, found that the slope ratios of the peaks appeared to be independent of the sample weight, whereas the width of the peak decreased with the amount.

According to Bayliss and Warne (44), the larger sample increases both the intensity of the reaction and the temperature at which they occur. The peak definition is decreased, however, because the sample approaches reaction equilibrium more slowly due to the necessity for the heat to transverse a longer distance through the sample to the central thermocouple.

Barrall and Rogers (50) found that the sample mass *vs.* peak area had a marked departure from linearity below a certain critical sample size. The depth or intensity of the peak varied in the same manner.

10. Effect of Diluent

The effect on the peak T_{max} values for various concentrations of kaolinite and halloysite diluted with alumina has been studied by Dean (79). For the former substance, the T_{max} values ranged from 525°C for a 10% mixture to 570°C for a 60% mixture. Similar results were found for the halloysite mixtures. De Jong (59) found that there was a linear relationship between peak area and weight fraction of kaolinite diluted with alumina, provided that the density of the mixtures did not change drastically. For illite–alumina mixtures, however, with a tendency for greater peak areas for higher illite concentrations, a linear relationship was not found.

TABLE V.5

Peak Area Obtained by 0.01 g Salicylic Acid Diluted with Various Materials[a] (76)

Diluent	Salicylic acid, %	Area/0.01 g of acid (mm²)
Carborundum	6.87	306
Iron metal	8.82	710
Iron(III) oxide	3.40	280
Glass beads, 0.029 mm	4.57	322
Glass beads, 0.29 mm	5.58	289
Alumina	8.60	313
Nujol	20.00	92

[a] ΔT sensitivity of 67 μV per in.; heating rate of 7.9°C min (76).

In a comprehensive study, Barrall and Rogers (76) determined the effect of diluents such as carborundum, iron metal, and iron(III) oxide, on the peak caused by the fusion of salicylic acid. This effect is illustrated in Table V.5. The variation in thermal conductivity of the diluent is probably the main cause of the peak area variation. Higher conductivity allows the thermal effect to be more efficiently conducted to the thermojunction in the center of the sample. It should be noted, however, that the diluent high thermal conductivity

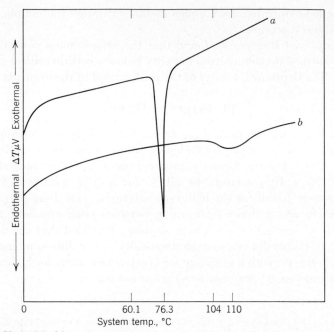

Fig. V.18. Masking effects of sample peaks caused by the diluent: (*a*) 8-quin-olinol diluted to 6.94% with carborundum; (*b*) 8-quinolinol diluted to 5.9% with alumina (76).

may decrease the peak area when the diluted sample is in direct contact with a metal sample block.

A "masking" effect has been noted (76) for certain peaks when the diluent reacts with the sample. This is illustrated in the case of 8-quinolinol diluted with carborundum and alumina, as shown in Figure V.18. When carborundum is used, the T_{max} obtained was 76.3°C; with an alumina diluent, no endothermic peak was observed in this temperature region. Apparently, a complex had been formed between the alumina and 8-quinolinol.

11. MISCELLANEOUS SAMPLE EFFECTS

The parameters of heat capacity, thermal conductivity, and packing density are not independent variables, but interact with each other for each sample. The packing density of the sample is very difficult to reproduce and unless very small samples are used, has a pronounced effect on the DTA curve, especially for quantitative studies. The heat capacity of the sample changes during the course of the experiment, due to a chemical or physical transformation. One method of maintaining an essentially constant sample-heat capacity is to use a diluent, as discussed previously. In this manner, the heat capacity of the sample is relatively small compared to that of the diluent.

Barrall and Rogers (76) have studied the effect of heat capacity and thermal conductivity of the sample on the peak areas so obtained. They found that in the case of a compound diluted with a diluent of high heat capacity, the curve peaks were smaller in area than if the compound had been diluted with a diluent of low heat capacity. For a sample using powdered iron as a diluent, the peak area was over twice that of carborundum; the thermal conductivities for these two diluents are 2×10^{-1} and 5×10^{-4} cal/s, respectively. The higher peak area must be due to the effective increase in thermal conductivity of the diluent.

The effect of sample packing on the DTA curve has been illustrated by Gruver (45), as shown in Figure V.19. In curve (a), the kaolin

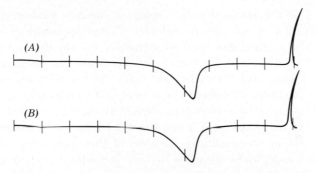

Fig. V.19. Effect of packing of the sample (kaolin): (a) tapping; (b) tamping (45).

sample was placed in the sample crucible and settled by a slight tapping action; in curve (b), the sample was tamped in place by use of a small glass rod. The curves obtained turned out to be identical. Admittedly, this is rather a crude method of testing this effect.

The effect of crystallinity of the sample is rather difficult to evaluate because of the definition of the term "degree of crystallinity." Carthew (71) defined the latter, in the case of kaolin samples, as the perfection of crystal orientation and not the size of the crystal. Using

five different samples of kaolin, he found that the area of the endothermic dehydration peak decreased with decrease in sample crystallinity. The peaks appeared to be sharper as the degree of crystallinity
of the sample increased. This effect of crystallinity was said to be
similar to that of change in particle size and could probably be explained in a similar manner.

D. Quantitative Differential Thermal Analysis

1. HEATS OF TRANSITION OR REACTION

Since the area obtained by integration of the differential temperature curve is proportional to the heat absorbed or evolved in the
sample transformation, the technique of DTA has been used to measure heats of transition and reaction of many substances. The heat
involved, ΔH, is equal to

$$\Delta H = \psi \int_{t_1}^{t_2} \theta \, dt \qquad (V.18)$$

where ψ is the proportionality constant, usually evaluated experimentally, but it can also be calculated from apparatus parameters
(59). The method has been so attractive for the determination of
heats of reaction that the term *microcalorimeter* has been applied to
the DTA apparatus (77). In most cases, the investigators have been
perhaps too optimistic about the results that were obtained, which in
many cases may have been fortuitous. It should be noted that the
results in quantitative DTA are affected by the same variables that
are present in the qualitative aspects of this technique. Thus, no
great accuracy can be obtained by this method unless these variables
are rigidly controlled, which in many cases is extremely difficult.

Vold (36) used the expression

$$\frac{\Delta H}{C_s} \left(\frac{df}{dt} \right) = \frac{dy}{dt} + A(y - y_s)$$

as the basis of her calculations to obtain the heats of fusion of stearic
and benzoic acids. The value of A in the expression was obtained by
plotting $\log (y - y_s)$ against time, t. These points fell on the straight
lines, as shown in Figure V.20. At the end of the transformation, the
base line y_s, was assumed to have its final value—i.e., C_s equal to the

heat capacity of the cell plus that of the melted sample. At the beginning of the transition, the point selected as $T_{max} - y_s$ was assumed to have its initial value.

The DTA curve in Figure V.21 shows a typical run from which the magnitudes of T_r, T_s, and y were evaluated. Although the results obtained were not of high precision, they were calculated independently of any empirical calibration.

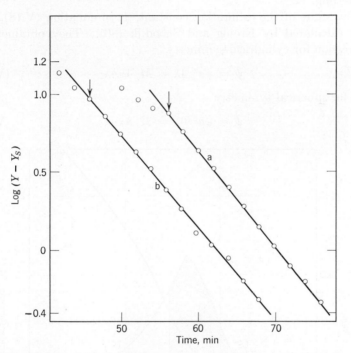

Fig. V.20. Plot for determining the constant, A. Arrows mark time at which transition is completed (36).

Wittels (77), using the theory of Speil et al. (29), found that the area enclosed by the curve peak was proportional to the heat absorbed in the decomposition of calcite, $CaCO_3$. A linear relationship was found, using sample weights from 0.30 to 3.00 mg. In another study, Wittels (78) elucidated the effect of heating rate and sample mass on the peak areas obtained by the thermal decomposition of tremolite, $Ca_2Mg_5Si_8O_{22}(OH)_2$. The relationship,

$$\Delta H = \frac{A}{\tan\left(\dfrac{\ln R(R - c)}{m}\right)} \tag{V.19}$$

was derived in which R is the heating rate, A is the peak area, and m and c are constants. The best response of the instrument was obtained at a heating rate of 30°C/min., and fell off rapidly below 15°C/min.

The value of the calibration constant, ψ, in equation (V.18), was first calculated by Kronig and Snoodijk (80). They obtained an expression for cylindrical symmetry

$$\psi = \varphi a^2/4\lambda = M/4\pi h\lambda \tag{V.20}$$

and for spherical symmetry

$$\psi = \varphi a^2/6\lambda = M/8\pi a\lambda \tag{V.21}$$

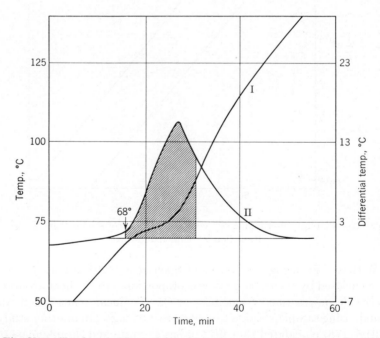

Fig. V.21. Total and differential heating curves for stearic acid. I. Heating curve for stearic acid; II. differential heating curve; shaded area is that used in calculating ΔH (36).

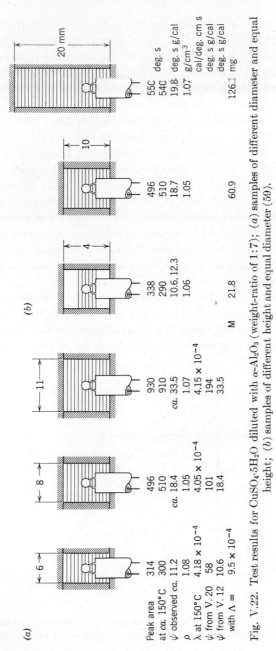

							units
	(a)				*(b)*		
	6	8	11	4	10	20 mm	
Peak area	314	496	930	338	496	55C	deg. s
at *ca.* 150°C	300	510	910	290	510	54C	deg. s
ψ observed *ca.*	11.2	*ca.* 18.4	*ca.* 33.5	10.6, 12.3	18.7	19.8	deg. s g/cal
ρ	1.08	1.05	1.07	1.06	1.05	1.07	g/cm^3
λ at 150°C	4.18×10^{-4}	4.05×10^{-4}	4.15×10^{-4}				cal/deg. cm s
ψ from V. 20	58	101	194				deg. s g/cal
ψ from V. 12	10.6	18.4	33.5	M 21.8	60.9	126.1 mg	deg. s g/cal
with $\Lambda =$	9.5×10^{-4}						

Fig. V.22. Test results for $CuSO_4 \cdot 5H_2O$ diluted with α-Al_2O_3 (weight-ratio of 1:7); *(a)* samples of different diameter and equal height; *(b)* samples of different height and equal diameter (59).

where φ is the sample density, a is the radius of the sample holder, and h is the height of the sample. These equations describe the temperature difference between the center of the reference material and the sample material, assuming very small thermocouple junctions and leads. The quantity, $4\pi h$ or $8\pi a$, is the geometrical shape factor, g, in Speil's theory. These results were similar to those obtained by Boersma (37) in which the influence of the heat loss through the thermocouple wires was taken into account (see p. 145).

De Jong (59) obtained ψ by calibration of his apparatus with compounds of known heat of reaction and compared it with values calculated by Boersma's equations. These results are shown in Figure V.22. It is seen that using equation (V.20), and ignoring the heat loss through the thermocouple leads, the value of ψ is five or six times as large as that observed by actual calibration. Using equation (V.9) however, which corrects for the thermocouple heat loss, with $\lambda = 9.5 \times 10^{-4}$ cal/deg cm s, gives values that correspond to the experimental values of ψ.

The variation of the calibration factor with different diameter thermocouple junctions is shown in Figure V.23. It can be seen that the ratio, $r_0/a = 0.2$, gave the largest peak areas. There is little gained, therefore, by decreasing the diameter of the thermojunction still further.

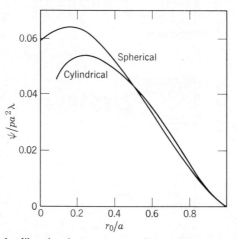

Fig. V.23. Plot of calibration factor, ψ, according to Boersma's equation for $\Delta/\lambda = 2$ and for different ratios of thermocouple junction r_0, vs. sample diameter (59).

Vold (36) obtained the constant, ψ, by an analysis of the exponential decay of the curve after the reaction had ceased. The relaxation time must have such a large value that after the reaction or transition is completed, the temperature relaxes over a range large enough to be interpretable. The apparatus used by de Jong (59) had too short a relaxation time to be used with this method. Allison (81), using Vold's method, calculated the heats of dehydration of clays using the unpublished data of Murray.

Sturm (82) proposed a method in which ψ was represented by the expression

$$\psi = M \, 2 \ln r \, \frac{(m_s c_s + m_w c_w)(T_2 - T_1)}{(t_2 - t_1)(T_0 - T_1)} \tag{V.22}$$

where $t_2 - t_1$ is the time interval; T_2, T_1 are the furnace temperature at times t_2 and t_1, respectively; m_s, m_w are the weights of sample and weight of portion of thermocouple wire embedded in the sample; c_s, c_w are the specific heats of the sample and thermocouple wires, respectively; M is an amplification factor depending on signal amplification; and r is the radius of the sample holder. The proportionality constant, ψ, was evaluated for each analysis in order to allow for differences in sample packing, particle size distribution, and variables due to heat leakage through the thermocouple wires. Because of the compositional change of the sample during the transformation, ψ is determined for temperature ranges before and after the reaction and the average value used. In determining the heat of fusion of $NaNO_3$ and KNO_3 by this method, excellent agreement between experimental and calculated values was obtained (83).

Yagfarov (84) has described a method of quantitative DTA which is based on an internal standard of known heat capacity. The method permits simultaneous measurements of heat capacity, thermal conductivity, thermal diffusivity, and the heat of reaction. It is based upon an analysis of the temperature field in the substance by passing through it a given heat flow set up by a known heat capacity. Heat capacity measurements were said to be within $\pm 1\%$ of the actual values.

Stone and Rase (85) determined the heat of physical adsorption, ΔH_p, for various catalysts, by use of the expression

$$\Delta = \frac{M_{tc}\Delta H_p}{W_t C} \tag{V.23}$$

where Δ is the difference between the temperature rise of the sample and reference materials; M_{tc} is the mass of test gas chemisorbed by the catalyst sample; W_t is the mass of catalyst; and C is the heat capacity of the catalyst and reference materials.

A number of investigations have been reported on the determination of heats of fusion, heats of polymerization, and entropy of fusion of polymeric materials. The heat of fusion of a semicrystalline polymer, as discussed by Ke and Sisko (86), is the amount of heat required to melt only the crystalline portion of it. The true heat of fusion, ΔH_f, is obtained from

$$\Delta H_f = (H_a - H_c)/x \qquad \text{(V.24)}$$

where H_a and H_c are the enthalpies of the amorphous and crystalline polymers, respectively $(H_a - H_c)$ is the measured heat of fusion, and x is the fractional crystallinity determined by independent methods. The heat of fusion was obtained by comparison of the peak area of the unknown polymer with the peak area of a polymer with a known heat of fusion.

The entropy of fusion, ΔS_f, is then

$$\Delta S_f = \Delta H_f / T_{\max} \qquad \text{(V.25)}$$

where $T_{\max}$ is the melting point of the polymer (87).

Klute and Viehmann (88) measured the heat of polymerization, ΔH_p, by use of the expression

$$-\Delta H_p = (1/n) \int_{\theta}^{\infty} K(t)\theta dt \qquad \text{(V.26)}$$

where K is the heat transfer coefficient for the apparatus; θ is the temperature difference between the sample and reference materials; t is the time; and n is the number of moles polymerized.

The results of the quantitative DTA studies are included in Chapter VII.

E. Reaction Kinetics

The kinetics of a thermal dissociation reaction of the type

$$\text{solid A} \xrightarrow{\text{heat}} \text{solid B} + \text{gas C}$$

can be determined by differential thermal analysis, using several different methods. These methods have been reviewed by Wend-

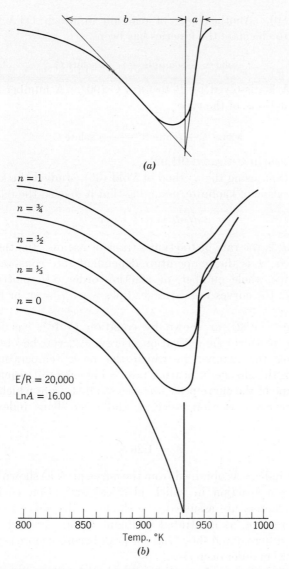

Fig. V.24. (a) Method for measuring amount of asymmetry of peak; (b) effect of order of reaction on plots of n vs. temperature. Shape index = S = a/s (52).

landt (20,89). Another type of reaction in which DTA has been employed to elucidate the kinetics has been

$$\text{solid A } + \text{ solute B } \xrightarrow{\text{solution}} \text{ solute C}$$

in which A is dissolved by B to form C (90). A number of homogeneous reactions, of the type

$$\text{solute A } + \text{ solute B } \xrightarrow{\text{solution}} \text{ solute C}$$

have also been investigated (91,92).

Allison (81), using the method of Vold (36), studied the kinetics of the dehydration of kaolinite, assuming that it obeyed the relationship

$$df/dt = k(1 - f)^n \tag{V.27}$$

where df/dt is the rate of fractional transformation; f is the amount transformed; k is the temperature-dependent rate constant; and n is a positive whole number, or reaction order. In plotting $\log k$ versus $1/T$, the curves were straight lines when $n = 1$, or first-order reactions.

Kissinger (51,52), as shown by equation (V.16), has derived an expression in which the activation energy, E^*, can be obtained by determining the manner in which the peak temperature, T_{max}, varies with the change in heating rate. The effect of reaction order on the shape of the curve peak was also studied, from which the relationship between reaction order, n, and peak shape index, S, was obtained:

$$n = 1.26\, S^{1/2} \tag{V.28}$$

The shape index was obtained from the curve peak as shown in Figure V.24. For a reaction in which identical activation energies and frequency factors are assumed, the shape of the curve varied with reaction order, n, as illustrated in Figure V.24. In each case, the curves are different and show that the peak becomes more asymmetric as the reaction order decreases.

Borchardt (93) has shown that the reaction-rate constant, k, can be obtained from

$$k = -\frac{d(n/n_0)}{dt} = \frac{\Delta T}{A} \tag{V.29}$$

where $-d(n/n_0)/dt$ is the rate of reaction in the fraction converted per unit time at the time where the peak height is Δt, and A is the peak area. From a rough triangulation of the curve peak,

$$A = \frac{1}{2}\tau\Delta T_{max} \tag{V.30}$$

where τ is the base of the triangle (peak), and ΔT_{max} is the height of the peak.

For a homogeneous reaction mixture, Borchardt and Daniels (91) have derived an equation which relates the rate constant with other parameters of the reaction mixture and apparatus. The equation is based on the following assumptions: (a) The temperature in the sample and reference materials is uniform; obviously, this can only be applied to stirred liquids and not to solids; (b) heat is transferred by conduction only, a condition easily met with liquids and the temperature ranges usually employed (the heat transfer through the thermocouple is neglected); (c) the heat transfer coefficients are identical for the sample and reference materials; and (d) the heat capacities of the sample and reference materials must also be identical; a condition approached if dilute sample solutions are investigated.

For a homogeneous reaction in which the order of reaction, n, is equal to one, the rate constant, k, is

$$k = \frac{C_p(d\,\Delta T/dt) + K\Delta T}{k(A - a) - C_p\Delta T} \tag{V.31}$$

where C_p is the heat capacity of the sample and reference materials, ΔT is the differential temperature, K is the heat-transfer coefficient for the sample and reference materials, A is total peak area, and a is the peak area up to time t.

If the temperature difference between the sample and reference materials is maintained at zero by supplying heat to the sample or reference, as in differential enthalpic analysis, the rate constant is

$$k = \frac{(AV/n_0)^{n-1}\,dH/dt}{(A - a)^n} \tag{V.32}$$

where H is the heat added, n is the reaction order, V is the volume, and n_0 is the number of moles initially present.

In equation (V.31), since the quantities $C_p(d\Delta T/dt)$ and $C_p\Delta T$

are of an order of magnitude smaller than the quantities to which they are added and subtracted, they may be neglected to obtain

$$k = \frac{\Delta T}{(A - a)} \qquad (V.33)$$

for a first-order reaction, or

$$k = \frac{(A V/n_0)^{n-1} \Delta T}{(A - a)^n} \qquad (V.34)$$

for the general case.

Padmanabhan et al. (94) and Agarwala and Naik (95) have used the simplified expression, as shown by equation (V.33), to determine the kinetics of a thermal decomposition reaction involving a powdered solid. The use of this expression for solid-state reactions does not appear to be valid in view of the original assumptions made in the derivation of the original equation. Further work is needed to determine if it is applicable to solid samples.

Baumgartner and Duhaut (92) also derive an expression for the determination of reaction kinetics for reactions in homogeneous solutions.

The role of the gaseous phase in solid-state reactions has also been discussed by Borchardt (96). Using constant temperature differential thermal analysis, Hall and Rase (97) studied the oxidation of carbonaceous deposits on silica–alumina catalysts. The approximate kinetic data was obtained through use of the expression

$$T = \frac{\Delta H \, kp \, Y_0}{WC(h/WC - kp)} \, [e^{-Tt} - e^{-ht/WC}] \qquad (V.35)$$

where T is the sample temperature referred to temperature before the reaction began; C is the specific heat of the sample; h is the heat transfer coefficient from sample to surroundings by all thermal processes; t is the time of reaction; p is the partial pressure of oxygen; Y_0 is the initial concentration of deposit on the catalyst; and W is the weight of sample.

F. Correlation of DTA and TGA Data

Since thermogravimetry is used as a complementary technique to aid in the interpretation of the DTA curve peaks, many attempts

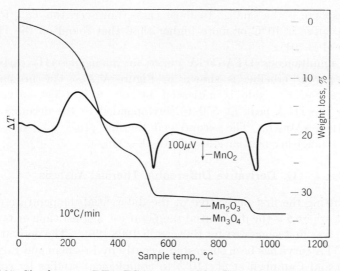

Fig. V.25. Simultaneous DTA–TGA curves of MnCO₃ (55). Heavy line DTA; Light line, TGA.

have been made to correlate TGA weight-loss temperatures with the DTA peak maxima temperatures. Generally, little agreement exists between the two types of experimental curves because of the different conditions of pyrolysis. The sample, in TGA, is exposed to a rather free diffusion environment, and is usually in a thin layer in the sample container. In DTA, larger samples are generally employed which are more densely packed in the sample holder thereby hindering free diffusion of the evolved gaseous decomposition products. Different heating rates are also normally employed; higher heating rates are generally used for DTA studies.

A discussion of the surrounding gaseous atmosphere on the DTA and TGA curves has been made by Notz and Jaffe (98) and Garn (99). If the environmental atmospheres are identical, there should be a good correlation between the DTA and TGA curves; this requires that dynamic gas atmospheres, not static, be employed. Notz and Jaffe (98) found this to be true for the thermal dissociation of anhydrous uranyl sulfate by DTA and TGA techniques.

The use of instruments capable of determining the DTA, TGA, and DTG curves simultaneously on the same sample under identical conditions eliminates the above problem as the environmental

atmosphere is the same.   In most cases, however, the T_{max} for the
DTA curve is 10°C or more higher than that found on the DTGA
curve (100,101).

A simultaneous DTA–TGA curve for manganese(II) carbonate
in a porous crucible is shown in Figure V.25.   The presence of
manganese(IV) oxide is indicated by the weight-loss curve (55)
while the DTA peak at 550°C corresponded to the decomposition
of $MnO_2{\rightarrow}Mn_2O_3$.   The second endothermic peak, T_{max} of 970°C,
is the change in oxidation state of $Mn_2O_3{\rightarrow}Mn_3O_4$.

G. Derivative Differential Thermal Analysis

Plotting the first derivative of the differential temperature curve,
$d\theta/dt$, where θ is the differential temperature, against time or temperature was first suggested by Burgess in 1908 (28).   The derivative of
the DTA curve has been suggested recently by Freeman and Edelman
(102) and Campbell et al. (103) to complement studies by conventional DTA.   The derivative differential thermal analysis (DDTA)
curves contain more detail of certain peaks that are frequently over-

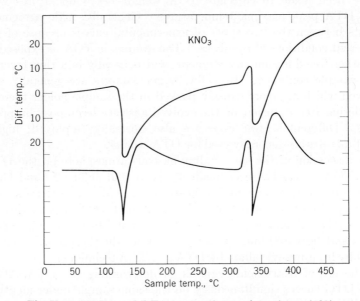

Fig. V.26. DDTA and DTA curves of potassium nitrate (103).

looked in DTA curves and are useful for qualitative characterization of substances as well as for kinetics studies.

A comparison between the DDTA and DTA curves for potassium nitrate is given in Figure V.26 (103). Although the DDTA curve theoretically will give two peaks, one below and one above the base line, for each single DTA curve peak, this is not very evident from Figure V.26. The peaks are due to the crystalline phase transition at 128 °C and the melting point at 340 °C.

Two methods have been used to obtain the DDTA curve of a sample. One is by direct differentiation of the DTA curve by a resistance–capacitance (R–C) system (103); the other is to maintain a temperature differential between two identical samples (102). The first method employs a recorder containing a retransmitting potentiometer coupled to the slidewire. The signal generated by the potentiometer circuit is differentiated by a simple R–C circuit and recorded on another recorder.

The second method, which is similar to that proposed for differential thermogravimetry by de Keyser (see p. 80), is based on the following. If two samples are heated simultaneously, their temperature differentials are:

(a) Sample 1:

$$\Delta T_s = T_s - T_r \tag{V.36}$$

(b) Sample 2:

$$\Delta T_{s'} = T_{s'} - T_r \tag{V.37}$$

where T_s and T_r represent sample and reference temperatures, respectively. If the temperature applied to both systems differs, subtracting equation (V.37) from (V.36) gives

$$\Delta T_s - \Delta T_{s'} = (T_s - T_{s'}) + (T_{r'} - T_r) \tag{V.38}$$

and, since the heating rates of both reference materials are the same,

$$\frac{d\,\Delta T_{s\cdot s'}}{dt} = \frac{dT_{s\cdot s'}}{dt} \tag{V.39}$$

The derivative DTA curve is obtained by using a single furnace and sample block, with an identical sample in place of the inert reference material. The temperature differential between the two samples will depend on the geometric arrangement of the system and the heat of transition. If it is too high, two DTA curves are obtained with a common base and opposite deflections. Where the temperature differential approaches zero, the true derivative plot is obtained.

Simultaneous DTA and DDTA curves can be obtained by the latter method (102) if a three-holed sample block, containing duplicate sample and an inert reference material, is employed. The DTA curve is obtained by using one of the samples and the reference, while the derivative curve is obtained simultaneously by recording the differential temperature between the two samples.

References

1. Murphy, C. B., *Anal. Chem.*, **30**, 867 (1958).
2. Murphy, C. B., *Anal. Chem.*, **32**, 168 (1960); **34**, 298R (1962).
3. Murphy, C. B., *Mod. Plastics*, **37**, 125 (1960).
4. Murphy, C. B., General Electric Co. Rept. No. 60GL60, April 1, 1960, 15 pp.
5. Pask, J. A., and M. F. Warner, *Bull. Am. Ceram. Soc.*, **33**, 168 (1954).
6. Norton, F. H., *J. Am. Ceram. Soc.*, **22**, 54 (1939).
7. Grim, R. E., *Ann. N. Y. Acad. Sci.*, **53**, 1031 (1951).
8. Ramachandran, V. S., and S. K. Bhattacharyya, *J. Sci. Ind. Res. (India)*, **13A**, 365 (1954).
9. Lehmann, H., S. S. Das, and H. H. Paetsch, *Tenind.-Ztg. u. Keram. Rundschau* (1954), p. 1.
10. Lukaszewski, G. M., and J. P. Redfern, *Lab. Pract.*, **10**, 630 (1961).
11. Garn, P. D., *Anal. Chem.*, **33**, 1247 (1961).
12. Redfern, J. P., *Thermal Analysis Review*, Stanton Instruments Ltd., London, 1962, No. 1.
13. Bhattacharyya, S. K., and N. D. Ganguly, *Proc. Natl. Inst. Sci. India*, **A27**, 588 (1961).
14. Smothers, W. J., Y. Chiang, and A. Wilson, *Bibliography of Differential Thermal Analysis*, University of Arkansas, Fayetteville, 1951.
15. Mackenzie, R. C., *Differential Thermal Analysis of Clays*, Central Press, Aberdeen, Scotland, 1957.
16. Smothers, W. J., and Y. Chiang, *Differential Thermal Analysis: Theory and Practice*, Chemical Publishing Co., New York, 1958.
17. Kissinger, H. E., and S. B. Newman, in *Differential Thermal Analysis in Analytical Chemistry of Polymers*, Vol. XII, Part II, G. M. Kline, ed., Interscience, New York, 1962.
18. Gordon, S., in *Encyclopedia of Science and Technology*, Vol. 13, McGraw-Hill, New York, 1960, pp. 556–559.
19. Gordon, S., and C. Campbell, in *Handbook of Analytical Chemistry*, L. Meites, ed., McGraw-Hill, New York, 1963.

20. Wendlandt, W. W., in *Technique of Inorganic Chemistry*, Vol. I, H. B. Jonassen and A. Weissberger, eds., Interscience, New York, 1963, p. 209.
21. Le Chatelier, H., *Bull. Soc. Franc. Mineral.*, **10**, 204 (1887).
22. Ashley, H. E., *Ind. Eng. Chem.*, **3**, 91 (1911).
23. Wholin, R., *Sprechsaal*, **46**, 749, 767, 781 (1913).
24. Rieke, R., *Sprechsaal*, **44**, 637 (1911).
25. Wallach, H., *Compt. Rend.*, **157**, 48 (1913).
26. Mellor, J. W., and A. D. Holdcraft, *Trans. Brit. Ceram. Soc.*, **10**, 94 (1910–1911).
27. Roberts-Austen, W. C., *Proc. Inst. Mech. Engrs.*, (*London*), (1899); *Metallographist*, **2**, 186 (1899).
28. Burgess, G. K., *Natl. Bur. Std.* (*U. S.*) *Bull.*, **5**, 199 (1908–1909).
29. Speil, S., L. H. Berkelhamer, J. A. Pask, and B. Davis, *U. S. Bur. Mines, Tech. Papers*, **664** (1945).
30. Houldsworth, H. S., and J. W. Cobb, *Trans. Brit. Ceram. Soc.*, **22**, 111 (1922–1923).
31. Fenner, C. N., *Am. J. Sci.*, **36**, 331 (1913).
32. Berkelhamer, L. H., *U. S. Bur. Mines, Rept. Invest.*, **R13762** (1944).
33. Kerr, P. F., and J. L. Kulp, *Am. Mineralogist*, **33**, 387 (1948).
34. Kauffman, A. J., and E. D. Dilling, *Econ. Geol.*, **45**, 222 (1950).
35. Foldvari-Vogl, M., *Acta Geol. Acad. Sci. Hung.*, **5**, 1 (1958).
36. Vold, M. J., *Anal. Chem.*, **21**, 683 (1949).
37. Boersma, S. L., *J. Am. Ceram. Soc.*, **38**, 281 (1955).
38. Tsang, N. F., ref. 16, Chap. V.
39. Mackenzie, R. C., and K. R. Farquharson, *Compt. Rend. 19ᵉ Congr. Geol. Inst. 19ᵉ Algeria*, **18**, 183 (1952).
40. Webb, T. L., *Nature*, **174**, 686 (1954).
41. Gita, G., *Rev. Chim.* (*Bucharest*), **9**, 313 (1958).
42. Arens, P. L., *A Study of the Differential Thermal Analysis of Clays and Clay Minerals*, Excelsiors Foto-Ottset, The Hague, 1951.
43. Gerard-Hirne, J., and C. Lamy, *Bull. Soc. Franc. Ceram.*, **1951**, 26.
44. Bayliss, P., and S. St. J. Warne, *Am. Mineralogist*, **47**, 775 (1962).
45. Gruver, R. M., *J. Am. Ceram. Soc.*, **31**, 323 (1948).
46. Mackenzie, R. C., *Nature*, **174**, 688 (1954).
47. Hauser, R. E., B. S. Thesis, N. Y. State College of Ceramics, Alfred, New York, 1953.
48. Vassallo, D. A., and J. C. Harden, *Anal. Chem.*, **34**, 132 (1962).
49. Smyth, H. T., *J. Am. Ceram. Soc.*, **34**, 221 (1951).
50. Barrall, E. M., and L. B. Rogers, *Anal. Chem.*, **34**, 1101 (1962).
51. Kissinger, H. E., *J. Res. Natl. Bur. Std.*, **57**, 217 (1956).
52. Kissinger, H. E., *Anal. Chem.*, **29**, 1702 (1957).
53. Murray, P., and J. White, *Trans. Brit. Ceram. Soc.*, **54**, 204 (1955).
54. Sewell, E. C., *Clay Minerals Bull.*, **2**, 233 (1953–1955).
55. Kissinger, H. E., H. F. McMurdie, and B. S. Simpson, *J. Am. Ceram. Soc.*, **39**, 168 (1956).
56. Skinner, K. G., "A Differential Thermal Analysis Apparatus for Temperatures up to 1575°C.," Naval Research Laboratory Report 4942, 1957, 12 pp.

57. Stross, F. H., and S. T. Abrams, *J. Am. Chem. Soc.*, **73**, 2825 (1951).
58. Grim, R. E., and R. A. Rowland, *J. Am. Ceram. Soc.*, **27**, 65 (1944).
59. de Jong, G. J., *J. Am. Ceram. Soc.*, **40**, 42 (1957).
60. Nathans, M. W., and W. W. Wendlandt, *J. Inorg. Nucl. Chem.*, **24**, 869 (1962).
61. Rowland, R. A., and D. R. Lewis, *Am. Mineralogist*, **36**, 80 (1951).
62. Schwenker, R. F., *Textile Res. J.*, **30**, 624 (1960).
63. Lodding, W., and L. Hammell, *Anal. Chem.*, **32**, 657 (1960).
64. Stone, R. L., *Anal. Chem.*, **32**, 1582 (1960).
65. Hodgson, A. A., *J. Sci. Instr.*, **40**, 61 (1963).
66. Crandall, W. B., and R. R. West, *Am. Ceram. Soc. Bull.*, **35**, 66 (1956).
67. Rowland, R. A., and E. C. Jonas, *Am. Mineralogist*, **34**, 550 (1949).
68. Rudin, A., H. P. Schrieber, and M. H. Waldman, *Ind. Eng. Chem.*, **53**, 137 (1961).
69. Reisman, A., *Anal. Chem.*, **32**, 1566 (1960).
70. Grimshaw, R. W., E. Heaton, and A. L. Roberts, *Trans. Brit. Ceram. Soc.*, **44**, 76 (1945).
71. Carthew, A. R., *Am. Mineralogist*, **40**, 107 (1955).
72. Martinez, E., *Am. Mineralogist*, **46**, 901 (1961).
73. Takahashi, H., *Bull. Chem. Soc. Japan*, **32**, 374 (1959).
74. Chihara, H., and S. Seki, *Bull. Chem. Soc. Japan*, **26**, 88 (1953).
75. Kulp, J. L., and A. E. Trites, *Am. Mineralogist*, **36**, 23 (1951).
76. Barrall, E. M., and L. B. Rogers, *Anal. Chem.*, **34**, 1106 (1962).
77. Wittels, M., *Am. Mineralogist*, **36**, 615 (1951).
78. Wittels, M., *Am. Mineralogist*, **36**, 760 (1951).
79. Dean, L. A., *Soil Sci.*, **63**, 95 (1947).
80. Kronig, R., and F. Snoodijk, *Appl. Sci. Research, Sect. A*, **3**, 27 (1951).
81. Allison, E. B., *Clay Minerals Bull.*, **2**, 242 (1953–1955).
82. Sturm, E., *J. Phys. Chem.*, **65**, 1935 (1961).
83. Sturm, E., unpublished results.
84. Yagfarov, M. S., *Russ. J. Inorg. Chem. (English Transl.)*, **6**, 1236 (1961).
85. Stone, R. L., and H. F. Rase, *Anal. Chem.*, **29**, 1273 (1957).
86. Ke, B., and A. W. Sisko, *J. Polymer Sci.*, **50**, 87 (1961).
87. Ke, B., *J. Polymer Sci.*, **42**, 15 (1960).
88. Klute, C. H., and W. Viehmann, *J. Appl. Polymer Sci.*, **5**, 86 (1961).
89. Wendlandt, W. W., *J. Chem. Educ.*, **38**, 571 (1961).
90. Blumberg, A. A., *J. Phys. Chem.*, **63**, 1129 (1959).
91. Borchardt, H. J., and F. Daniels, *J. Am. Chem. Soc.*, **79**, 41 (1957).
92. Baumgartner, P., and P. Duhaut, *Bull. Soc. Chim. France*, **1960**, 1187.
93. Borchardt, H. J., *J. Inorg. Nucl. Chem.*, **12**, 252 (1960).
94. Padmanabhan, V. M., S. C. Saraiya, and A. K. Sundaram, *J. Inorg. Nucl. Chem.*, **12**, 356 (1960).
95. Agarwala, R. P., and M. C. Naik, *Anal. Chim. Acta*, **24**, 128 (1960).
96. Borchardt, H. J., *J. Am. Chem. Soc.*, **81**, 1529 (1959).
97. Hall, J. W., and H. F. Rase, *IEC Process Design Develop.*, **2**, 25 (1963).
98. Notz, K. J., and H. H. Jaffe, *J. Am. Ceram. Soc.*, **43**, 53 (1960).
99. Garn, P. D., *Anal. Chem.*, **33**, 1247 (1961).

100. Erdey, L., F. Paulik, and J. Paulik, *Acta Chim. Acad. Sci. Hung.*, **10,** 61 (1956).
101. Powell, D. A., *J. Sci. Instr.*, **34,** 225 (1957).
102. Freeman, E. S., and D. Edelman, *Anal. Chem.*, **31,** 624 (1959).
103. Campbell, C., S. Gordon, and C. L. Smith, *Anal. Chem.*, **31,** 1188 (1959).

CHAPTER VI

DIFFERENTIAL THERMAL ANALYSIS
INSTRUMENTATION

A. Introduction

Like thermogravimetry, a large number of different types of differential thermal analysis instruments have been described. These instruments vary widely concerning types of furnace and sample holder assemblies, temperature controllers, recording devices, etc. For this reason, there is little agreement, at times, between the DTA thermograms obtained on the same sample by different instruments. With the advent of several commercial instruments, however, some standardization has taken place in that fairly reproducible results can be obtained under identical pyrolysis conditions by the same type of instrument located in different laboratories.

A typical DTA instrument is illustrated in Figure VI.1. The instrument generally consists of (a) a furnace or heating device, (b) sample holder, (c) low-level dc amplifier, (d) differential temperature detector, (e) furnace temperature controller, (f) recorder, and (g) control equipment for maintaining a suitable atmosphere in the furnace and sample holder. Many modifications have been made of this basic design, but all instruments measure the differential temperature of the sample as a function of temperature or time (assuming that the temperature rise is linear with respect to time).

1. SAMPLE HOLDERS

Sample holders constructed from glass, metal, or ceramic materials, in a variety of shapes and dimensions (1), have been described. Construction materials include alumina, zirconia, borosilicate glass, Vycor glass, fused quartz, beryllia, stainless steel, nickel, platinum–platinum–10% rhodium, Inconel, silver, palladium–stainless steel, aluminum, copper, brass, graphite, and the sample itself. Obviously, the choice of material depends upon the temperature range to be studied, as well as the nature of the sample itself.

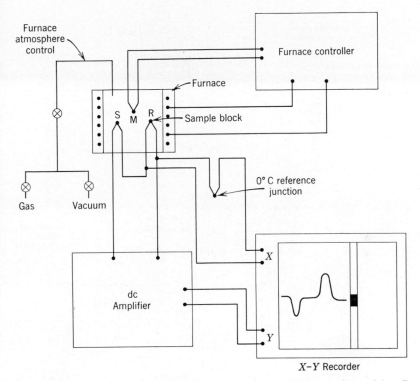

Fig. VI.1. Typical differential thermal analysis instrument (schematic). S, sample TC; R, reference TC; M, monitor TC.

Several of the more common types of sample holders are illustrated in Figure VI.2.

In (a), the sample and reference materials are placed in intimate contact with the thermojunction; the removable ceramic or metal sleeve aids in cleaning out the spent sample material. A removable sample cup is shown in (b); the cup can be easily removed from the apparatus for weighing, cleaning, etc. An advantage of this type of holder is that the sample is not in direct contact with the thermojunction as the cup makes contact with the junction from the bottom. In (c), volatile samples, i.e., liquids, can be studied. The tube can be sealed off or alternatively, closed with a suitable cover or stopper. Again, the sample does not come in contact with the thermojunction. The thermojunction is introduced into the sample from the top of the

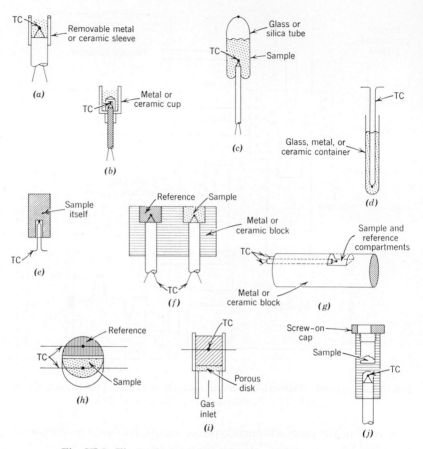

Fig. VI.2. Illustrative sample holders for DTA instruments.

container in (d).   In the case of some sample materials, such as clays, the sample can be compressed into the shape as shown in (e) and thus serve as its own container.   A very common type of sample holder is shown in (f).   The container may be constructed of a metallic or ceramic material.   A similar sample holder is illustrated in (g) except that it is mounted in a horizontal, rather than a vertical position.   A ceramic crucible has been used as a sample and reference container as shown in (h).   A partition separates the two materials.   To allow the passage of a gas through the sample material, the holder in (i) has been described.   A porous ceramic plate in the bottom of the con-

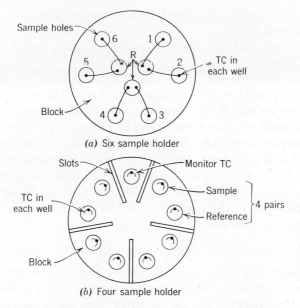

(a) Six sample holder

(b) Four sample holder

Fig. VI.3. Multiple sample holder arrangements.

tainer allows easy passage of the gas into the chamber.   An isobaric sample holder, as described by Bohon (24), is illustrated in *(j)*.   The holder contains a screw-on stainless steel cap which is made gas-tight by a copper washer.

To increase the number of samples that can be studied at any one given time, various multiple sample holders have been described, capable of studying three, four, five, or six samples simultaneously. Several arrangements of these holders are illustrated in Figure VI.3.

The arrangement in *(a)*, which is due to Kulp and Kerr (2,3), contained six sample wells and three reference wells.   Each sample and reference well was $1/4$ in. in diameter and $3/8$ in. deep, drilled in a nickel metal block.   A multipoint recorder was used to record the temperature differences for each sample–reference combination.

A more recent multiple sample holder, as shown in *(b)*, is used in the Deltatherm instrument (see p. 200).   Four separate sample–reference pairs are employed, as well as a monitor thermocouple.   Slits are cut at various radial intervals in the block to prevent thermal gradients from one sample interfering with an adjacent reference well.   Four separate dc amplifiers are used in conjunction with a novel four-channel recorder.

A five sample multiple sample block has also been described by Cox and McGlynn (4).

The size of the sample that is placed in the various sample holders varies over a wide range. Sample sizes from 5 to 6 g of material down to 10 to 100 μg (5) have been employed, although the most commonly used size ranges from 100 to 400 mg. For the extremely small samples mentioned above, the differential thermojunction contained a small cavity which acted as a microcrucible for the sample. For liquid samples, the temperature detection devices may be inserted into tubes containing the liquid or the liquid may be placed upon a thermally inert substance, such as α-alumina, and run in the conventional manner.

2. Differential Temperature Detection Devices

The choice of a temperature detection device depends upon the maximum temperature desired, the chemical reactivity of the sample, and the sensitivity of the dc amplifier and recording equipment. The most common means of differential temperature detection is with thermocouples, although thermopiles, thermistors, and resistance elements have been employed. For high-temperature studies, an optical pyrometer may also be practical.

Thermocouples have been constructed from platinum vs. platinum–10% rhodium; gold–40% palladium vs. platinum–10% rhodium; platinum–10% rhodium vs. palladium–20% gold or palladium–10% gold; iron vs. Constantan; Chromel vs. Alumel, copper vs. Constantan, and platinum vs. platinum–13% rhodium. For temperatures up to 3000°C, tantalum carbide vs. graphite has been suggested (6).

To increase the output signal from the differential thermocouples without the use of an amplifier, thermopiles have been employed (4,7,14). The advantage of such a system is the greater output signal with a lower noise level, due to lack of electronic amplification.

Fairly high resistance thermistors 100 000 Ω at ambient temperature, connected in a bridge circuit have been used to detect the differential temperature (8,9). This method does not normally require the use of a dc amplifier. Because their resistance decreases rapidly with increase in temperature, thermistors are generally only useful up to about 300°C (8).

3. FURNACES AND FURNACE TEMPERATURE CONTROLLERS

Again, as in the preceding part, the choice of furnace heating element and type of furnace depends upon the temperature range under investigation. DTA furnaces have been described which operate in the range from −190 to 2800°C. The furnace may be mounted vertically or horizontally; it may be heated by a resistance element, infrared radiation (10,11), high-frequency rf oscillation (6,12), or by a coil of tubing through which a heated or cooled liquid or gas is circulated (13).

Resistance elements are perhaps the most widely used in furnace construction. Some resistance elements and their approximate temperature limits are given in Table VI.-1. These temperature limits, are of course, dependent upon the furnace design and insulation.

TABLE VI.1
Temperature Limits for Furnace Resistance Elements

Element	Approximate temperature, °C
Nichrome	1000
Kanthal	1350
Platinum	1400
Platinum–10% rhodium	1500
Rhodium	1800
Tantalum	1330
Globar	1500
Kanthal Super	1600
Molybdenum	1200
Platinum–20% rhodium	1500
Chromel A	1100
Tungsten	2800

In an attempt to control the atmosphere within the furnace and sample holder, various techniques have been employed. They include: (a) flooding the furnace with a gaseous atmosphere (15,16, 21,24); (b) vacuum furnaces (15–20, 22, 23); and (c) a dynamic gas flow atmosphere (15,16,25,26).

In order to obtain satisfactory DTA curves, the furnace temperature must be increased at a constant, uniform rate. Heating rates from 0.1 to 300°C/min have been employed; the most common is from 10 to 15°C/min. The rate of temperature increase can be controlled by increasing the voltage into the furnace heater coils. One method of accomplishing this is to connect the furnace windings to the output of a variable-voltage transformer, which is rotated at a slow, fixed rate by a synchronous motor. A properly constructed and insulated furnace will give an approximately linear heating-rate curve. More refined furnace temperature controllers, employing a feedback circuit which is controlled by a thermocouple in the furnace, are also commonly employed. A wide choice of heating rates is available using commercial instruments.

Although most DTA instruments have only one furnace, to increase the number of samples that can be run each day, several furnaces may be used in conjunction with the sample holder, amplifier, and recording system. In fact, an instrument that contains four different furnaces (27) has been described.

4. DC AMPLIFIERS AND RECORDERS

Unless a sensitive recorder is used, the differential thermocouple emf output must be amplified by a stable, low-noise level, dc microvolt amplifier. Low-output thermocouples, such as platinum vs. platinum–10% rhodium, require more amplification than do the Chromel vs. Alumel or copper vs. Constantan types. Thermistors and thermopiles seldom require the use of amplifiers.

Various recorders have been described, from photographic light-beam galvanometer types to modern electronic potentiometric recorders. Burgess (28) gives an excellent discussion of some of the earlier recording devices.

Probably the first to use modern potentiometric recorders, especially the multipoint type, were Kerr and Kulp (3) and Kauffman and Dilling (29). This type of recorder, plus the use of multiple sample holders, increased the usefulness of DTA for the qualitative identification of geological materials. Another technique, using a two-point recorder, is to record both the differential temperature and the reference material temperature as a function of time on the same chart paper. More useful perhaps is the modern $X-Y$ recorder in which the differential temperature is plotted directly as a function of reference material temperature. Thus, a direct recording of the differential temperature vs. temperature is obtained. A wide choice of recorders and recording ranges are available.

B. Commercial DTA Instruments

Stone has described several DTA instruments which are now commercially available (Robert L. Stone Co., 3314 Westhill Drive,

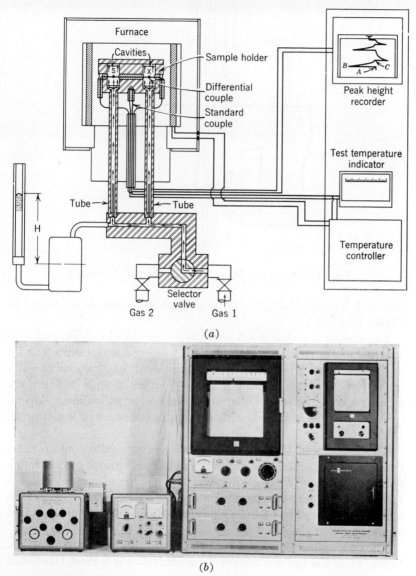

(a)

(b)

Fig VI.4. Schematic illustration of the Stone DTA apparatus (25),

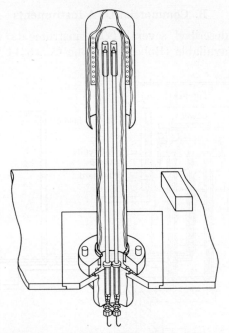

Fig. VI.5. Apparatus Manufacturers, Inc., DTA assembly.

Austin 4, Texas) (19,25,26).   One of the instruments is illustrated in
Figure VI.4.

The sample chamber is 1.5 in. in diameter, 0.75 in. thick, and constructed of Inconel.   The sample and reference cavities are 0.25 in.
in diameter, 0.375 in. deep, and contain identical platinum vs. platinum–10% rhodium thermojunctions.   Other sample holders are
available, constructed of either stainless steel or palladium.   Several
furnaces may be obtained, with maximum temperature limits up to
1400°C.

The bottoms of the sample and reference cavities contain a refractory, porous disk that permits the passage of various gases through
them.   By use of a selector valve, the change of several gases is
facilitated.   The apparatus is also equipped with a vapor generator,
which can be used to produce superheated water vapor or vaporized
organic compounds.

The dc amplifier employed is of the Leeds and Northrup or A.R.A.
types, while the furnace temperature controller is a West Gardsman

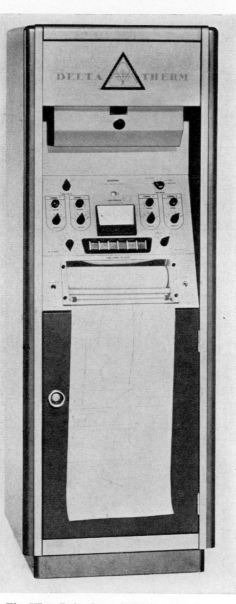

Fig. VI.6. Deltatherm DTA instrument.

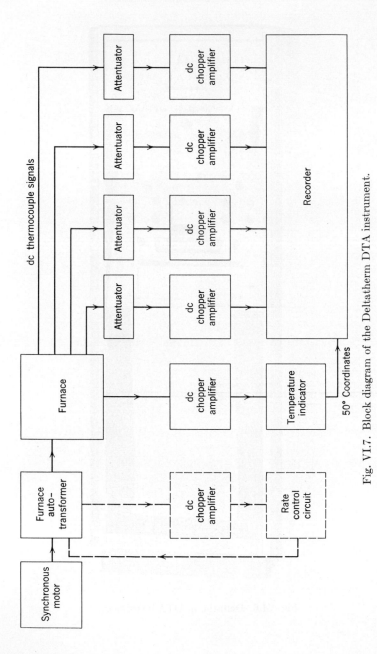

Fig. VI.7. Block diagram of the Deltatherm DTA instrument.

Fig. VI.8. The Deltatherm sample holder.

Stepless Controller. Heating rates for the furnace or from 1 to 15°C/min are available.

The Apparatus Manufacturers, Inc. (Box 47, Green Village, New Jersey) DTA furnace and sample holder assembly is illustrated in Figure VI.5. Apparently only the above is supplied by the manufacturer, the remaining instrumentation is to be furnished by the purchaser.

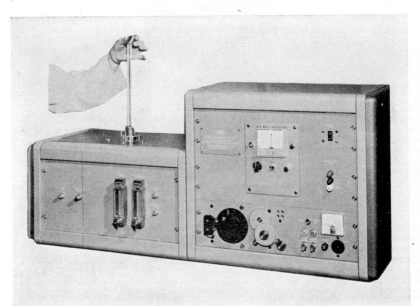

Fig. VI.9. The Thermoanalyzer DTA instrument.

The assembly is basically a controlled-atmosphere, controlled-pressure dynamic atmosphere unit of the Lodding–Hammell type (15,16). Three types of sample holders are supplied: (a) nickel, ceramic or stainless steel block containing two sample cavities and a monitor thermocouple opening; (b) ceramic open-ended tubes such as described in Figure VI.2a; and (c) ceramic closed-end tubes. The latter sample holder is useful for maintaining a self-generated atmosphere. Two optional furnaces are available with maximum temperature limits of 1200 and 1600°C, respectively. The furnace chamber is pressure and leak-tested above 100 psig.

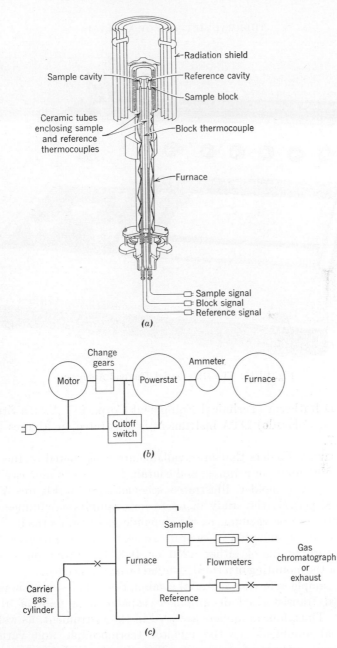

Fig. VI.10. Schematic diagram of: (a) furnace and sample holder assembly; (b) furnace programmer; and (c) flow control system.

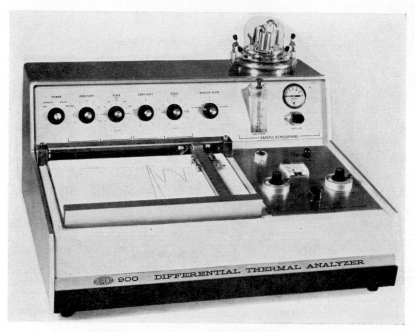

Fig. VI.11. The Differential Thermal Analyzer.

The Deltatherm (Technical Equipment Corp., 917 Acoma Street, Denver 4, Colorado) DTA instrument is illustrated in Figures VI.6 and VI.7.

The sample holders that are available are constructed of Inconel, copper, aluminum, or ceramic, and contain from two to nine cavities. The nine-cavity holder, illustrated schematically in Figures VI.3b and VI.8, permits the study of up to four samples simultaneously, under pressure or vacuum, or the dynamic gas flow method. Two furnaces can be mounted in each instrument. These furnaces have temperature limits of either 1250 or 1600°C. Provision is also made for the mounting of a third external furnace if needed.

Each sample–reference material combination has its own chopper-stabilized transistorized dc amplifier, capable of a gain of about 50,000. Thus, four amplifiers are used in the instrument, as well as additional amplifiers for the monitor thermocouple and variable heating-rate furnace programmer. The outputs of the four sample amplifiers are fed into a unique four-channel, strip-chart recorder. In this recorder, the dc signal from the amplifier is compared to a sawtooth voltage synchronized with the travel of small electrodes fastened to a chain which travels across the 12 in. wide paper at a 90° angle to the chart paper travel direction. An electrical pulse is produced when the sawtooth voltage passes the dc voltage signal, which is then amplified and used to print a dot on the electrosensitive paper. The dots that are printed on the paper blend into a line, giving a tracing of voltage vs. time. At 50°C intervals of temperature, a solid black line is printed on the recording chart.

The furnace-temperature rise is controlled either by a motor-driven variable transformer or a feedback-type programmer. Heating rates from 2 to 20°C/min are available.

The Thermoanalyzer DTA instrument (American Instrument Co., 8030 Georgia Ave., Silver Spring, Maryland) is illustrated in Figures VI.9 and VI.10.

The furnace and sample holder are of the Lodding–Hammell (15,16) type with a maximum furnace temperature of 1000°C. Two such furnaces are supplied with the instrument. The flow-control system permits the use of the dynamic gas flow technique in that various gases can be passed through the sample and reference materials (16).

The furnace-temperature programmer is basically a motor-driven, variable voltage transformer which, through a gear interchange, permits heating rates of 2, 4, 8, and 16°C/min.

Although a recorder is not furnished with the instrument, an X–Y recorder is recommended to record the differential temperature curves.

The Differential Thermal Analyzer (E. I. du Pont de Nemours & Co., Instrument Products Division, Wilmington 98, Delaware) is illustrated in Figures VI.11 and VI.12.

The furnace and sample holder, previously described by Chiu (30), consist of an aluminum block, heated by a heater cartridge, which can be operated up to 500°C. Sample and reference materials are placed in glass melting-point capillary tubes, which are located symmetrically around the heater cartridge. Thermocouples are inserted into the samples through the top of the open glass tubes, as is illustrated in Figure VI.2d. A glass bell jar, seated on a neoprene O-ring, is placed over the entire sample and furnace assembly to permit a controlled atmosphere.

The output from the dc amplifier is recorded on a modified Moseley $X-Y$ recorder with provision for zero offset of the temperature axis. The heating and cooling rate of the furnace can be varied from $+30$ to $-30°C$ min.

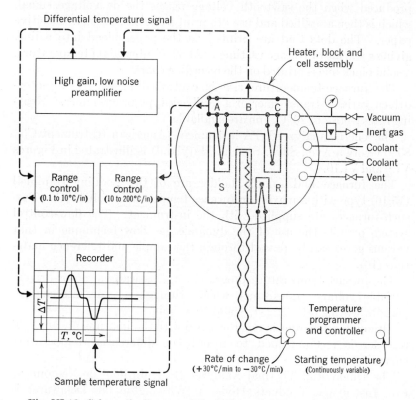

Fig. VI.12. Schematic diagram of the Differential Thermal Analyzer.

The Harrop DTA instrument (Harrop Precision Furnace Co., 3470 East Fifth Ave., Columbus 19, Ohio) is illustrated in Figure VI.13.

A total of three furnace and sample holders which contain such furnace heater windings as Nichrome (1050°C), platinum, and molybdenum (1500°C) may be chosen. Controlled atmospheres are provided for at moderate pressures and under a vacuum. Nickel-sample holder blocks or platinum–10% rhodium metal sample

Fig. VI.13. Harrop DTA instrument.

cups are available.   The furnace temperature programmer permits the use of heating rates from 1 to 20°C/min.

In contrast to the previously described instruments, the Bolton DTA instrument (A. R. Bolton & Co., Ltd., Bankhead Drive, Sighthill, Edinburgh, Scotland) employs a horizontally mounted furnace and sample holder.   An Inconel block is used with a sample capacity of about 200 mg.   Various controlled atmospheres, pressure and vacuum, can be employed.   Furnace heating rates of 2.5, 10, 20, and 40°C/min are permitted.   A two-channel strip-chart recorder simultaneously plots the differential temperature and furnace temperature as a function of time.

The Rigaku Denki Differential Thermal Analyzer–Specific Heat Measurement (DTA–SHM) instrument (Rigaku Denki Co., Ltd., 8, Kanda-Daidokorocho, Chiyoda-Ku, Tokyo, Japan; sold in U.S.A. by Erb and Gray Scientific Co., Houston, Texas) is a multiple function instrument which may be used to measure either the specific heat (and heat of reaction) or the differential temperature of the sample as a function of time or furnace temperature.

In the SHM mode of operation, the sample temperature is maintained in an adiabatic condition to the furnace by applying periodic

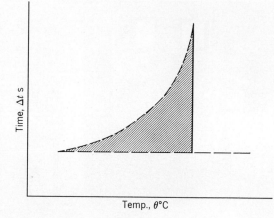

Fig. VI.14. Determination of the heat of transformation by a SHM curve.

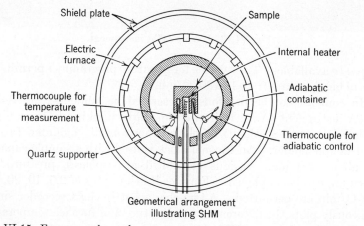

Geometrical arrangement
illustrating SHM

Fig. VI.15. Furnace and sample arrangement for SHM measurements (schematic).

amounts of heat by means of an electric heater located inside of the sample. The specific heat, at constant pressure, of the sample, C_p, is calculated from

$$C_p = \frac{0.239\ W\,\Delta t}{M\,\Delta Q} \qquad (VI.1)$$

where Δt is the time, in seconds, in which the sample at $Q°C$ is heated by $\Delta Q°C$, M is the mass of the sample, and W is the supplied

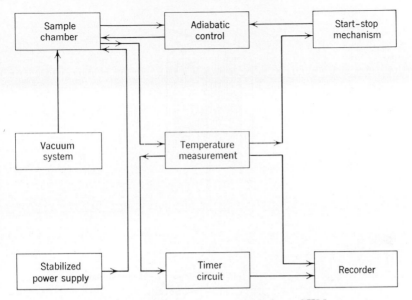

Fig. VI.16. Schematic diagram of components for a SHM apparatus.

heat, in watts. The total heat of transformation (reaction) is the area enclosed by the curve as shown in Figure VI.14.

A schematic diagram of the furnace and sample arrangement is shown in Figure VI.15, while a block diagram of the SHM apparatus is given in Figure VI.16. The novel spherical furnace arrangement is said to give better uniformity of temperature distribution, good heating efficiency, and greater ease of operation than the conventional tube type furnaces. The furnace atmosphere may be vacuum, controlled gas, or air, while the sample may be either a powder, solid, or liquid of any shape.

By simple modification of the sample block, the apparatus may be used to obtain DTA measurements. Such a modification is shown by the sample holder in Figure VI.17. The sample and reference materials are placed in quartz or metal containers as shown in the illustration. The unique spherical furnace is said to practically eliminate base-line drift. Temperature limits of the standard furnace are from ambient to 1000°C.

A manually recording, portable DTA instrument (Eberbach Corp., Ann Arbor, Michigan) widely used for the analysis of clay and soil

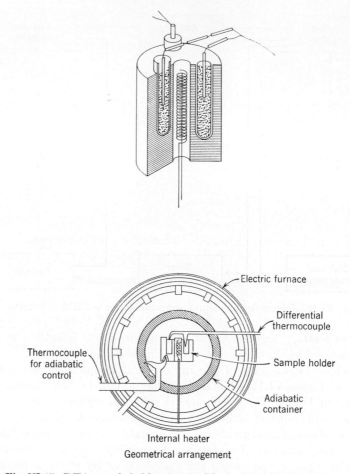

Fig. VI.17. DTA sample holders for the Rigaku Denki DTA apparatus.

samples in the field is also available.   Three crucible cells are available, each of which is fitted with a thermocouple.   Temperature
differences between the sample and reference materials are measured
with a sensitive galvanometer; the furnace temperature is measured
by a third thermocouple.   The results are manually plotted on graph
paper.

A DTA apparatus based upon a different principle than previously
described here is available from the Perkin-Elmer Corporation and is

called a Differential Scanning Calorimeter (DSC) (Perkin-Elmer Corporation, Instrument Division, Norwalk, Connecticut).

The instrument is illustrated in Figures VI.18 and VI.19. The apparatus, unlike DTA, maintains a sample temperature isothermal to a reference substance (or furnace block) by supplying heat to the sample or reference material. The amount of heat required to maintain these isothermal conditions is then recorded as a function of time (or temperature). In addition to recording the enthalpy

Fig. VI.18. Differential Scanning Calorimeter (DSC).

curve, if the sample evolves a volatile material during the heating process, the gas evolved by the sample is recorded.

The instrument contains two "control loops," one for the average temperature control, the other for the differential temperature control. In the former, a programmer provides an electrical output signal that is proportional to the desired temperature of the sample and reference holders. The programmer signal, which reaches the average temperature amplifier, is compared with signals received from platinum-resistance thermometers permanently embedded in the sample and reference holders via an average temperature computer.

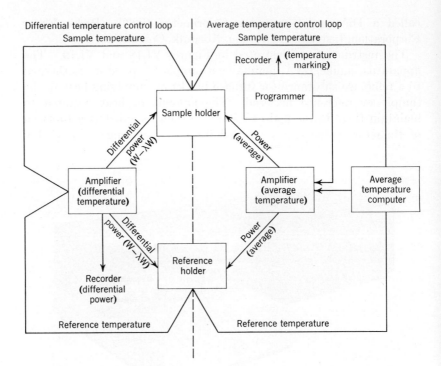

Fig. VI.19. Schematic diagram of the Differential Scanning Calorimeter.

In the differential temperature loop, signals representing the sample and reference temperatures, as measured by the platinum-resistance thermometers, are fed to the differential temperature amplifier via a comparator circuit, which determines whether the reference or sample temperature is greater. The differential temperature-amplifer output then adjusts the differential power increment put into the reference and sample heaters in the direction and magnitude necessary to correct any temperature difference between them. A signal proportional to the differential power is also transmitted to the pen of a galvanometer recorder, giving a trace of differential power vs. time (temperature). The area under a peak, then, is directly proportional to the heat energy absorbed or liberated in the transition.

Various furnace heating rates are available, ranging from 0.6 to 80°C/min. Output sensitivity can be varied from 0.002 to 0.032 cal/s for a half-scale deflection. The furnace chamber has a temperature range of -100 to $550\,°C$, and can be flooded with various gases at atmospheric pressure or under vacuum (> 10 mm Hg).

C. Noncommercial DTA Instruments

A large number of DTA instruments have been described in the literature; in fact, each investigator has apparently built his own instrument, each of which is slightly different from the other. In recent times, however, some standardization has taken place by the use of commercially available recording devices, dc amplifiers, and furnace temperature programmers. The only variable part of the instrument, and perhaps the most important, is the furnace and sample holder assembly. Unfortunately, many investigators still construct this part of the instrument, and hence a wide variation in DTA curves is still obtained. An attempt will be made here to illustrate a selected few of the many instruments that have been described. Each, it is hoped, will illustrate a specific type of instrument or temperature range. In many cases, only the furnace and sample holder arrangements will be shown.

One of the first precision, vacuum or inert atmosphere instruments was designed and constructed by Whitehead and Breger (18). The furnace and sample block assembly are illustrated in Figure VI.20.

The furnace was constructed from an Alundum core, 9 in. in length by 2 in. inside diameter, wound with Chromel A resistance wire. The core was shielded by four sheet nickel cylinders, mounted on three posts, and the entire assembly placed inside a 12 in. $\times$ 24 in. Pyrex bell jar. All electrical connections were made through the bottom of the bell jar mounting base. The sample block was made in the dimensions shown from Type 446 or 309 stainless steel.

The furnace heating rate was controlled by a Leeds and Northrup Micromax controller; the differential temperatures were recorded on a Beckman Photocell recorder.

Wendlandt (20) has also described a simple vacuum or controlled atmosphere DTA furnace and sample holder, which is illustrated in Figure VI.21.

The furnace tube was 19 cm in length, 2.5 cm in diameter, and partially constructed of fused silica. The lower end of the tube contained two Pyrex glass 25 mm inside diameter O-ring joints, which were attached to the fused silica tube by a Nylon seal, machined to the dimensions of the glass O-ring joint, and attached to it by a com-

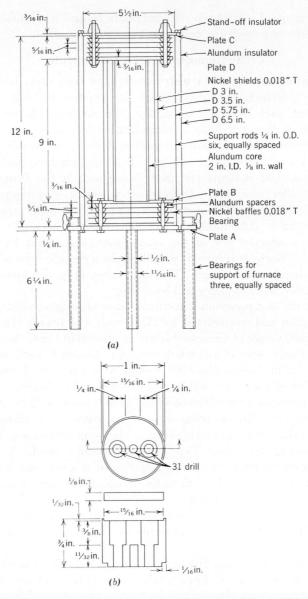

Fig. VI.20. Vacuum furnace and sample holder assembly of Whitehead and Breger (18).

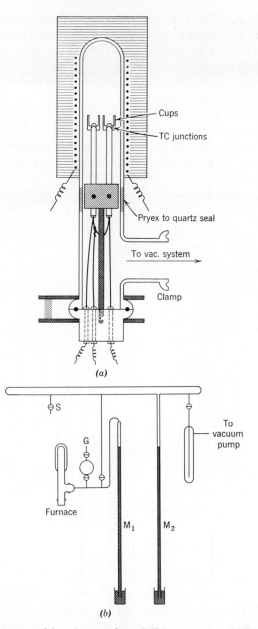

Cups

TC junctions

Pryex to quartz seal

To vac. system

Clamp

(a)

S

G

To
vacuum
pump

Furnace

M₁

M₂

(b)

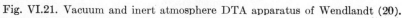

Fig. VI.21. Vacuum and inert atmosphere DTA apparatus of Wendlandt (20).

pression clamp. The Chromel vs. Alumel thermocouple wires were brought into the furnace zone by use of 3.0 mm diameter, two-holed ceramic tubing. The sample and reference cups made of Inconel were 7 mm in diameter, 10 mm in length, and had a volume of 0.8 ml. The cups fit snuggly on the insulator tube and were in intimate contact with the thermojunctions.

The furnace was wound, either on the insulated fused silica tube or on an external ceramic tube, which fit closely about the silica tube, with Nichrome resistance wire. The furnace temperature programmer consisted of a variable-voltage transformer driven by a synchronous motor (31).

The differential temperature signal was amplified by a Leeds and

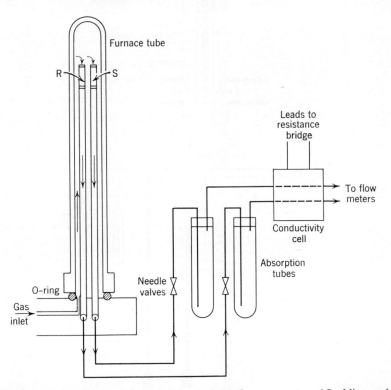

Fig. VI.22. DTA furnace, sample holder, and gas-flow apparatus of Lodding and Hammell (15,16).

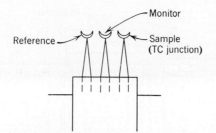

Fig. VI.23. Sample and reference holder of Mazieres (5).

Northrup dc microvolt amplifier and recorded against temperature on a Houston Instruments Corp. X–Y recorder.

The DTA furnace and gas flow system of Lodding and Hammell (15,16) is illustrated schematically in Figure VI.22.

The furnace consisted of a recrystallized alumina tube, $1^1/_8$ in. inside diameter, heated from the outside by a double helix of Kanthal A resistance wire. The insulating jacket, which fit loosely over the furnace windings of the tube, was made by lining a stainless steel beaker with insulating brick. The jacket could be removed from the furnace to permit rapid cooling of the furnace. The furnace was mounted in a vertical position on a horizontal aluminum plate.

The sample and reference material holders were identical to those shown in Figure VI.2a and were constructed of Mullite. The thermocouples were brought into the furnace chamber through two-holed Mullite insulator tubes fastened to a movable aluminum block. Provision was made for external thermocouple connections and gas inlet and outlet connections through this block. The two-holed Mullite tubes permitted the flow of a gas through the sample and reference materials, thus providing a controlled atmosphere inside of the furnace chamber. Pressures of 28 atm at 1200°C, as well as a vacuum, may be employed in the furnace.

A novel sample holder has been described by Mazieres (5) and is illustrated in Figure VI.23. The junctions of the Chromel vs. Constantan thermocouples are drilled out to form a cavity in which the sample is contained. A suitable DTA curve could be obtained with only 40 μg of sample.

A DTA furnace and sample block, which employed standard 18 mm × 150 mm test tubes as sample and reference material con-

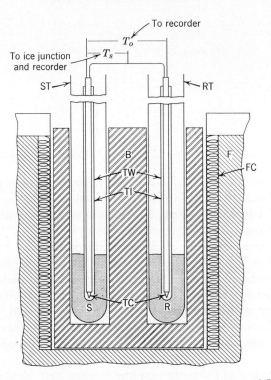

Fig. VI.24. DTA heating block and sample tube arrangement of Campbell and Weingarten (12). F, furnace, 110 V, 550 W; FC, furnace coil and core; B, block, steel, $2\,^7/_8$ in. by 4 in.; ST, sample tube, Pyrex, 18 mm by 150 mm; RT, reference tube; TW, thermocouple well, Pyrex; T1, thermocouple insulating tube, round, double bore; TC, thermocouple, Chromel-Alumel, BS 2 8; T_d, differential temperature; T_s, sample temperature.

tainers, have been described by Campbell and Weingarten (12). The apparatus is illustrated in Figure VI.24. The heating rate of the furnace, normally 15°C/min, was controlled by a West Instruments Co. Gardsman-cam type, stepless, proportioning pyrometer-controller. For faster heating rates, up to 330°C/min, the sample block was placed in the heating coil of a 2.5 kw Lepel high-frequency induction heater. For the lower heating rate, 0.25 g of sample was employed.

A DTA apparatus capable of operation up to 1575°C has been described by Newkirk (32) and Skinner (33). The apparatus described by the former is shown in Figure VI.25.

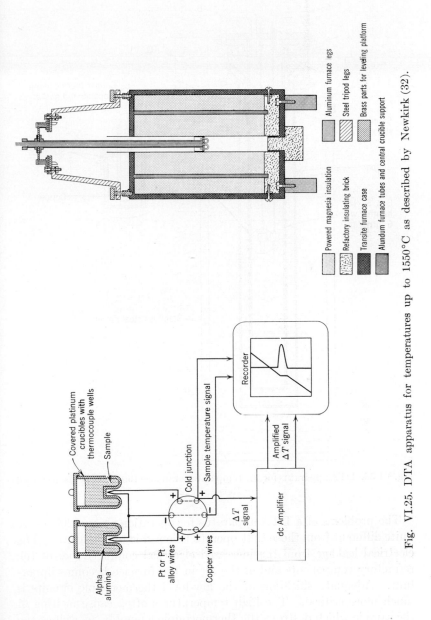

Fig. VI.25. DTA apparatus for temperatures up to 1550°C as described by Newkirk (32).

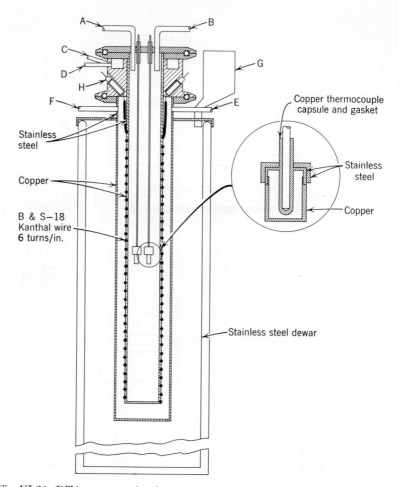

Fig. VI.26. DTA apparatus for the temperature range −190 to 400°C as described by Reisman (22).

The problems of a DTA apparatus for operation above 1200 °C are quite different from those that operate below this temperature. The electrical leakage from the increased electrical conductivities of the refractory components and of the air in the furnace becomes important. Adequate shielding of the low-level thermocouple circuits is much more critical. The high temperatures often cause melting of the sample which destroys the thermocouple assembly, as well as the

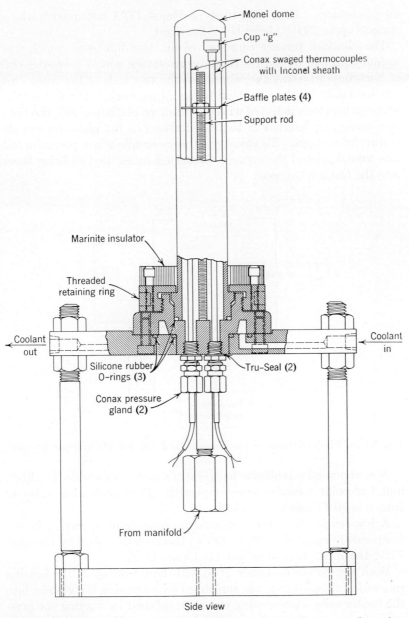

Side view

Fig. VI.27. DTA apparatus for explosives and propellant samples after Bohon (24).

sample holders.   Even with these problems, DTA instruments which operate up to 2800 °C have been described.

The Newkirk furnace consisted of an Alundum core, which was wound with platinum–20% rhodium resistance wire.   A booster coil of Nichrome wire was also wound on the two ends of the core; this was used only for the very high temperature work.   The differential temperatures were detected with platinum vs. platinum–10% rhodium thermocouples, inserted in the indentations of the platinum sample and reference cups.   To shield the thermocouple wires, platinum foil was wound around the ceramic insulating tubes used to bring them into the furnace hot zone.

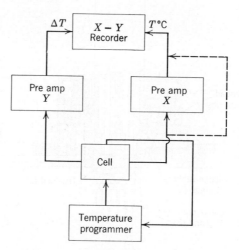

Fig. VI.28. Block diagram of the Vassallo and Harden DTA apparatus (34).

A commercially-available temperature programmer, dc amplifier, and two-point recorder were employed.   Furnace-heating rates of from 0 to 30 °C/min were possible.

A low-temperature DTA apparatus, capable of operation in the temperature range of −190 to 400 °C, has been described by Reisman (22); the apparatus is illustrated in Figure II.26.

With the Dewar container filled with liquid nitrogen, the heating rate of the sample block was controlled by increasing the voltage into the heater coils, while cooling was accomplished by varying the pressure of the gas present in the outer chamber.   Commercially avail-

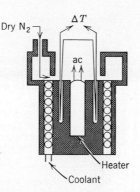

Fig. VI.29. Cross section of heater and sample block of Vassallo and Harden (34).

able dc amplifiers and recorders were employed in the apparatus to record the DTA curve.

An extremely rugged DTA furnace and sample holder has been described by Bohon (24) and is illustrated in Figure VI.27.

In this apparatus, the differential thermocouples are isolated from the sample to avoid destruction from explosions or chemical reaction with the sample. This was accomplished by employing Chromel vs. Alumel thermocouples encased in an Inconel sheath. The furnace tube and auxiliary pressure manifold were made from Monel metal. Pressures up to 1000 psig have been sustained in the furnace tube assembly at 350°C, and 400 psig at temperatures up to 500°C.

A highly sensitive DTA apparatus which permitted the determination of phase transition temperatures of ±0.5°C over a wide range of heating rates has been described by Vassallo and Harden (34). The overall instrument components and the sample holder and heating block are illustrated in Figures VI.28 and VI.29.

The apparatus is conventional in the differential temperature measuring circuit, but in the furnace temperature-measuring circuit a dc amplifier and zero-suppressing circuit are used when temperature accuracies of better than ±0.5°C are required.

The heating block permits the use of 1.5–2.0 mm × 30 mm melting point capillary tubes as sample and reference material containers, with the thermocouples inserted into the sample through the top of the tube (see Fig. VI.2d). The block was heated by a 30 W cartridge heater placed in the center of the block. The double coil of copper tubing served as a cooling line. One coil was immersed in a coolant

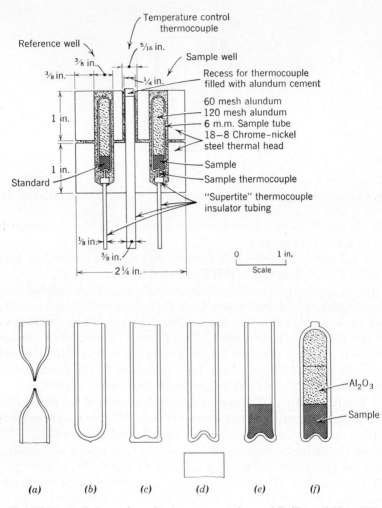

Fig. VI.30. Sealed sample and reference containers of Bollin and Kerr (36).

contained in the lower part of the flask, while the second coil surrounded the block. The block was cooled by a flow of air or nitrogen through the lower coil, thence to the coil surrounding the block. A temperature range from −150 to 450°C could be covered by the apparatus.

The use of sealed glass or silica sample and reference tubes has been

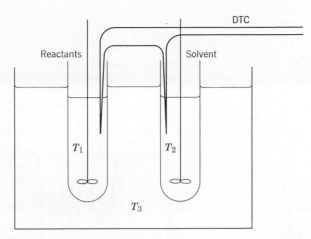

Fig. VI.31. Solution DTA apparatus of Borchardt and Daniels (38).

described by recent investigators (35–37). These containers are especially useful when volatile or highly corrosive materials are studied, but appear to be difficult to use. The arrangement used by Bollin and Kerr (36) is illustrated in Figure VI.30.

The sample containers were constructed of either Pyrex, Vycor, or fused silica tubing, 6 mm in diameter. The final tube was about 4 in. in length and contained a mixture of the sample (1–2 mg) and aluminum oxide, and was evacuated to 10 μ pressure before being sealed off at the top. The sample and reference containers were placed on thermocouple junctions contained in a stainless steel block. Powdered Alundum was placed between the containers and the block for better heat transfer.

In the apparatus described by Gasson (37), three samples could be studied simultaneously.

For studying the kinetics of homogeneous reactions in solution, Borchardt and Daniels (38) used the glass apparatus illustrated schematically in Figure VI.31. The cells consisted of two Pyrex tubes, 1.25 in. in diameter and 5 in. in length, each having a volume of about 60 ml. The thermocouples, contained in Kel-F covered copper tubes, were inserted into the tube contents from the top. The bath temperature and hence the sample and reference materials, was gradually increased by use of a heater connected to a variable-voltage transformer.

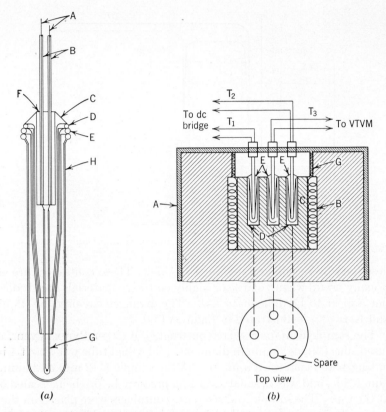

Fig. VI.32. DTA apparatus of Pakulak and Leonard (8). (a) Thermistor probe: A, output leads; B, teflon sleeving; C, electric resistor cement; D, 1 mm centrifuge tube; E, 1.5 mm centrifuge tube; F, two-hole ceramic tube; G, thermistor; H, test tube. (b) Furnace cross section: A, furnace; B, furnace coil and well; C, block, aluminum; D, sample tubes; E, thermistor containers; T_1, T_2, T_3 thermistors; G, glass ring 1 in. $\times$ $3^1/_4$ in.

A DTA apparatus containing thermistors as the differential temperature detection devices has been described by Pakulak and Leonard (8) and is illustrated in Figure VI.32, while the dc thermistor bridge circuit is shown in Figure VI.33.

The matched thermistors, 100 000 Ω at 25 °C, were contained in glass tubes and centered in each of the sample and reference tubes. A third thermistor was used to detect the temperature of the furnace. All three thermistors and tubes were placed into a furnace constructed

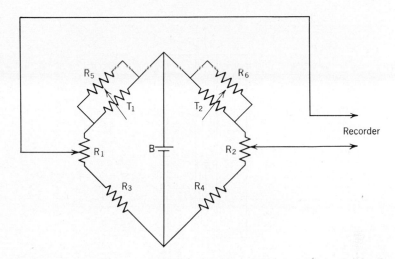

Fig. VI.33. Direct current bridge for thermistor DTA apparatus (8). R_1, R_2, 100 Ω potentiometer; R_3, R_4, 1000 Ω ± 1%; R_5, R_6, 2000 Ω ± 1%; T_1, T_2, thermistors-100 000 Ω at 25°C; B, $1^1/_2$ V dry cell.

of aluminum. The heating rate of the furnace was controlled by increasing the furnace windings voltage by means of a variable voltage transformer. A heating rate of 2°C/min was normally employed.

It should be noted that a dc amplifier was not required since the bridge unbalance voltage signal was large enough to be recorded by the recorder.

A rather novel DTA apparatus has been described by Nedumov (39) in that the differential temperature between the sample and reference materials was measured by tungsten resistance thermometers, which were not directly in contact with the sample. Hence the name, noncontact thermography. The crucible containing the sample material was placed in a cavity in the furnace block. Two identical tungsten resistance elements were placed at fixed positions on the outside of the crucible. One measured the sample temperature (for sample temperature vs. time recording) and the other measured the differential temperature. To decrease the temperature gradient between the sample and the surface of the resistance element, the mass, and hence the heat capacity of the compartment, was made much greater than that of the heating element. The changes in the resistance of the elements were measured by a bridge circuit and recorded

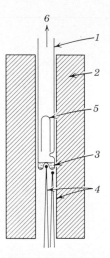

Fig. VI.34. DTA apparatus for measuring the saturated vapor pressure of a substance (40). (*1*) Quartz tube; (*2*) furnace; (*3*) substance; (*4*) two Pt/Pt–Rh thermocouples connected in a differential circuit; (*5*) small tube quartz for inserting the substance; (*6*) to vacuum installation.

on a photocell recorder. The furnace consisted of a tungsten wire heater element, capable of operation up to 2800 °C. To prevent volatilization of the tungsten, the wire was covered with a 5–6 μ thick layer of rhenium metal.

A DTA apparatus which has been used to determine the saturated vapor pressure of slightly volatile substances has been described by Novikov and Polyachenok (40) and is illustrated in Figure VI.34.

The sample, about 100 mg in weight, was placed inside of the fused silica tube, which was seated on one junction of a two-junction differential temperature thermocouple system. Pressure changes within the tube were effected by connection of the tube to a variable pressure vacuum system. By plotting the differential temperature of the sample vs. the pressure of the system, the saturated vapor pressure of the sample material could be obtained.

D. Multiple Instruments Containing a Differential Thermal Analysis Apparatus

The technique of DTA has been combined with other thermal techniques so that a simultaneous recording of the two or more

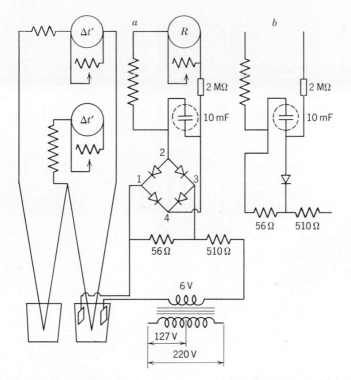

Fig. VI.35. Schematic diagram of simultaneous recording of DTA–electrical conductivity of a sample. (a) with four rectifiers; (b) with one rectifier (41).

techniques can be obtained on the same sample under identical conditions of pyrolysis. Other techniques that have been combined with DTA include thermogravimetry, gas evolution analysis (effluent gas analysis), electrical conductivity, differential thermogravimetry, gas chromatography, mass spectrometry, radioactivity, optical microscopy, and dilatometry.

The instrumentation for the simultaneous recording of DTA–TGA and DTA–gas evolution curves has been discussed in Chapters II and IX, respectively. An apparatus for the simultaneous recording of DTA–electrical conductivity curves has been described by Berg and Burmistrova (41) and is illustrated schematically in Figure VI.35.

The electrical conductivity of the sample is measured by placing the sample between two small platinum electrodes while the differential

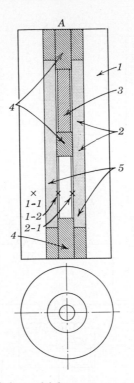

Fig. VI.36. Sample block for multiple apparatus for DTA, heat capacity, thermal diffusivity of Yagfarov (42,43). (*1*) Cylinder of heat-resisting steel (or aluminum or nickel); (*2*) internal cylinder of heat-resisting steel (or nickel); (*3*) material of known reproducible thermal capacity; (*4*) heat insulating partitions in variant A (these were hermetically sealed at the top, the thermocouple leads passed through them, the lower rings were removable for insertion of the substance under test); (*5*) the substance under test in A and B.

temperatures are measured by a small thermocouple placed in the sample. The electrodes were usually spaced 10 mm apart but at times were only 1 mm apart; for qualitative purposes, the distance was not critical. Part of a 6 V ac voltage was impressed upon the platinum electrodes and changes in the current in this circuit were detected, rectified to dc, and recorded as a function of temperature. The differential temperature and the reference material temperature were recorded simultaneously by light-beam galvanometers.

The simultaneous determination of the heat capacity, thermal conductivity, thermal diffusivity, and DTA of a sample could be obtained in the apparatus described by Yagfarov (42,43), the sample holder of which is illustrated in Figure VI.36.

The instrument consisted of a furnace, two differential thermocouples, the sample block, and a temperature recording device. The sample block consisted of a hollow cylinder, whose length was at least four times its diameter equipped with heat insulating blocks fixed to its ends. The standard sample was a solid cylinder, located in the lower half of the holder, while the sample material was placed in the upper half of the holder. The temperature differences between the main cylinder and the standard material, and between the main cylinder and the center of the sample material were measured with thermocouples indicated in the figure by a number and an x. The thermocouples at 1–1 and 1–2 measured the temperature drop due to the thermal diffusivity of the sample, and at the same time, the junctions at 2–1 and 2–1 measured the temperature drop in the substance caused by the known heat capacity of the standard.

Bussiere et al. (44) have described an apparatus in which the weight change, DTA, and radioactivity emission were measured simultaneously. The system was constructed of glass and contained a recording balance, DTA sample and reference containers, a scintillation counter, and auxiliary counting equipment.

An apparatus capable of simultaneously measuring the DTA and dilatometric properties of a sample material has been described by Pearce and Mardon (45). The DTA readout was on an automatic recorder, while the dilatometer readout consisted of a dial gage actuated by a push rod from the sample contained in the furnace assembly. The dial gage was made into an automatic recording unit by installation of a wiper-arm for contact on a potentiometer wire. The entire apparatus was installed in a glove-box.

References

1. Wendlandt, W. W., "Differential Thermal Analysis," in *Technique of Inorganic Chemistry*, H. B. Jonassen and A. Weissberger, eds., Interscience, New York, 1963, Volume 1, Chapter 6.
2. Kulp, J. L., and P. F. Kerr, *Science*, **105**, 413 (1947).
3. Kerr, P. F., and J. L. Kulp, *Am. Mineralogist*, **33**, 387 (1948).
4. Cox, D. B., and J. F. McGlynn, *Anal. Chem.*, **29**, 960 (1957).
5. Mazieres, C., *Compt. Rend.*, **248**, 2990 (1959).
6. Brewer, L., and P. Zavitsanos, *J. Phys. Chem. Solids*, **2**, 284 (1957).

7. Lodding, W., and E. Sturm, *Am. Mineralogist*, **42**, 78 (1957).
8. Pakulak, J. M., and G. W. Leonard, *Anal. Chem.*, **31**, 1037 (1959).
9. Weaver, E. E., and W. Keim, *Proc. Indiana Acad. Sci.*, **70**, 123 (1960).
10. Hill, J. A., and C. B. Murphy, *Anal. Chem.*, **31**, 1443 (1959).
11. Hogan, V. D., and S. Gordon, *Anal. Chem.*, **32**, 573 (1960).
12. Campbell, C., and G. Weingarten, *Trans. Faraday Soc.*, **55**, 2221 (1959).
13. Clampitt, B. H., *Anal. Chem.*, **35**, 577 (1963).
14. Joncich, M. J., and D. R. Bailey, *Anal. Chem.*, **32**, 1578 (1960).
15. Lodding, W., and L. Hammell, *Rev. Sci. Instr.*, **30**, 885 (1959).
16. Lodding, W., and L. Hammell, *Anal. Chem.*, **32**, 657 (1960).
17. Martin, A. J., and K. L. Edwards, *J. Sci. Instr.*, **36**, 170 (1959).
18. Whitehead, W. L., and I. A. Breger, *Science*, **111**, 279 (1950).
19. Stone, R. L., *J. Am. Ceram. Soc.*, **35**, 76 (1952).
20. Wendlandt, W. W., *J. Chem. Educ.*, **40**, 428 (1963).
21. Rudin, A., H. P. Schreiber, and M. H. Waldman, *Ind. Eng. Chem.*, **53**, 137 (1961).
22. Reisman, A., *Anal. Chem.*, **32**, 1566 (1960).
23. Chihara, H., and S. Seki, *Bull. Chem. Soc. Japan*, **26**, 88 (1953).
24. Bohon, R. L., *Anal. Chem.*, **33**, 1451 (1961).
25. Stone, R. L., and H. F. Rase, *Anal. Chem.*, **29**, 1273 (1957).
26. Stone, R. L., *Anal. Chem.*, **32**, 1582 (1960).
27. Levandowsky, J., and N. Sacovy, *Inst. franc. petrole XI*, 818 (1956).
28. Burgess, G. K., *U. S. Bur. Std., Bull.*, **5**, 199 (1908–1909).
29. Kauffman, A. J., and E. D. Dilling, *Econ. Geol.*, **45**, 222 (1950).
30. Chiu, J., *Anal. Chem.*, **34**, 1841 (1962).
31. Wendlandt, W. W., *J. Chem. Educ.*, **38**, 571 (1961).
32. Newkirk, T. F., *J. Am. Ceram. Soc.*, **41**, 409 (1958).
33. Skinner, K. G., Naval Research Laboratory Rept. No. **4942**, May 24, 1957, 12 pp.
34. Vassallo, D. A., and J. C. Harden, *Anal. Chem.*, **34**, 132 (1962).
35. Bollin, E. M., J. A. Dunne, and P. F. Kerr, *Science*, **131**, 661 (1960).
36. Bollin, E. M., and P. F. Kerr, *Am. Mineralogist*, **46**, 823 (1961).
37. Gasson, D. B., *J. Sci. Instr.*, **39**, 78 (1962).
38. Borchardt, H. J., and F. Daniels, *J. Am. Chem. Soc.*, **79**, 41 (1957).
39. Nedumov, N. A., *Russ. J. Phys. Chem. (English Transl.)*, **34**, 84 (1960).
40. Novikov, G. I., and O. G. Polyachenok, *Russ. J. Inorg. Chem. (English Transl.)*, **6**, 996 (1961).
41. Berg, L. G., and N. P. Burmistrova, *Russ. J. Inorg. Chem. (English Transl.)*, **5**, 326 (1960).
42. Yagfarov, M. S., *Dokl. Akad. Nauk. SSSR*, **127**, 615 (1959).
43. Yagfarov, M. S., *Russ. J. Inorg. Chem. (English Transl.)*, **6**, 1236 (1961).
44. Bussiere, P., B. Claudel, J. Renouf, Y. Trambouze, and M. Prettre, *J. Chim. Phys.*, **58**, 668 (1961).
45. Pearce, J. H., and P. G. Mardon, *J. Sci. Instr.*, **36**, 457 (1959).

CHAPTER VII

APPLICATIONS OF DIFFERENTIAL THERMAL ANALYSIS

A. Introduction

As discussed previously, the DTA curve consists of a series of peaks (sometimes called bands) in an upward (exothermic) or downward (endothermic) direction on the Y-axis. The positions (on the temperature or X-axis), shape, and the number of peaks are used for purposes of qualitative identification of a substance, while the areas of the peaks (with reference to the base line, $\Delta T = 0$), since they are related to the enthalpy of the reaction, are used for quantitative estimation of the reactive substance present or for thermochemical determinations. Because of the various factors which effect the DTA curve of a sample, the peak temperatures and the shape of the peak are rather empirical. Generally, however, the DTA curves are reproducible for any given instrument so that they can be useful in the laboratory. This usually necessitates the employment of previously studied standard materials or compounds of known composition and purity. By use of various calibration substances, the areas enclosed by the DTA curve peaks can be related to heats of reaction, transition, polymerization, fusion, and so on. Or, if the heat of the reaction is known, the amount of reacting substance can be determined.

The origins of the endothermic or exothermic peaks in a DTA curve are summarized in Table VII.1. Any phenomena that produce an enthalpic change can be detected by DTA, provided that the instrument has the required sensitivity. These phenomena are caused by fundamental changes in state, chemical composition, changes in intramolecular reactivity of the substance, and so on. The shape of the peaks and also the peak maximum temperature, T_{max}, are controlled basically by the reaction kinetics, although they are also influenced by the sample packing and geometrical parameters, heating rate, furnace atmosphere, and reference temperature. The area of the peak is determined by the enthalpic change and also by the instrumental fac-

TABLE VII.1
Physicochemical Origin of the Peaks in Differential Thermal Analysis (1)

Phenomena	Enthalpic change	
	Endothermal	Exothermal
Physical		
Crystalline transition	x	x
Fusion	x	
Vaporization	x	
Sublimation	x	
Adsorption		x
Desorption	x	
Absorption	x	
Chemical		
Chemisorption		x
Desolvation	x	
Dehydration	x	
Decomposition	x	x
Oxidative degradation		x
Oxidation in gaseous atmosphere		x
Reduction in gaseous atmosphere	x	
Redox reactions	x	x
Solid-state reaction	x	x

tors such as sample size, thermal conductivity and specific heat of the sample, and sample particle size.

The technique of DTA has been employed by geologists, ceramicists, and metallurgists for many years. The technique proved to be a rapid analytical tool for the determination and identification of clays and other minerals, phase transitions and phase diagrams, high-temperature kiln reactions, and so on. Normally, the technique is supplemented by x-ray diffraction, dilatometry, thermogravimetry, electrical conductivity, and other techniques. Within only fairly recent times has the chemist become interested in this technique, although many classic chemical studies were carried out in the 1930's. Mention should be made of the excellent studies by Kracek (2,3). The list of applications to chemical problems has grown very rapidly, with applications being made to all the basic disciplines of chemistry. Specific areas of investigation are summarized in Table VII.2. Indeed, nearly every chemical field has been touched by this technique,

TABLE VII.2
Specific DTA Applications in Chemistry

Substances	Types of studies
Catalysts	Decomposition reactions
Polymeric materials	Phase diagrams
Lubricating greases	Reaction kinetics
Fats and oils	Solid-state reactions
Coordination compounds	Dehydration reactions
Carbohydrates	Radiation damage
Amino acids and proteins	Catalysis
Metal salt hydrates	Heats of adsorption
Metal and nonmetal oxides	Heats of reaction
Coal and lignite	Heats of polymerization
Wood and related substances	Heats of sublimation
Natural products	Heats of transition
Organic acids	Desolvation reactions
	Solid–gas reactions

although the emphasis has been mainly in analytical, inorganic, and physical chemistry.

The applications cited here will be concerned chiefly with problems in analytical chemistry. In this area of chemistry, DTA can be used as a control or routine tool for comparing similar but not identical materials. As a control technique (4), it may be used to distinguish between raw materials quickly and easily in those cases in which the treatment of the material must be modified if slight changes in the material are encountered. As a comparison technique, DTA may be used in some cases to test materials that yield anomalous results by other tests. Lastly, by suitable calibration of the instrument, DTA may be used for the quantitative estimation of a substance or mixture of substances.

B. Applications to Analytical Chemistry

Because of the large number of applications to analytical chemistry, only a limited number will be reported here. The applications discussed here were chosen to represent illustrative examples of problems that can be investigated by DTA. No attempt was made, however, to make this a comprehensive survey of all of the analytical applications.

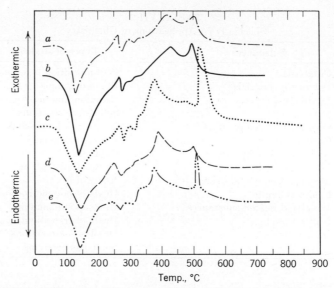

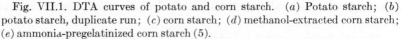

Fig. VII.1. DTA curves of potato and corn starch. (a) Potato starch; (b) potato starch, duplicate run; (c) corn starch; (d) methanol-extracted corn starch; (e) ammonia-pregelatinized corn starch (5).

The characterization of starch and related polysaccharides by DTA has been carried out by Morita (5). The DTA curves obtained for several samples of potato and corn starch are given in Figure VII.1. The samples were prepared into a compressed "sandwich" type packing prepared by placing 150 mg of sample between two 200 mg layers of calcined alumina and compressing at 200 psi.

The thermograms of the starches were characterized by endothermic peaks in the 135–310°C region, followed by two distinct exothermic peaks in the 375–520°C range. The curves illustrate very nicely the effect of pretreatment on the starches.

Since starch is a polymeric glucoside composed of α-1,4- and α-1,6-linked glucopyranosidic units, it was of interest to examine the thermal properties of the linear polymeric fraction of starch, namely, that of amylose. The DTA curves for various amylose fractions, prepared from the same starches as shown in Figure VII.1, are illustrated in Figure VII.2. Examination of the three fractions reveals three distinct features: the endothermic peaks with T_{max} of about 150 and 225°C, and a shoulder peak with a T_{max} of 315°C. There

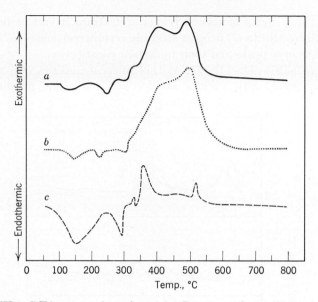

Fig. VII.2. DTA curves of amylose. (a) Potato amylose; (b) amylose from ammonia-pregelatinized corn starch; (c) amylose from methanol-extracted corn starch (5).

were pronounced exothermic peaks in the 490–510°C temperature range.

The mechanism of the thermal degradation reactions are not known and are probably quite complicated. The DTA curves serve not merely to characterize or identify these carbohydrates, but will eventually lead to information pertaining to the relationship between molecular composition and chemical properties.

Morita (6) also studied the DTA of several α- and β-linked polyglucosans, as well as rice starch. An interesting feature of this investigation was the study of the effect of moisture on the DTA curves obtained. This was illustrated by the study of rice starch stored in various types of atmospheres such as vacuum, 100% relative humidity water vapor, and so on. The presence of moisture altered the endothermic peak with a T_{max} of 130°C, but not the 275 or 310°C peaks. The results suggest that the original 130°C peak is not entirely due to the loss of residual moisture, and that the dehydration process is not completely reversible.

The DTA curves of several bacterial dextrans have also been determined by Morita (7) in order to study certain relationships between the DTA curve peaks and their molecular constitution.

Anderson (8) studied the DTA of six different epoxides, both reacted and unreacted, with various amines and anhydride polymerizing

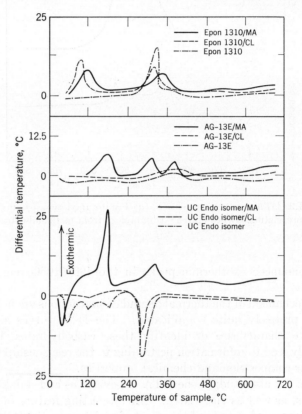

Fig. VII.3. DTA curves of catalyzed and uncatalyzed epoxides; MA is maleic anhydride; CL is *m*-phenylenediamine; heating rate of 2.5°C/min (8).

agents. The samples, varying in weight from 1 to 3 g, were intimately mixed with equal weights of aluminum oxide. After placing the mixture in the sample tube, the tube was weighed before and after the heating cycle so that the loss in weight of the sample could be obtained.

The DTA curves of three catalyzed and uncatalyzed epoxides are given in Figure VII.3. The epoxides studied were Epon 1310 (tetraglycidyl ether of tetrakis(hydroxyphenyl)ethane); Diepoxide AG-13E (bis-epoxydicyclopentyl ether of ethyleneglycol), and UC Endo isomer (dicyclopentadiene dioxide) All the uncatalyzed epoxides, except the UC Endo isomers, exhibited exothermic peaks in the 300–400°C region. These peaks were believed to be due to the isomerization of the epoxy group to carbonyl groups (aldehydes for primary epoxides and ketones for secondary epoxides) The appearance of vapors in the tubes indicated that volatilization and decomposition also occurred simultaneously with isomerization and polymerization. The Endo isomer showed an endothermic peak because of the heat absorbed by volatilization, and decomposition masked any heat resulting from the slower rate of isomerization and etherification polymerization of its epoxy groups. The peak at T_{max} of 184°C corresponded to the melting point of the Endo isomer.

When the above three epoxides were mixed with the catalysts (maleic anhydride or m-phenylenediamine), except for the AG-13E/CL and UC Endo isomer/CL, all of the mixtures exhibited two exothermic peaks. One of these peaks was in the 100–150°C temperature range, the other was in the 300–400°C range. The AG-18E/CL system showed only one exothermic peak, broad and weak, in the latter temperature range, while the UC Endo isomer showed no exothermic peaks and only one endothermic peak. This latter peak corresponded to the boiling points and/or decomposition points of both the epoxide and the catalyst.

The DTA curves obtained on the above system may be used confidently as a characterization index. This technique offers unique advantages over other instrumental methods, especially those involving insoluble and amorphous crosslinked epoxy systems which exhibit diffuse x-ray patterns and which, because of their inherent intractable physical state, do not give reproducible infrared spectra.

The DTA and TGA of some hydrazine, guanidine, and guanidinium picrates, styphnates, and sulfates have been investigated by Fauth (9). These compounds are useful for identification of the various bases and are rather sensitive to detonation both by impact and by rapid heating. The decomposition temperatures of these compounds was generally considerably lower than those reported in the literature. A comparison of the DTA decomposition temperatures and the literature melting point values is given in Table VII.3. This is to be expected, however, because at the higher heating rates, thermodynamic equilibrium is not attained and the existence of large thermal gradients in the sample is probably conducive to the formation of "hot spots" which lead to rapid decomposition or, in the case of the styphnates, detonation.

TABLE VII.3

Comparison between Melting Points and DTA Decomposition Temperature for Some Picrates (9)

Compound	T_{max}, °C	M.P., °C
Hydrazine picrate	115	201
N-Methylguanidine picrate	180	201
N-Ethylguanidine picrate	195	180
Guanidine picrate	222	333
Guanylurea picrate	190	265
Aminoguanidine picrate	160	Not available

In a roughly related study, Chiu (10) investigated the formation of an organic derivative by DTA. Chiu, instead of using the traditional method of preparing the derivative from the sample and reagent, replaced it with a one-step process. The sample was heated with a specific reagent at a programmed heating rate in a selected atmosphere. The DTA curve showed the derivative forming reaction, the physical transitions of the sample or the reagent in excess, and the physical transitions of the intermediates and products. Glass capillary tubes were employed as the sample holder in the apparatus previously described on p. 201.

The formation of the acetone hydrazone derivative with p-nitrophenylhydrazine is illustrated in Figure VII.4. Curve a shows the endothermic peak for the boiling of acetone, with a T_{max} of 58°C. For p-nitrophenylhydrazine, the endothermic peak at a T_{max} of 160°C was caused by the fusion of the compound. A mixture of acetone and p-nitrophenylhydrazine, however, in the 54–80°C temperature range, gave a complex endothermic peak which was attributed to the net result of evaporation of excess acetone, solution of p-nitrophenylhydrazine in acetone, and hydrazone formation. The fusion of the hydrazone was indicated by the endothermic peak with

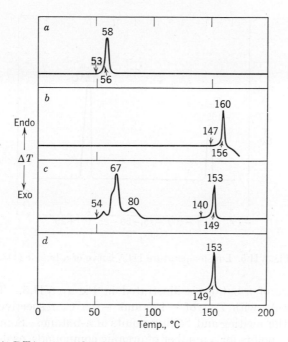

Fig. VII.4. DTA curves showing formation of p-nitrophenylhydrazone of acetone. (a) acetone; (b) p-nitrophenylhydrazine; (c) Reaction mixture of acetone and p-nitrophenylhydrazine; (d) Rerun of residue from (c) (10).

a T_{max} of 153°C. A rerun of the residue gave only a single endof thermic peak, with a T_{max} of 153°C. The reported melting point o- the hydrazone derivative is 152°C. Similar examples, such as the reactions of triethylamine with picric acid and dextrose with propylamine, were illustrated.

The method described is rapid and dynamic in nature, and requires that: (a) a specific reagent should form a derivative with the sample rapidly; (b) the derivative so produced should show a discernible physical transition or a characteristic DTA curve; (c) one reactant more volatile than the other should be used in excess; (d) one reactant should serve as the solvent for the other; and (e) a catalyst may be used.

Using the precision apparatus described on p. 219, Vassallo and Harden (11) used the DTA technique to determine the melting and boiling points of a number of organic compounds. A low-temperature

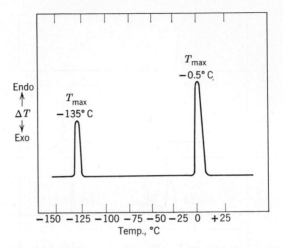

Fig. VII.5. Low-temperature DTA curve of n-butane (11).

DTA curve of n-butane is illustrated in Figure VII.5. The endo-thermic peaks with T_{max} of -135 and $-0.5\,°C$, respectively, corre-spond to the melting and boiling points of n-butane. Some melting and boiling points for a number of organic compounds, as determined by DTA, are given in Table VII.4. The precision of the method was $\pm 0.3\,°C$ over a wide range of heating rates.

The technique of DTA has been used to study the thermal degrada-tion of balsam fir wood by Arseneau (12). Using air-dried wood and also various samples of wood that had been extracted with several re-

TABLE VII.4

Transition Temperatures of Various Compounds Determined by DTA (11)

| | Melting point, °C | | Boiling point, °C | |
Compound	Found	Reported	Found	Reported
n-Pentane	-129.5	-129.7	36.2	36.0
n-Hexane	-94.5	-95.3	69.0	68.8
Benzoic acid	121.8	121.8	—	—
Toluene	—	—	111.1	110.6
Benzene	5.2	5.5	80.5	80.1
Acetic acid	16.5	16.6	118.4	118.1
n-Dodecane	—	—	215.5	216.0
Water	0.0	0.0	100.0	100.0

TABLE VII.5
Summary of DTA Curve Peaks for Air-Dried Wood (12)

Peak, °C	Compound
(1) Endotherm at 145	Alcohol–water extract
(2) Endotherm at 163	Alcohol–water extract
(3) Exotherm at 210	Unaccounted
(4) Exotherm at 265	Possibly acid lignin
(5) Exotherm at 285	Benzene–alcohol extract
(6) Exotherm at 300	Sum of benzene–alcohol extract and acid lignin
(7) Exotherm at 330	Cellulose
(8) Exotherm at 360	Same as (6)

agents, Arseneau attributed the various DTA curve peaks to the reactions summarized in Table VII.5.

The thermal decomposition of a number of organic acids has been studied by DTA by Wendlandt and Hoiberg (13,14). The Deltatherm DTA apparatus was employed as previously described on p. 200. Since the acids were decomposed in an argon atmosphere, only

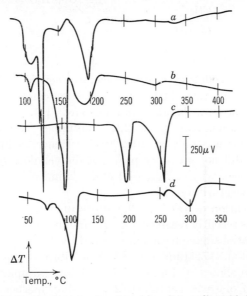

Fig. VII.6. DTA curves of some organic acids: (a) oxalic acid dihydrate; (b) malonic acid; (c) succinic acid; and (d) glutaric acid (13).

endothermic peaks were observed in the DTA curves.   These peaks were caused by such reactions as dehydration, decarboxylation, sublimation, decomposition, and phase transitions from the solid to the liquid state.   The maximum peak temperatures for the phase transitions were 10° to 30° higher than the reported melting point temperatures.   The DTA curves for some of the acids are given in Figure VII.6.

The DTA curve for oxalic acid dihydrate, the only acid studied containing water of hydration, had dehydration peaks with T_{max} values of 110, 120, and 125 °C, respectively.   All other curve peaks for the organic acids were caused by fusion and decomposition reactions. For example, the second endothermic peak in the succinic acid curve was probably caused by dehydration reaction, resulting in anhydride formation, of the type:

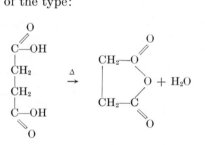

The DTA of cellulose, cellulose acetate, cellulose nitrate, pentaerythritol, pentaerythrityl trinitrate, and other compounds of this type has been studied by Pakulak and Leonard (15).   Using a thermistorized DTA apparatus (see p. 222), the upper temperature limit of the instrument was only about 200 °C.   Hence, cellulose and cellulose acetate did not give any peaks, while cellulose nitrate gave an exothermic peak with a T_{max} of 180 °C.   Similar results were noted for the pentaerythritol series.

The application of DTA to the study of polymers and polymeric materials has recently received a great amount of attention.   Some of these applications have been summarized by Murphy (16).

Murphy et al. (17) studied the DTA of Vibrin 135 resins, the results of which are shown in Figure VII.7.   Three samples of resin were studied, two of them contained 2% *tert*-butylperbenzoate catalyst, the other 0.5%.   Each catalyst–resin mixture was then heated (cured) for a definite period of time.   The DTA curves in (*1*) and (*2*) showed that two low-temperature exothermic peaks were observed, with T_{max} values of 150 and 180 °C, respectively. This first peak was missing from the post-baked (180 °C for 24 hr) sample, although the 320 °C peak was found in all three curves. The presence of the low-temperature exothermic peak was attributed to the further polymerization of the under-cured resin, especially the polyester portion of the

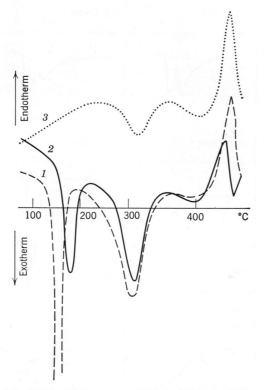

Fig. VII.7. DTA curves of Vibrin 135 resins (17).

resin. The high-temperature exothermic peak was caused by the curing of the triallyl cyanurate portion of the resin.

Murphy et al. (18) further demonstrated the effect of different catalysts on the curing of Vibrin 135 resin by a DTA method. The catalyst, benzoyl peroxide, effected the most complete cure for the resin.

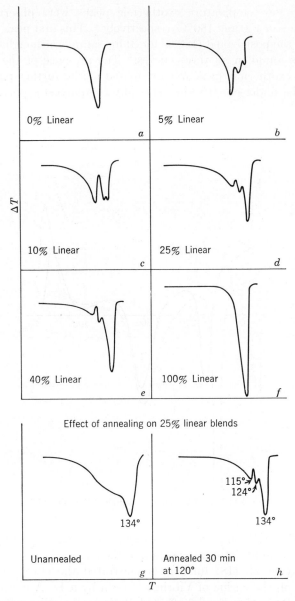

Fig. VII.8. DTA curves of linear high-pressure polyethylene blends (19).

The technique of DTA has been used by Clampitt (19) for the estimation of the linear content of polyethylene blends. The DTA curves for several polyethylene blends are given in Figure VII.8.

Careful examination of the unannealed polyethylene sample curve indicated a peak with a T_{max} of 134 °C, and also a shoulder peak. On annealing the sample for 30 min at 120 °C, the shoulder peak was resolved into two peaks, with T_{max} values of 115 and 124 °C, respectively. Using the above annealing procedure, but varying the percentage of the linear content of the samples, the DTA curves in Figure VII.8 were obtained. The curves contained endothermic peaks with T_{max} values of 115, 124, and 134 °C, respectively. For the pure components, however, only one peak was obtained with the high-pressure polyethylene, with a T_{max} of 110 °C, and for the linear polyethylene, a T_{max} of 135 °C. The area under the 115 °C peak decreased and the area under the 134 °C peak increased as the amount of linear polymer increased. The 115 °C peak was associated with the presence of crystals of high-pressure polyethylene, while the 134 °C peak presumably was due to crystals of linear polyethylene.

If it is assumed that all of the linear polyethylene is crystallized, then, using a proportionality constant and the area under the 134 °C peak, the amount of linear content of the sample can be calculated. Using this method, fairly good agreement was obtained between the true blend composition and the calculated linear content.

Schwenker and Beck (20) studied by the DTA technique the thermal degradation of polymeric materials used in textile manufacturing in air and nitrogen atmospheres. The polymers studied were Dacron, nylon 66, Neoprene W, and Orlon. From the results obtained, the reactions, such as rearrangements, crosslinking, and depolymerization, taking place in the polymers on thermal degradation can be detected and identified. DTA can detect relatively small changes in polymer composition or the presence of substituents on the polymer backbone, as well as prove quite valuable for thermal degradation mechanism studies.

The DTA curves of nylon 66 fabric and Neoprene W, in air and in nitrogen, are given in Figure VII.9.

At about 100 °C, a weak endothermic peak due to the loss of sorbed water was observed in the nylon 66 curve. In air there was an exothermic reaction initiating at about 185 °C, and forming a small endothermic peak at about a T_{max} of 250 °C, the latter being caused by the

fusion of the polymer (m.p. *ca.* 255 °C).   In nitrogen, the exothermic
peaks were not present, suggesting that the air reactions were due to
an oxidation reaction.   The two endothermic peaks in the nitrogen

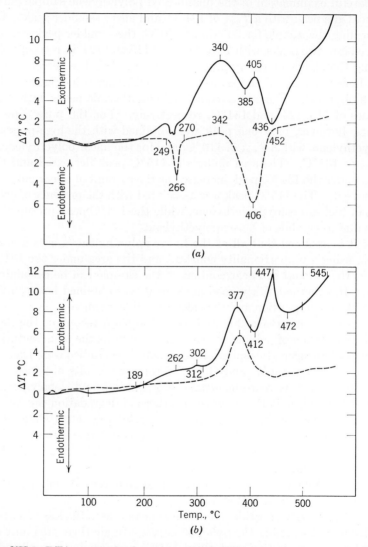

Fig. VII.9. DTA curves of polymeric materials (20). ———, in air; - - - , in nitrogen. (*a*) nylon 66; (*b*) neoprene W.

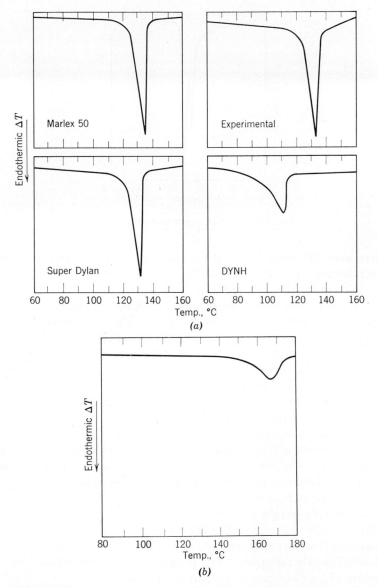

Fig. VII.10. DTA curves of some polyolefins (21). (a) Polyethylenes; (b) poly-propylene.

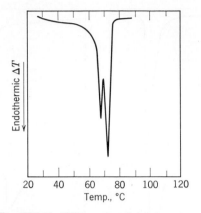

Fig. VII.11. DTA curve of dotriacontane (21).

curve were due to the fusion of the polymer and to the depolymerization reaction.   It is obvious that the thermal degradation mechanisms
are different for the air and nitrogen atmospheres.

In the DTA curves for Neoprene W, both curves exhibited an exothermic peak with a T_{max} of about 377 °C.   This peak was attributed
to the elimination of HCl and the crosslinking of the residue.

The melting points and degree of crystallinity of a number of polyolefins have been studied by DTA by Ke (21).   Five polyolefin DTA
curves are given in Figure VII.10.

From the curves, the peak maximum temperature, T_{max}, was used
for the determination of the polymer melting point.   Results obtained by DTA were within ±1 °C of the reported literature values,
although several of them had a 15 °C melting point range, as indicated
by the distance between the initial departure from the base line and
the peak.   Isotactic polypropylene gave a somewhat broader endothermic peak at T_{max} of 169 °C.   The end point of the transition was
somewhere beyond the peak at a point not known exactly.

Ke (21) also determined the DTA curve of mixtures of polyolefins
and found that the components could be identified if the melting points
were sufficiently far apart.   The peak areas were proportional to the
amount of each component present in the mixture.

The degree of crystallinity of polyethylenes was calculated by comparing the area of the respective endothermic peak with the double
peak of dotriacontane, the DTA curve of which is given in Figure

TABLE VII.6
Degree of Crystallinity of Polyethylenes (21)

Polyethylene	Crystallinity, %	
	Found	Literature
Marlex 50	91	93
Super Dylan	81	65–85
Experimental (polyethylene)	86	87
DYNH	52	40–60

VII.11.   The curve contains two peaks, the first of which is due to a chain-rotational transition a few degrees below the melting point. The resulting degree of crystallinity values agreed well with the literature values, as shown in Table VII.6.

The effect of diluents on the melting behavior of polyethylenes has also been studied by Ke (22).   A comparison between the melting transitions of solution and melt-crystallized polyethylene (23) has been made.   The measurement of the melting and second-order transitions of polyethylene terephthalate by DTA has been studied by Scott (24).   Rudin et al. (25) measured the oxidation resistance of various polymers and rubbers by a DTA method.   A comparison of the melting and freezing curves before and after oxidation provided the indication of the extent to which the polymer had been damaged or oxidized.

The melting and glass transitions in commercial Nylons and both homo- and copolyamides prepared by interfacial polycondensation have been studied by DTA by Ke and Sisko (26).   The DTA curves for a number of the polyadipamides and polysebacamides are given in Figure VII.12.

The polyadipamides were made from diamines containing both even and odd numbers of carbon atoms and the polysebacamides from diamines containing an even number of carbon atoms.   All curves exhibited a peak caused by the melting of the polymer, the melting point of which decreased with an increase in the number of carbon atoms in the diamine chain.

The application of DTA to the detection of changes induced in biphenyl, polyvinyl chloride, Teflon, and Versalube F-50 has been reported by Murphy and Hill (27).   The curves for biphenyl and irradiated biphenyl are shown in Figure VII.13.

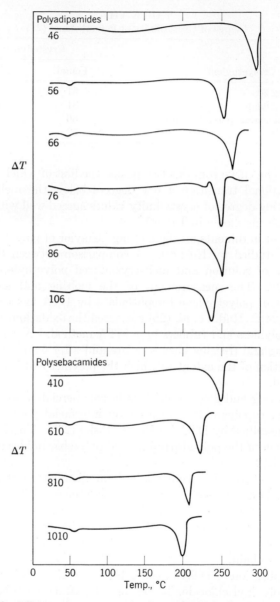

Fig. VII.12. DTA curves of some polyadipamides and polysebacamides (26).

The nonirradiated sample gave a curve with two endothermic peaks which were caused by the fusion (70 °C peak) and volatilization (175 °C peak) of the compound. The irradiated sample gave the first two peaks, as well as an exothermic peak at about 370 °C. The melting peak occurred at a slightly lower temperature. It was assumed that the 370 °C exothermic peak was caused by air oxidation of the nonvolatile, radiation-induced biphenyl polymer remaining in the sample holder after volatilization of low-molecular-weight materials. The lowering of the melting point was also caused by the irradiation of the sample. Similar results were noted for polyvinyl chloride samples.

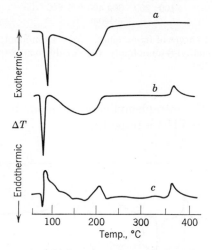

Fig. VII.13. DTA curves of biphenyl. (a) nonirradiated; (b) irradiated; and (c) irradiated vs. nonirradiated samples (27).

It was noted that by proper selection of materials on the basis of the relationship of peak area to radiation dose, DTA might be applied to dosimetry over a wide range of energy levels.

The DTA technique has been applied to an epoxy resin and 32 synthetic polymeric systems consisting of unsaturated polyesters copolymerized with styrene by Anderson and Freeman (28). The endothermic peaks in the 250–450 °C temperature range were used as a basis for comparison between the various systems.

A DTA study of 8-quinolinol tetraphenylboron and its derivatives has been reported by Wendlandt et al. (29). The DTA curves of the

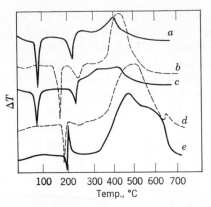

Fig. VII.14. DTA curves of free amines. (*a*) 8-Quinolinol; (*b*) 5,7-dichloro-8-quinolinol; (*c*) 2-methyl-8-quinolinol; (*d*) 5,7-dibromo-8-quinolinol; (*e*) 5,7-diiodo-8-quinolinol (29).

free amines and the tetraphenylboron compounds are illustrated in Figures VII.14 and VII.15, respectively.

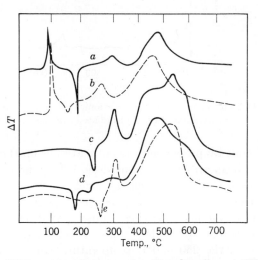

Fig. VII.15. DTA curves of some amine tetraphenylboron (TPB) salts. (*a*) 8-Quinolinol TPB; (*b*) 2-methyl-8-quinolinol TPB; (*c*) 5,7-dichloro-8-quinolinol TPB; (*d*) 5,7-dibromo-8-quinolinol TPB; (*e*) 5,7-diiodo-8-quinolinol TPB (29).

For the 2-methyl-, and 8-quinolinol TPB salts, the DTA curves exhibited exothermic peaks in the 90–100°C temperature region. Apparently, an exothermic crystalline phase transition or rearrangement takes place in which a portion of the initial compound sublimes off. These were the only two TPB compounds that exhibited this behavior, the other compounds gave curves which contained an endothermic peak followed by exothermic air oxidation peaks. The free amines DTA curves contained endothermic peaks due to melting and/or decomposition, followed by air oxidation exothermic peaks

DTA studies on coal and related substances have been carried out by a large number of investigators, included among them are Breger and Whitehead (30) and Gamel and Smothers (31).

Breger and Whitehead (30), using the vacuum DTA apparatus previously described on p. 209, studied the thermal properties of cellulose, wood, lignite, and various coals. It was found that the low-temperature peaks for lignin disappeared or were masked in peat and then reappeared in the lignites. The decomposition peaks for lignin were suppressed in bituminous coals and were absent in the curves for anthracites.

Gamel and Smothers (31) related the areas under the decomposition peaks to the concentration of a Utah Mine coal in a coal–alumina mixture. A linear area vs. concentration curve was obtained for 0–12.0% coal mixtures. They also found that the area under the curve peak was directly proportional to the BTU-lb values for the coal. This relationship is illustrated in Table VII.7.

TABLE VII.7

Heating Values of Selected Arkansas Coals as Measured DTA and Peroxide Bomb Methods in BTU/lb (31)

Sample	Area under curve, in.^{2}	BTU/lb of coal
Paris Mine	0.345	13,347
Utah Mine	0.460	14,476
Jerome Mine	0.415	13,994
Quality Excelsior Mine	0.470	14,531

A rapid method for the determination of the moisture content of "nearly dry" powdered substances had been described by Stone (32). Using the dynamic gas flow apparatus described on p. 193, Stone placed samples of the substance in the DTA sample holder at room

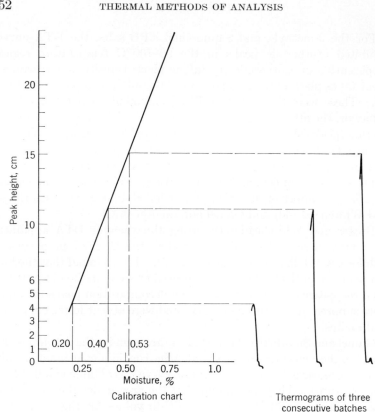

Fig. VII.16. Method of determining moisture content of dry powders by evacuation and DTA (room temperature) (32).

temperature and atmospheric pressure. When the system was evacuated at a fixed rate, the DTA curve peak began at the point where the external water vapor pressure was less than the partial pressure of the water vapor pressure of the sample. From the peak height, using the calibration curve in Figure VII.16, the amount of moisture in the sample could be determined. The calibration curve was made from samples containing known amounts of water.

Using the DTA technique for quality control purposes, Garn and Flaschen (4) studied the thermal decomposition of different samples of magnesium carbonate and talc. The DTA curves for the different magnesium carbonate samples are given in Figure VII.17, while the talc curves are shown in Figure VII.18.

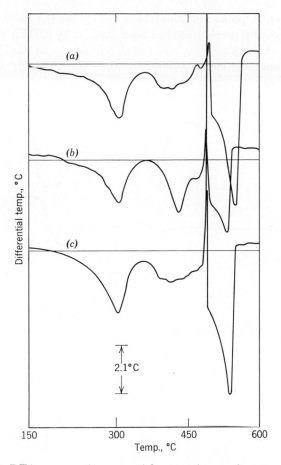

Fig. VII.17. DTA curves of commercial magnesium carbonate samples (4). (a) Lot No. 6, Baker; (b) Lot No. 3, Merck; (c) Lot No. 2, Merck.

The curves for the magnesium carbonate samples showed distinct differences due to their different thermal histories. Each of the talc curves exhibited a strong exothermic peak, starting at about 850 °C. The magnitude of the reaction was about the same in each case, but differences in impurities caused pronounced differences in the curves. The Montana and Sierramic talcs gave a small endothermic peak at about 570 °C, while the latter talc gave a pronounced endothermic peak at about 700 °C.

The effect of potassium chlorate impurity on the thermal stability of ammonium perchlorate has been studied by a DTA method by Petricciani et al. (33). The effect of this impurity on the DTA curve of ammonium perchlorate is illustrated in Figure VII.19.

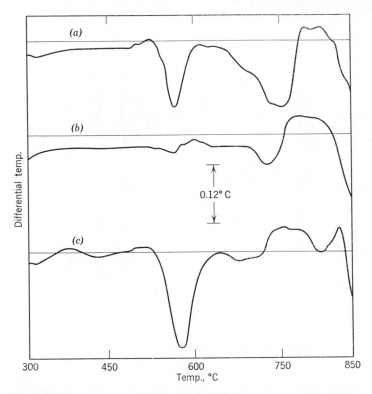

Fig. VII.18. DTA curves of: (a) Sierramic; (b) Yellowstone; and (c) Montana talcs using platinum cups (4).

The curves clearly illustrate the presence of an increasingly large exothermic reaction after the 244°C lattice transition of the ammonium perchlorate. In the 0.1% $KClO_3$ region of impurity, the heat evolved after the lattice transition was great enough to initiate complete thermal decomposition of the sample. This represents an effective 150° lowering of the thermal decomposition temperature of the pure material, which normally decomposes at about 400°C. The

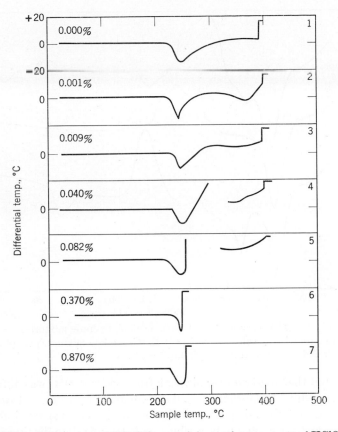

Fig. VII.19. DTA curves of NH_4ClO_4 containing various amounts of $KClO_3$ (33).

DTA technique could be used to detect the approximate amount of impurity in the ammonium perchlorate.

Wendlandt et al. (34), in studying the thermal decomposition of the thorium, uranium, and rare-earth metal oxalate hydrates by DTA, also studied mixtures of the rare-earth oxalate hydrates. The DTA curves of mixtures of lanthanum–cerium and praseodymium–neodymium oxalate mixtures are given in Figure VII.20.

In curve a, a 1:1 physical mixture of La–Ce oxalates is presented, while curve b is a 1:1 mixture of La–Ce oxalates that was precipitated by the homogeneous precipitation method. The physical mixture exhibited dehydration endothermic peaks at the appropriate temper-

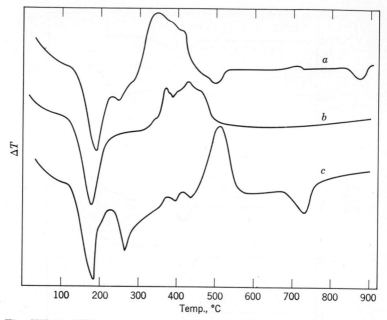

Fig. VII.20. DTA curves of rare-earth oxalate hydrate mixtures. (*a*) 1:1 La–Ce oxalate mixture (physical); (*b*) 1:1 La–Ce oxalate mixture (precipitated); (*c*) 1:1 Pr–Nd oxalate mixture (precipitated) (34).

atures, but the broad exothermic peak from 300 to 450 °C was different from the individual lanthanum and cerium oxalate curves. However, the 875 °C endothermic peak was still present. The 1:1 precipitated mixture of La–Ce gave only a single endothermic dehydration peak, while the broad exothermic decomposition peak began at a slightly higher temperature. The curve was devoid of any peaks beyond 500 °C, in contrast to curve *a*. Curve *c* is a 1:1 precipitated mixture of Pr–Nd oxalates. The double dehydration peaks were present, although shifted to slightly higher temperatures, while the praseodymium oxalate exothermic peak at 460 °C was shifted to a higher temperature, 510 °C, in the mixture. In contrast, the 768 °C neodymium endothermic peak shifted to a lower temperature, 670 °C, while the 675 °C neodymium oxalate exothermic peak disappeared entirely. It is apparent from the precipitated mixture curves that the resultant curves are not the same as the sum of the curves for the individual oxalates.

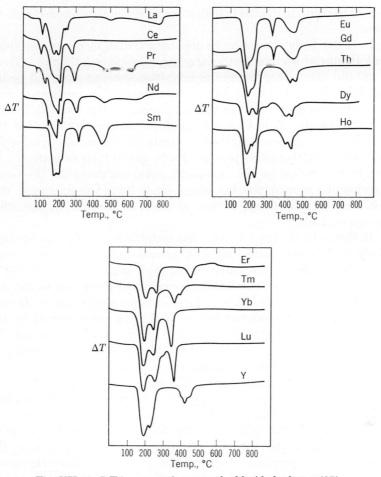

Fig. VII.21. DTA curves of rare-earth chloride hydrates (35).

Wendlandt and Bear (35) used the technique of DTA to characterize the rare-earth chloride hydrates. The DTA curves of these compounds are given in Figure VII.21.

On the basis of the thermograms, it is convenient, for purposes of discussion, to classify the thermal decomposition patterns into four main groups: Group I, La, Ce, Pr, and Nd; Group II, Sm, Eu, and Gd; Group III, Tb, Dy, Y, Ho, Er, and Tm; Group IV, Yb and Lu. These groups are just arbitrary, but results on the thermal decomposition of the rare-earth nitrate hydrates reveal much the same classification.

In Group I, the thermograms are characterized by one or two small endotherms which precede the large dehydration endotherms. These small endotherms are thought to arise from the heat absorbed by the partial fusion of the metal salts. Also observed in this group, with the exception of cerium, are the endotherms in the 400–650 °C temperature range. It is known from thermobalance studies that the terminal thermal decomposition products are the metal oxychlorides and these endotherms are presumed to be due to their formation. As the atomic weight of the rare-earth metal ion increased, the metal oxychlorides were obtained at progressively lower temperatures; this could explain the disappearance of these endotherms in the other groups studied.

In Group II, the large dehydration endothermic peaks consisted entirely of just one maximum with several small endothermic peak shoulders. There were sharp endothermic peaks in the 160–400 °C temperature range. The latter are presumed to be due to the formation of metal oxychlorides; thermobalance studies appear to confirm this. The compounds in Group II were characterized by the splitting of the dehydration exothermic peaks into two peaks and also the splitting of the oxychloride formation peaks. The splitting of the former resulted in the formation of peaks in the 175–190 and 205–240 °C temperature ranges. It is of interest to observe that the curve for yttrium appears to fit nicely between dysprosium and holmium, in agreement with results found from separation studies.

In Group IV, the splitting of the dehydration endothermic peak was observed again, but new endothermic peaks appeared in the 310–325 °C temperature range. These new peaks were characterized by their rather sharp, narrow appearance, in contrast to the broad endothermic peaks found in this region in the Group III compounds.

The determination of goethite (α-FeO·OH) and gibbsite [Al(OH)$_3$] by themselves, and in mixtures, has been carried out by a DTA method by Lodding and Hammell (36). If goethite is heated in the controlled atmosphere DTA apparatus, previously described on p. 213, in a reducing atmosphere (hydrogen), it dehydrates below 300 °C and the iron(III) ion present is immediately reduced to amorphous Fe$_3$O$_4$ which recrystallizes to magnetite between 300 and

360 °C.   If the hydrogen atmosphere is now replaced by nitrogen after reaching 400 °C, and then air, an exothermic peak is formed due to the oxidation of magnetite to maghemite, γ-Fe_2O_3.   A second exothermic peak, due to the conversion of γ-Fe_3O_3 to α-Fe_2O_3, occurs at 775–836 °C.   This peak is usually a doublet and the integrated area under it is proportional to the amount of newly formed hematite, which is, therefore, equal to the amount of hydrated iron oxide present in the original sample.   The amount of gibbsite can then be determined by the difference from the area under the dehydration peak.

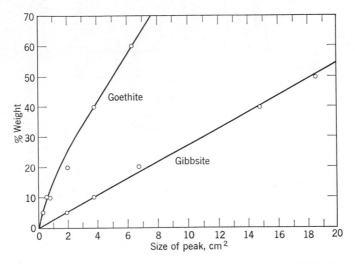

Fig. VII.22. Calibration curves of peak areas for dehydration of gibbsite and goethite (36).

The hematite or magnetite present in the sample was said to have a negligible influence on the area of the conversion peaks.

The calibration curves of peak area to amounts of goethite and gibbsite present in the mixtures are given in Figure VII.22.   A similar curve for the $\gamma \rightarrow \alpha$-$Fe_2O_3$ conversion was also presented by Lodding and Hammell (36).

The thermal decomposition of some metal 8-quinolinolates has been studied by DTA by Wendlandt and Horton (37) and by Charles (38). The DTA curves of several of the hydrated and anhydrous metal chelates are given in Figure VII.23 (37).

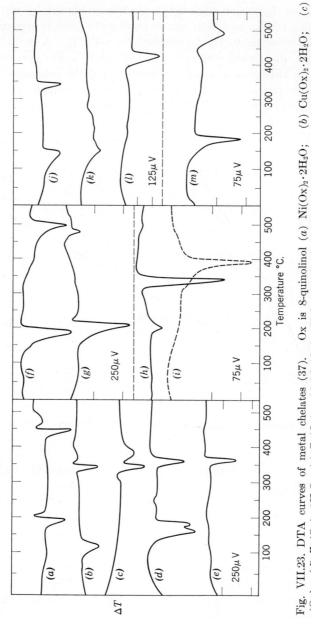

Fig. VII.23. DTA curves of metal chelates (37). Ox is 8-quinolinol (a) Ni(Ox)₂·2H₂O; (b) Cu(Ox)₂·2H₂O; (c) Cu(Ox)₂; (d) Zn(Ox)₂·2H₂O; (e) Zn(Ox)₂; (f) Mn(Ox)₂·2H₂O; (g) Co(Ox)₂·2H₂O; (h) Fe(Ox)₃; (i) Co(Ox)₃·1H₂O; (j) Pb(Ox)₂·1.5H₂O; (k) Sc(Ox)₃·HOx; (l) UO₂(Ox)₂; (m) Cd(Ox)₂·1H₂O.

The metal 8-quinolinol chelates decomposed to give a DTA curve containing a series of endothermic peaks which were caused by dehydration, sublimation, and/or decomposition reactions. However, only in the case of the nickel and aluminum chelates was sublimation detected. All of the dehydration reactions took place in the temperature range from about 100 to 250 °C. with peak maxima temperatures from 115 to 210 °C. Although most of the hydrated compounds contained 2 moles of water per mole of complex, only in the case of zinc was there any evidence that they were evolved stepwise. If the peak maximum temperature may be used as a measure of the thermal stability of the hydrated compounds, the stability decreased in the order: Co(II) = Al > Ni > Co(III) > Mn > Cd = Bi > Zn > Pb > Cu.

For the anhydrous metal chelates (38), using the peak maxima temperatures, the order of thermal stability was: Ca > Mg > Sr > Cd > Mn > Ba > Co > Ni > Zn > Pb > Cu. This order is the same as that found from TGA studies.

The endothermic peak in the 350–500 °C temperature range has been attributed to the melting of the complexes with, in some cases, thermal decomposition as well (37,38). Since two different instruments were used in these studies, it is of interest to compare the results obtained for the peak maxima temperatures, as shown in Table VII.8. As can be seen, the results are in quite good agreement.

To determine the effect of substitution on the 8-quinolinol ring on the thermal stability of the metal chelate, metal chelates of a divalent ion, Cu(II), a trivalent ion, Al(III), and a quadrivalent ion, Th(IV), with the various substituted 8-quinolinols were studied. The peak maxima temperature variations for the three series of complexes are given in Table VII.9. The order of stability was very different for the three metal ions. For the thorium chelates, substitution on the 8-quinolinol ring decreased the thermal stability, while for the other two metal ions, the general trend was an increase in stability. For the copper and aluminum chelates, the order of decreasing thermal stability was: 5,7-dichloro- > 8-quinolinol > 5-iodo-7-chloro- > 5,7-dibromo- > 5,7-diiodo- > 5-iodo- > 2-methyl-. For a given chelating agent, 8-quinolinol, the thermal stability of the complexes with various central metal ions was in the order: Al > Th > Cu. For the 5,7-dichloro- and 5,7-dibromo-metal chelates, the order was: Al > Cu > Th.

TABLE VII.8

Comparison of Peak Maxima Temperatures Obtained by Two Different Instruments for the Metal 8-Quinolinol Chelates

| | Peak maxima temp., °C | |
Compound	Wendlandt and Horton (37)	Charles (38)
$Ni(Ox)_2$	450	450
$Cu(Ox)_2$	335	334
$Zn(Ox)_2$	365	356
$Mn(Ox)_2$	490	502
$Co(Ox)_2$	475	466
$Co(Ox)_3$	335	
$Fe(Ox)_3$	390	
$Pb(Ox)_2$	330	321
$Sc(Ox)_3 \cdot HOx$	155	
$UO_2(Ox)_2$	420	
$Cd(Ox)_2$	490	506
$Bi(Ox)_3$	360	
$Sb(Ox)_3$	310	
$Al(Ox)_3$	415	
$Th(Ox)_4$	270	

TABLE VII.9

Peak Maxima Temperatures for Metal Chelates Containing Substituted 8-Quinolinols (37)

Chelating agent	Copper chelates, °C	Aluminum chelates, °C	Thorium chelates, °C
8-Quinolinol	335	415	270[a]
2-Methyl-	230	Unknown[b]	440
5,7-Dichloro-	340 (exo)[c]	335	245 (exo)
5,7-Dibromo-	315 (exo)	405	200
5,7-Diiodo-	290 (exo)[d]		200
	330 (exo)		
5-Iodo-7-chloro-	315 (exo)	350	240 (exo)
5-Iodo-	260	330	240

[a] All were normal chelates, $Th(Ox)_4$.
[b] Cannot be prepared.
[c] exo = exothermic peak; all others are endothermic.
[d] Small peak.

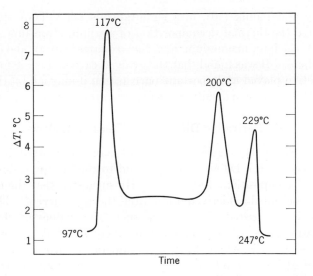

Fig. VII.24. DTA curve of pure lithium stearate. Heating rate 1.5°C/min (39).

All of the aluminum chelates with the substituted 8-quinolinols gave DTA curves which contained only endothermic peaks, while for the other metal ions, the 5,7-dihalochelates all gave exothermic peaks. These exothermic peaks must be related to the oxidation of the halogen, although it is not known why this effect does not take place with aluminum. Perhaps it is related to the thermal stability of the metal halide which might be formed as an intermediate compound.

Cox and McGlynn (39) studied several lubricating greases by the technique of DTA. In Figure VII.24 is illustrated the DTA curve for pure lithium stearate.

The first peak in the curve had a T_{max} of 117°C, while the second was at 200°C. The third peak, however, varied from 225 to 229°C, depending on the heating rate and the amount of alumina in the sample mixture. This variation in the third peak was caused by the fact that there were two different phase changes taking place simultaneously. The first of these occurred probably at 225°C or slightly higher, and the second at 229°C. The DTA apparatus was not able to separate the two peaks.

The phase diagram of lithium stearate-n-hexadecane was also determined by DTA by Cox and McGlynn (39).

Erdey and Paulik (40), in a simultaneous DTA–TGA study, investigated the thermal decomposition of barium, strontium, manganese(II), calcium, magnesium, and zinc oxalates in an air and nitrogen atmosphere.   It was found that the evolved carbon dioxide formed in the reaction played an important part in that it may inhibit the progress of the reaction and shift the peak temperatures to higher values.

C. Derivative Differential Thermal Analysis

Frederickson (41) suggested the use of manually plotted first derivative curves of the DTA curve as an aid to the interpretation of the thermal decomposition of kaolinite.   He suggested that the curve so obtained be called a "derived differential thermal curve."   The manual plotting consisted of observing successive values of change of temperature $(T - T')$ for equal increments of T.   This was expressed as $\Delta(T - T')/\Delta T$, where ΔT was a temperature increment of 10 °C. A plot of $\Delta(T - T')/\Delta T$ vs. T is thus the first derivative of the DTA curve.   The derived DTA curve peak area was said to be reproducible to $\pm 3\%$.

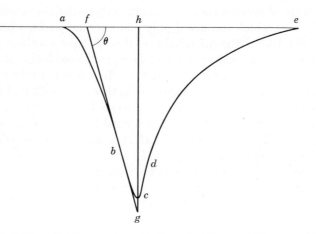

Fig. VII.25. Differential temperature vs. time for the crystalline transition of potassium nitrate (42).

Since the magnitude of the first derivative curve peak is proportional to the amount of reactant present for a zero-order reaction, such as a crystalline phase transition or melting, Campbell et al. (42) de-

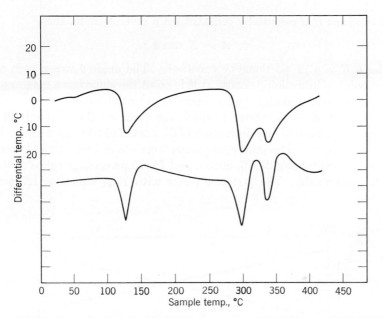

Fig. VII.26. Normal and derivative DTA curves for 50% KNO₃ and 50% KClO₄ mixture (42).

termined the concentration of the components in potassium nitrate–potassium perchlorate mixtures.

The method is based on the following analysis of the DTA curve, as given in Figure VII.25.   If it is assumed that the thermal effect of the reaction is completed at point c, then the enthalpy change is the area enclosed by the triangle, fgh.   Because the area of this part of the peak is proportional to the quantity of reactant involved, the area, A, is then

$$A = \tfrac{1}{2} BH$$

or

$$\tan \theta = H/B$$

where B is the base, fh, H is the altitude of the triangle, hg, and θ is the angle subtended by the altitude.   The area is then

$$A = \tfrac{1}{2} B^2 \tan \theta$$

If the base B is essentially constant for a given system, then

$$A = K \tan \theta$$

where K is a proportionality constant. The angle θ was chosen at the point of inflection, because at this point the slope has a maximum value and consequently the maximum area was obtained.

Verification of the above method was made on the KNO_3–$KClO_4$ system, the normal and derivative DTA curves of which are shown in Figure VII.26. The pure compounds were studied as well as binary mixtures containing 25:75, 50:50, and 75:25 percentage ratios of the two compounds. The first two peaks with T_{max} values of 128 and

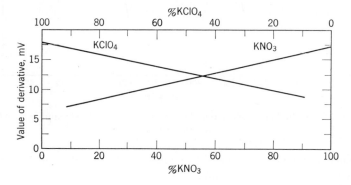

Fig. VII.27. Derivative peaks vs. sample composition for both crystalline transitions (42).

300 °C, corresponded to the crystalline phase transitions of the KNO_3 and $KClO_4$, respectively. The third peak was caused by the melting of KNO_3 and had a T_{max} of about 340 °C. In all cases, the points of inflection, as defined by the derivative peaks, occurred at the temperatures cited.

The linearity of the peak derivatives as a function of sample composition for both transitions is given in Figure VII.27. As can be seen, there was excellent agreement between the experimental and theoretical values for both compounds in the mixtures.

Freeman and Edelman (43) reported the derivative DTA (DDTA) curves of potassium nitrate, calcium oxalate 1-hydrate, and potassium perchlorate.

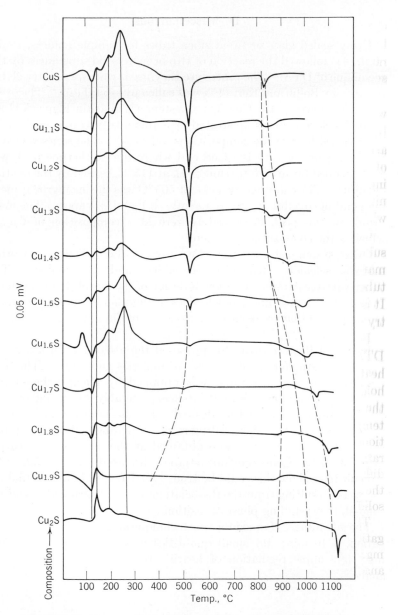

Fig. VII.28. Pyrosynthesis curves for the system CuS–Cu₂S (45).

D. Miscellaneous

Using sealed glass or fused silica tubes for sample holders, Bollin et al. (44) followed the reaction of two or more solid substances by the technique of DTA. The procedure they used, which was later elaborated on by Bollin and Kerr (45), was called pyrosynthesis. The pyrosynthesis curves of the CuS–Cu_2S system are given in Figure VII.28.

In the eleven curves illustrated, the amounts of copper and sulfur were varied to give the compositions indicated. The series was synthesized, starting with the CuS end where the exothermic peak was accompanied by an endothermic peak at 115 °C, caused by the melting of sulfur. The endothermic peak at 505 °C was the incongruent melting point of covellite (CuS) to digenite + liquid + vapor. The magnitude of this peak decreased to zero at a composition of $Cu_{1.8}S$, which is the composition of digenite.

Other systems studied were FeS–FeS_2, $CuFeS_2$, $FeS_{1.5}$, and other sulfides, selenides, tellurides, arsenides, and antimonides. The many variable parameters, such as design of the sample holder, sample tubes, heating rate, and particle sizes of the sample were determined. It is expected that pyrosynthesis would be useful in inorganic chemistry as well.

Berg and Rassonskaya (46) proposed the use of high heating rate DTA apparatus for rapid analysis of minerals and clays. The high heating rate, 80–100 °C/min, was obtained by placing the sample holder into a previously heated furnace, preferably 300 °C higher than the final sample temperature desired. It was claimed that the peak temperatures, at this high heating rate, for melting and boiling transitions, were the same as those obtained at the 3–6 °C/min. heating rate. Judging from previous studies discussed on p. 152, it is difficult to see how this could be true. Similar results were found for the peaks resulting from the dissociation of metal carbonates and for solid-state crystalling phase transition.

The advantages claimed for this technique are: (a) speed of investigation, 3–10 min; (b) small quantities of sample required, 20–100 mg; (c) simple regulation of heating rate; and (d) cheapness of analysis.

References

1. Gordon, S., *J. Chem. Educ.*, **40**, A87 (1963).
2. Kracek, F. C., *J. Phys. Chem.*, **33**, 1281 (1929).
3. Kracek, F. C., *J. Phys. Chem.*, **34**, 225 (1930).
4. Garn, P. D., and S. S. Flaschen, *Anal. Chem.*, **29**, 271 (1957).
5. Morita, H., *Anal. Chem.*, **28**, 64 (1956).
6. Morita, H., *Anal. Chem.*, **29**, 1095 (1957).
7. Morita, H., *J. Am. Chem. Soc.*, **78**, 1397 (1956).
8. Anderson, H. C., *Anal. Chem.*, **32**, 1592 (1960).
9. Fauth, M. I., *Anal. Chem.*, **32**, 655 (1960).
10. Chiu, J., *Anal. Chem.*, **34**, 1841 (1962).
11. Vassallo, D. A., and J. C. Harden, *Anal. Chem.*, **34**, 132 (1962).
12. Arseneau, D. F., *Can. J. Chem.*, **39**, 1915 (1961).
13. Wendlandt, W. W., and J. A. Hoiberg, *Anal. Chim. Acta*, **28**, 506 (1963).
14. Wendlandt, W. W., and J. A. Hoiberg, *Anal. Chim. Acta*, **29**, 539 (1963).
15. Pakulak, J. M., and G. W. Leonard, *Anal. Chem.*, **31**, 1037 (1959).
16. Murphy, C. B., *Mod. Plastics*, 125, Aug. (1960).
17. Murphy, C. B., J. A. Palm, C. D. Doyle, and E. M. Curtiss, *J. Polymer Sci.*, **28**, 447 (1958).
18. Murphy, C. B., J. A. Palm, C. D. Doyle, and E. M. Curtiss, *J. Polymer Sci.*, **28**, 453 (1958).
19. Clampitt, B. H., *Anal. Chem.*, **35**, 577 (1963).
20. Schwenker, R. F., and L. R. Beck, *Textile Res. J.*, **30**, 624 (1960).
21. Ke, B., *J. Polymer Sci.*, **42**, 15 (1960).
22. Ke, B., *J. Polymer Sci.*, **50**, 79 (1961).
23. Wunderlich, B., and W. H. Kashdan, *J. Polymer Sci.*, **50**, 71 (1961).
24. Scott, N. D., *Polymer*, **1**, 114 (1960).
25. Rudin, A., H. P. Schreiber, and M. H. Waldman, *Ind. Eng. Chem.*, **53**, 137 (1961).
26. Ke, B., and A. W. Sisko, *J. Polymer Sci.*, **50**, 87 (1961).
27. Murphy, C. B., and J. A. Hill, *Nucleonics*, **18**, 78 (1960).
28. Anderson, D. A., and E. S. Freeman, *Anal. Chem.*, **31**, 1697 (1959).
29. Wendlandt, W. W., J. H. Van Tassel, and G. R. Horton, *Anal. Chim. Acta*, **23**, 332 (1960).
30. Breger, I. A., and W. L. Whitehead, *Fuel*, **30**, 247 (1951).
31. Gamel, C. M., and W. J. Smothers, *Anal. Chim. Acta*, **6**, 442 (1952).
32. Stone, R. L., *Anal. Chem.*, **32**, 1582 (1960).
33. Petricciani, J. C., S. E. Wimberley, W. H. Bauer, and T. W. Clapper, *J. Phys. Chem.*, **64**, 1309 (1960).
34. Wendlandt, W. W., T. D. George, and G. R. Horton, *J. Inorg. Nucl. Chem.*, **17**, 273 (1961).
35. Wendlandt, W. W., and J. L. Bear, *Anal. Chim. Acta*, **21**, 439 (1959).
36. Lodding, W., and L. Hammell, *Anal. Chem.*, **32**, 657 (1960).
37. Wendlandt, W. W., and G. R. Horton, *Anal. Chem.*, **34**, 1098 (1962).
38. Charles, R. G., *Anal. Chim. Acta*, **27**, 474 (1962).
39. Cox, D. B., and J. F. McGlynn, *Anal. Chem.*, **29**, 960 (1957).

40. Erdey, L., and F. Paulik, *Acta Chim. Acad. Sci. Hung.*, **7**, 27 (1955).
41. Frederickson, A. F., *Am. Mineralogist*, **39**, 1023 (1954).
42. Campbell, C., S. Gordon, and C. L. Smith, *Anal. Chem.*, **31**, 1188 (1959).
43. Freeman, E. S., and D. Edelman, *Anal. Chem.*, **31**, 624 (1959).
44. Bollin, E. M., J. A. Dunne, and P. F. Kerr, *Science*, **131**, 661 (1960).
45. Bollin, E. M., and P. F. Kerr, *Am. Mineralogist*, **46**, 823 (1961).
46. Berg, L. G., and I. S. Rassonskaya, *Dokl. Akad. Nauk S.S.S.R.*, **73**, 113 (1950).

CHAPTER VIII

THERMOMETRIC TITRIMETRY

A. Introduction

Although not a "thermal" method in the same sense of the word as are TGA, DTA, etc., thermometric titrimetry is included here because it has become an important analytical tool along with potentiometric, conductometric, spectrophotometric, and other titrimetric procedures. In contrast with other thermal methods, in which a physical property of the system is continuously monitored as a function of temperature, thermometric titrations involve the measurement of the temperature change in a system as a function of time or volume of titrant. The methodology of the technique consists of the detection and measurement of the change in temperature of a solution as the titrant is added to it, under as nearly adiabatic conditions as possible. In practice, the titrant is added from a thermostated constant delivery buret into the titrate (solution titrated) which is contained in an insulated container such as a Dewar flask. The resultant temperature–volume (or time) curve thus obtained is similar to other titration curves in that the beginning and end points of the reaction can be readily ascertained. Since all reactions involve a detectable endothermic or exothermic enthalpy change, the technique has wide application in analytical chemistry, particularly in those cases where other more common methods are not applicable. Use of this titration method has been applied to neutralization, precipitation, complexation, and oxidation–reduction reactions in aqueous solvents and also to reactions in nonaqueous solvents. Although the literature on this subject is rather extensive, excellent reviews have been written by Zenchelsky (16) and Jordan (17,18,65).

Over the past fifty years or so that it has been in existence (1) the nomenclature of this titration technique has been a rather confused one. Starting from about 1924, the term "thermometric titration" has been in general use (2), although calorimetric titration was used by one of the same authors (3) in 1925. Other terms used have been enthalpy titrations (22,23), thermochemical titrations (4), thermal titrations (5), and thermovolumetry (6). In 1952, the Committee on Nomenclature of the Division of Analytical Chemistry of the American Chemical Society stated that the term "thermometric" was not recommended (7). However, at the 1957 Symposium on Thermoanalytical Titrimetry, New York, it was the consensus that the term "thermometric titration" be adhered to in the future (1).

Perhaps the first description of this technique was by Bell and Cowell (8) who applied it to the titration of a citric acid solution with ammonia to obtain ammonium citrate. Using a Dewar flask, a platinum stirrer, and a 0.1°C calibrated thermometer, they found

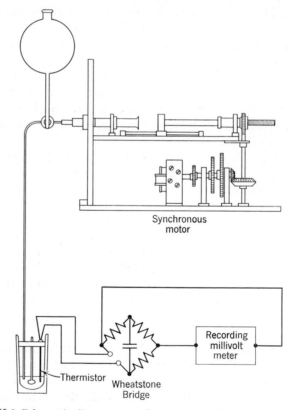

Fig. VIII.1 Schematic diagram of a thermometric titration apparatus (66).

that the end point of the reaction could easily be ascertained from the temperature–volume curve. The work of Dutoit and Grobet (9), as applied to acid–base, complexation, and precipitation reaction systems, probably was the first to demonstrate the general utility of the method. Other early applications were the thermometric titration of a soluble sulfate with barium chloride by Dean and Watts (2) and of a soluble chloride with silver nitrate by Dean and Newcombe (3). These studies were followed by other analytical determinations such as the titration of calcium, strontium, and barium chlorides with $(NH_4)_2C_2O_4$, H_3AsO_3 with $KBrO_3$, and $KMnO_4$ with $H_2C_2O_4$, as described by Mayr and Fisch (10). The technique has also been used to study the formation of metal hydroxo- and other anionic complexes by various Indian investigators (11–15,19,20).

All of the early work consisted of the laborious point-by-point plotting of temperature, as detected by a Beckmann thermometer, and volume, as measured by a buret, to obtain the titration curve. Various errors were possible such as the excessive time of titration which could result in heat leaks into the system, the long time constant of the thermometer, stirring errors, dilution effects, and, of course human error. These effects were minimized when Linde et al. (21) introduced a virtually automatic system consisting of a constant delivery flow buret, a thermistor temperature detector, and a strip-chart recorder. It was at this point that modern thermometric titrators and, hence, more reliable thermometric titration data came into existence.

B. Apparatus

A schematic diagram of a thermometric titration apparatus is given in Figure VIII.1.

The experimental apparatus consists of (a) an automatic buret, (b), an adiabatic titration cell, (c) a temperature measuring device (d) a strip-chart or other type of recorder. For purposes of calibration, a calorimetric calibrator (c) is employed. Various automatic burets have been used, from a gravity flow type (21) to a motor driven syringe type such as described by Lingane (24) and which are now commercially available. The adiabatic titration cell is normally a Dewar flask of 250 ml capacity, which contains an efficient stirrer and stirring motor to agitate the flask contents. Thermistors are used to detect the temperature of the titration solution

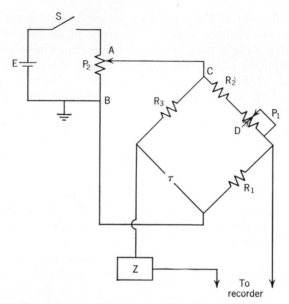

Fig. VIII.2. Thermistor bridge circuit (25). E, 1.5-V source; P_1, 1300-Ω potentiometer; P_2, 50-Ω potentiometer; τ, thermistor; R_1, R_3, 2000-Ω resistors; R_2, 1500-Ω resistor; S, Single-pole, single-throw switch; Z, Zero adjuster (4).

mainly because of their rapid response time (21) although for precision measurements, Schlyter (23) recommended a platinum resistance thermometer. The thermistor is used in conjunction with a dc current balanced Wheatstone bridge circuit as illustrated in Figure VIII.2.

The sensitivity of the bridge circuit, expressed in terms of unbalance potential per given change in thermistor resistance, is regulated by varying the voltage to the bridge, as described by Muller and Stolten (26). The unbalance potential, π, is equal to

$$\pi = \gamma_{AB} \left(\frac{\tau}{\tau + R_3} - \frac{R_1}{R_1 + R_{CD}} \right) \qquad \text{(VIII.1)}$$

where γ_{AB} is the potential drop between points A and B which is equal to the bridge input voltage, R_{CD} is the resistance between C and D; and τ, R_1, and R_2 are the resistances of the thermistor and fixed resistors, respectively. Using this circuit, Jordan and Alleman (25) found that at the maximum sensitivity setting in the 24–26°C

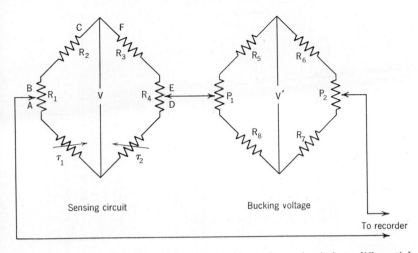

Fig. VIII.3. Temperature-sensing and bucking voltage circuit for a differential titrator (27). P_1, 50-Ω 10-turn potentiometer; P_2, 1000-Ω potentiometer; R_1, 4000-Ω potentiometer; R_2, 16 000-Ω resistor; R_3, 18 000-Ω resistor; R_4, 2000-Ω potentiometer; R_5 to R_8, 5000-Ω resistors; V, variable voltage from dry cells, 0. to 22.5 V; V', 6-V dry cell; $\tau_1 = \tau_2 =$ sets of four 51Al thermistors in parallel. Resistance at 25°C 25 900 Ω.

temperature range with $\gamma_{AB} = E = 1.5$ V, $R_1 = R_{CD} = R_3 = \tau = 2000$ Ω, a 1°C change corresponded to an unbalance potential of 15.7 mV or 176 cm on the recorder chart ordinate. This was equivalent to about 0.15°C per full scale deflection and since the chart ordinate could be read to an accuracy of about ±0.03 cm, corresponded to ±0.0002°C.

The recorders employed are usually of the potentiometric strip-chart type. Since the delivery volume of titrant is linear with time, a plot of bridge unbalance (temperature) and volume (time) is thus obtained. An equally feasible system would be to use an X-Y recorder and plot temperature on the Y-axis, and volume, as determined by a retransmitting potentiometer mounted on the buret motor, on the X-axis.

A differential titration apparatus has been described by Tyson et al. (27). Matched thermistors are placed in both the sample and blank solutions. In order to utilize a low-input impedance recorder and still have the advantage of the high-temperature coefficient of high-resistance thermistors −4.6% per °C for 100 000-

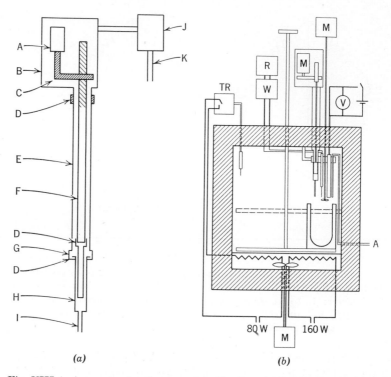

Fig. VIII.4. Apparatus for thermometric titrations in fused salt solvents (29). (a) Buret; A, motor; B, mechanism housing; C, worm gear; D, brass collar nuts; E, stainless steel tubing; F, stainless steel push rod; G, syringe plunger; H 1-ml syringe; I, capillary tip; J, constant voltage transformer; K, power line, 110-V ac. (b) General view: A, Argon inlet; M, motors for stirrer, fan, and automatic titrator; R, Recorder; TR, thermistor thermoregulator; V, heater circuit for simulated titration; W, thermistor bridge.

Ω thermistors compared to -4% per °C for the 2000-Ω type (25), it was necessary to connect several thermistors in parallel. For a differential circuit, two sets of identical thermistors were used; such a circuit is illustrated in Figure VIII.3.

An interesting titration apparatus which was used for titrations in a molten lithium nitrate–potassium nitrate eutectic solvent at 158°C has been described by Jordan et al. (28,29). The apparatus is shown in Figure VIII.4. The buret employed was a modified Aminco-Koegel Meniscomatic type driven by a dc servomotor. The ser-

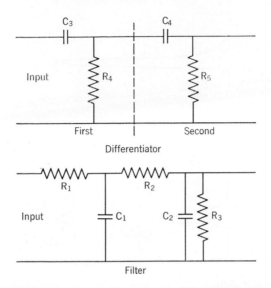

Fig. VIII.5. Differentiator and filter circuits (30). R_1, R_2, R_3. 0.5 MΩ· R_4, R_5, 1 MΩ; C_1, C_2, 10 mF, Pyranol; C_3, C_4, 0.5 mF, paper.

vomotor was connected to a worm gear which gave a vertical motion to a stainless steel push rod attached to the plunger of a 1 ml Pyrex syringe. The syringe-buret delivered 2–4 μl of titrant per second with a precision of ±0.02 μl/s.

The calorimeter consisted of a Dewar flask inserted in an electric thermostated oven for proper temperature environment. Four such flasks were mounted on a turntable at 90° radial intervals. By rotating the turntable, it was possible to position the Dewars in succession opposite an asbestos stopper containing the thermistor, stirrer, calibration heater, inert gas inlet tube, and syringe end of the titrator. A high resistance, 100 000 Ω at 25°C, bead-type thermistor was employed; its resistance at 170°C was 1600 Ω.

Since the thermometric titration curves frequently resemble conductometric titration curves, it is difficult at times to locate the end point of the titration by extrapolation procedures. By taking the first derivative of the curve, Zenchelsky and Segatto (30) found that the end points were easier to detect. The differentiator and filter circuits are shown in Figure VIII.5. Both consist of simple R–C circuits which yield only the approximate second derivative of

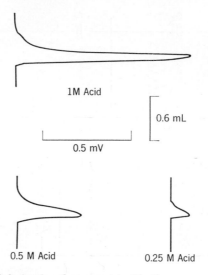

Fig. VIII.6. Second derivative thermometric titration curves of an acid solution (30).

the curve. Titration curves for acid solutions of different concentrations are illustrated in Figure VIII.6.

A commercially available instrument, the Titrathermomat, has recently been introduced (American Instrument Co., 8030 Georgia Ave., Silver Spring, Maryland). The instrument is shown in Figure VIII.7.

All of the necessary components, the motor-driven syringe, the "adiabatic" titration tower, and thermistor and bridge assembly, are encased in a single unit. Operation of the apparatus is entirely automatic with the temperature–volume (time) presentation being made on a standard strip-chart potentiometric recorder.

C. Theory

Two thermometric titration curves for an exothermic process are given in Figure VIII.8.

In Figure VIII.8 a is illustrated an idealized curve, while VIII.8b illustrates the actual curve showing the extrapolation correction for curvature due to incompleteness of reaction. For an endothermic process, the curve would deflect in the opposite direction. In (a),

Fig. VIII.7. The Titrathermomat.

line AB is the temperature–time blank which in most cases has a slight slope due to heat leakage into or out of the titration cell. As the titrant is added to the titrate, the curve deviates from the base line at point B and levels off again at the idealized end point of the reaction, point C. Line $C'D$ is the excess titrant line with a slope due to heat leakage and temperature difference between titrant and titrate.

In an actual titration, Figure VIII.8, curve B, the curve has a pronounced curvature before point C is attained thus necessitating the correction. In both cases ΔT is the corrected temperature change of the reaction and ΔV is the end-point volume of titrant.

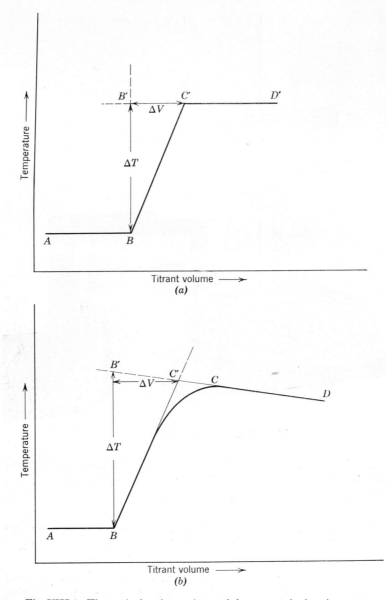

Fig. VIII.8. Theoretical and experimental thermometric titration curves.

The number of moles of unknown substance, N_m, titrated is (18):

$$N_m = \Delta V C_t \qquad \text{(VIII.2)}$$

or

$$N_m = -\frac{0.001g}{\Delta H} \qquad \text{(VIII.3)}$$

where ΔV is the volume of titrant; C_t is the concentration of the reagent; g is the number of calories evolved by the reaction, as obtained from ΔT and a calibration constant of the calorimeter; and ΔH is the effective enthalpy change of the reaction in kcal per mole.

If the cell or calorimeter constant, Q, which actually represents the effective heat capacity of the system, is known, the heat of reaction can be calculated by

$$\Delta H = -\frac{Q \Delta T}{N_m} \qquad \text{(VIII.4)}$$

Keily and Hume (31) have considered the theoretical aspects of the thermometric titration curve. Consider a titration in which the titrant is isothermal with the initial solution and in which the only process contributing to the temperature change is the chemical reaction. Since the reaction must be rapid to be practical, then

$$-dH = \Delta H dn = -C_p dT \qquad \text{(VIII.5)}$$

where ΔH is the isothermal heat of reaction at T, in kcal per mole, and dn is the increment of titrant in millimoles. Because $dn = M dV$, where V is expressed in ml, and because V is linear with time t,

$$\frac{dT}{dV} = \frac{\Delta H M}{C_p} \qquad \text{(VIII.6)}$$

where C_p is the heat capacity, in cal, of the titration cell and its contents. The plot of T vs. V should then be linear if ΔH and C_p are constant. However, the variation in C_p due to added titrant is significant. If C_p is considered to consist of two terms—the heat capacity of the liquid and the heat capacity of the titration cell, stirrers, and so on, then

$$C_p = (cd)V + C' \qquad \text{(VIII.7)}$$

where c is the specific heat of the liquid (assumed constant), d is its density, and C' is the heat capacity of the titration apparatus. Integrating equation (VIII.6) between the initial and final temperatures, T_1 and T_2, and the corresponding volumes in the Dewar flask, V_1 and V_2, the relationship between the total temperature rise and the volume of the titrant is

$$\Delta T = \int_{t_1}^{t_2} dT = - \Delta HM \int_{v_1}^{v_2} \frac{dV}{cdV + C'}$$

$$= \frac{-2.3 \,\Delta HM}{cd} \log \left[\frac{cdV_2 + C'}{cdV_1 + C'} \right] \quad \text{(VIII.8)}$$

The nonlinearity of the titration curve caused by the changing heat capacity introduces no difficulty in locating end points because these are usually very clear and sharp for most reactions. It would appear that the nonlinearity of the curves would affect the calculation of ΔH from ΔT, but it is found that the first 30% of the titration curve follows very closely to linearity. Thus, using the initial slope of the curve and equation (VIII.6) both difficulties can be circumvented. The advantages of the initial slope method are: (a) curvature in the vicinity of the end point caused by incompleteness of reaction does not affect results; (b) errors due to a difference in temperature between the titrant reservoir and the titration solution are minimized; and (c) the heat capacity of the initial system, which can be measured readily, is appropriate for the calculations.

If the titrant and solution are not isothermal, which is the usual case in an actual titration, the rate of temperature change due to mixing with titrant of a different temperature, T_3, is (31)

$$\frac{dT}{dV} = \frac{(T_3 - T_1)cd}{C_p} \quad \text{(VIII.9)}$$

and correspondingly,

$$\Delta T = \int_{T_1}^{T_2} dT = 2.3 \,(T_3 - T_1) \log \left[\frac{cdV_2 + C'}{cdV_1 + C'} \right] \quad \text{(VIII.10)}$$

It is assumed that both the specific heat and density are the same for titrant and solution. It can easily be seen that a plot of T vs. V would not be linear.

Keily and Hume (31) have also derived expressions whereby it is possible to calculate heats of solution and heats of dilution from a thermometric titration. Indeed, thermometric titrimetry provides a simple and direct method for measuring differential heats of solution in an infinitely dilute solution.

Using the differential thermometric titration technique, Tyson, et al. (27) used the following equation to calculate the heat of reaction:

$$\Delta H = \frac{E_1 E_2 S_1}{(4.185)R_3 \, NFS_2} = \text{cal/meq} \qquad \text{(VIII.11)}$$

where E_1 is the voltage across the heating cell; E_2 is the voltage across the standard resistor; R_3 is the resistance of the standard resistor in ohms; N is the normality of titrant; F is the flow rate of the buret, in ml per second; S_1 is the slope of titration curve; and S_2 is the slope of the heating curve.

D. Applications

A summary of the applications of thermometric titrations is given in Table VIII.1. For the analytical chemist, the determination of

TABLE VIII.1
Summary of Applications of Thermometric Titrations (17)

Information obtainable		Procedure for calculating data from curve
Analytical applications	Concentration of an unknown	Direct thermometric
	Amount of an unknown	End point determinative
	Heat of reaction	From extrapolated ordinate heights
Fundamental applications	Free energy of reaction	From curvature in equivalence point region
	Entropy of reaction	From thermodynamic equations
	Reaction stoichiometry	End point determinative

the concentration of an unknown substance is of prime importance especially if other analytical methods are not applicable. Linde et al. (21) have shown that even thick slurries have no significant effect on the end point of the titration. The accuracy of the titration is given by (18)

$$P_n \approx |C_n \, \Delta H| \qquad \text{(VIII.12)}$$

where P_n is the "enthalpimetric sensitivity index," expressed in cal per liter; C_n is the minimum concentration, expressed in mmoles per l, of unknown which can be determined with a relative accuracy of n per cent; and ΔH is the heat of reaction. The quantity, P_n, depends upon the characteristic experimental apparatus but is independent of concentration whenever $C \geq C_n$. In order to minimize dilution curvature, ΔT should be at least $0.01\,°C$ and C_t, from equation (VIII.2), should be at least 100 times the concentration of the unknown.

The limits of applicability will be set by a number of factors (21). The reaction must be rapid or serious curvature will appear and the end point of the reaction may be displaced. Adequate mixing of large volumes of solution is a problem at times and heat loss due to evaporation becomes serious for small titration volumes. If the solutions are too dilute, the amount of heat generated will be difficult to measure. Another factor present when the heat evolved or absorbed is small is that excessive care is necessary to equalize the temperature of the titrant and the titration solution.

Thermometric titrations have been applied to acid–base (neutralization), precipitation, complex formation (complexation), and oxidation–reduction reactions in both aqueous and non-aqueous systems.

1. Acid–Base Reactions

The thermometric titration of strong acids and bases presents no inherent difficulties. With weak acids and bases, excellent results have also been obtained. The most important potentialities and limitations of acid–base thermometric titrations are due to the fact that the heats of neutralization of various acids differ by 50% or less (32). This energetic significance is apparent from the following. Generally, the heat of neutralization of an acid with a strong base can be additively equated to its heat of ionization, ΔH_i^0, plus the heat of neutralization of strong acids ($-13.5\,\text{kcal/mole}$):

$$10\,\text{kcal/mole} < - \Delta H_n^0 = (- \Delta H_i^0 + 13.5) < 15\,\text{kcal/mole}$$

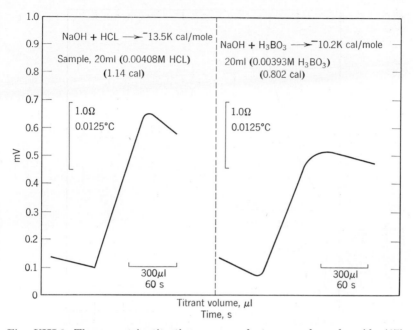

Fig. VIII.9. Thermometric titration curves of strong and weak acids (17). Titrant, 0.2610M NaOH, 600 μl/min.

In turn, the enthalpy of ionization is an additive function of a free energy and an entropy term:

$$\Delta H_i^0 = \Delta F_i^0 + T\Delta S_i^0 = -RT \ln K_i + T\Delta S_i \quad \text{(VIII.13)}$$

For a given acid, then, ΔF_i^0 is energetically compensated for by the $T\Delta S_i^0$ term, yielding a ΔH_i^0 value which varies considerably less from acid to acid than either ΔS_i^0 or ΔF_i^0. Although potentiometric titration curves are quite different for a series of acids, the thermometric titration curves were fairly similar, as was shown for boric, acetic, monochloroacetic, and trichloroacetic acids (32).

Typical thermometric titration curves for a strong acid, HCl, and a weak acid, H_3BO_3, are given in Figure VIII.9. In this case, boric acid is acting as a monoprotic acid. The potentiometric titration curves of the two acids are very different yielding a large end-point inflection for HCl, $K_a \approx \infty$, and virtually none for H_3BO_3, $K_a \approx 10^{-10}$. The corresponding curves are practically identical

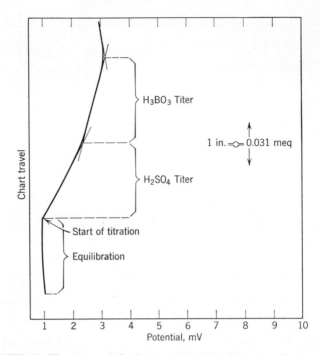

Fig. VIII.10. The sequential thermometric titration of sulfuric and boric acids (33). Solution titrated: 1.00 ml 0.102N H_3BO_3 + 0.10 ml 0.908N H_2SO_4 + dist. H_2O to make 5.00 ml. Titrant: 1.00N NaOH.

(17) because the heats of neutralization of HCl and H_3BO_3 are -13.5 and -10.2 kcal/mole, respectively. As a result the two acids can be determined with comparable ease, precision, and accuracy while direct free energy methods are bound to fail with H_3BO_3. In fact, mixtures of a strong acid and a weak acid can be titrated as was shown by Miller and Thomason (33). The titration of a mixture of sulfuric and boric acids is illustrated in Figure VIII.10.

A summary of the acid–base titrations that have been carried out in aqueous solvents is given in Table VIII.2.

In the titration of strong acids and bases, the concentration of the titrant is normally about $1N$ while the substance to be titrated must be present in concentrations greater than about $0.002N$ in order to obtain an accuracy of $\pm$ 2 to 3% (21). For weak acids or bases titrated with a strong base or acid, the concentration of the solution to be titrated must be greater than about $3 \times 10^{-3}N$ for an accuracy of $\pm 1\%$ (32). The effect of concentration of the weak acid on the accuracy of the titration has been studied in detail (32).

TABLE VIII.2

Thermometric Titrations of Acids and Bases in Aqueous Solutions

Titrate	Titrant	Precision and accuracy, %	Ref.
NaOH	HCl	0.11[a]	21
NH$_3$	HCl	0.56	21
H$_3$PO$_4$	NaOH	2.8	21
2nd H$^+$	NaOH	2.1	21
3rd H$^+$	NaOH	0.85	21
CH$_3$COOH	NaOH	0.99	21
H$_3$BO$_3$	NaOH	0.38	21
C$_5$H$_5$N	HCl	4.7	21
OH$^-$ + CO$_3^{--}$	HCl	0.84	21
H$_2$SO$_4$ + H$_3$BO$_3$	NaOH	1.19	33
H$_3$BO$_3$ + mannitol	NaOH	1.19	33
Ethylenediamine, over-all	HCl	0.1	27
1st NH$_2$	HCl	1.7	27
2nd NH$_2$	HCl	2.0	27
Ethanolamine	HCl	0.9	27
2-Amino-1-butanol	HCl	0.9	27
2-Methyl-2-amino-1-propanol	HCl	0.6	27
2-Methyl-2-amino-1,3-propanediol	HCl	0.5	27
Tris(hydroxymethyl)-aminomethane	HCl	0.4	27
Alanine	NaOH	±2[b]	34
Glutamic acid	NaOH	±2	34
Aspartic acid	NaOH	±2	34
Glycine	NaOH	±2	34
H$_3$AsO$_4$	NaOH		35
H$_3$AsO$_3$	NaOH		36
H$_3$PO$_4$ + HCl	NaOH		37
H$_4$P$_2$O$_7$ + H$_2$SO$_4$	NaOH		37
HPO$_3$ + H$_4$P$_2$O$_7$	NaOH		37
HPO$_3$ + H$_4$P$_2$O$_7$ + H$_3$PO$_3$	NaOH		37, 38
Citric acid	NH$_3$		8
Monochloroacetic acid	NaOH	±1	32
Trichloroacetic acid	NaOH	±1	32

[a] σ values.

[b] Accuracy values, in %.

2. Precipitation Reactions

The formation of a slightly soluble substance, MX, can be followed nicely by thermometric titrimetry. Such a reaction can be followed due to the heat of reaction, ΔH, evolved or absorbed, as shown by the reaction:

$$M^+(aq) + X^-(aq) \to MX(s) \pm \Delta H$$

The titration of silver nitrate with hydrochloric acid or a soluble metal chloride results in curves that are very similar to strong acid–strong base curves. A great amount of work has been done on this type of reaction beginning with the titration of soluble sulfate with barium chloride (2) in 1924. This method has also been used to detect the presence of various intermediate compounds which may be formed during the precipitation reaction.

A summary of some precipitation reactions that have been studied by thermometric titrimetry is given in Table VIII.3. It is difficult to separate precipitation reactions from complex-formation reactions because in many cases, the complexes precipitate out of solution.

TABLE VIII.3
Summary of Precipitation Reactions in Aqueous Solutions

Titrate	Titrant	Precipitate	Ref.
$Pb(C_2H_3O_3)_2$	$K_4Fe(CN)_6$	$Pb_2Fe(CN)_6$	35
$HgCl_2$	KCN	$Hg(CN)_2$	35
$HgCl_2$	KI	HgI_2	39
$NiSO_4$	KCN	$Ni(CN)_2$	39
$Zn(NO_3)_2$	KCN	$Zn(CN)_2$	39
$Co(NO_3)_2$	KCN	$Co(CN)_2$	39
KCN	$AgNO_3$	AgCN	2
NaCl	$AgNO_3$	AgCl	2
$CaCl_2$	$(NH_4)_2C_2O_4$	CaC_2O_4	10
$SrCl_2$	$(NH_4)_2C_2O_4$	SrC_2O_4	10
$BaCl_2$	$(NH_4)_2C_2O_4$	BaC_2O_4	10
$Hg(NO_3)_2$	$(NH_4)_2C_2O_4$	HgC_2O_4	10
Pb^{2+}	$H_2C_2O_4$	PbC_2O_4	10
Mg^{2+}	$C_2O_4^-$	MgC_2O_4	40

Linde et al. (21) state that under ordinary conditions and using solution concentrations from 0.02 to 0.005N, a precision of a few parts per thousand can be obtained.   Tyson et al. (27) found errors of from −0.2 to +1.9% in the differential thermometric titration of silver nitrate with hydrochloric acid.

3. Complex-Formation or Complexation Reactions

The thermometric titration technique has been used to study complex formation in solution, since the first application by Dutoit and Grobet (9) in 1922.   Since this first investigation, much work has been done on the detection of various types of complexes involving such ligands as thiosulfate, cyanide, ferrocyanide, acetate, and iodides.   There is considerable doubt about the reliability and accuracy of much of the early data mainly because of errors due to

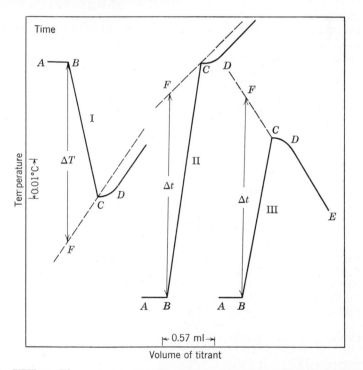

Fig. VIII.11. Thermometric titration curves of 1.000M EDTA with divalent cations (25).   I: 0.01080M Mg^{++}, titrant warmer than reactant.   II: 0.01170M Cu^{++}, titrant warmer than reactant.   III: 0.01170M Cu^{++}, titrant colder than reactant curves shifted arbitrarily along vertical axis.

TABLE VIII.4

Some Complexation Reactions That Have Been Studied by Thermometric Titrations

Titrate	Titrant	Complex formed	Ref.
Pb^{2+}	$EDTA^{4-}$	$Pb(EDTA)^{2-}$	25
Cd^{2+}	$EDTA^{4-}$	$Cd(EDTA)^{2-}$	25
Cu^{2+}	$EDTA^{4-}$	$Cu(EDTA)^{2-}$	25
Ni^{2+}	$EDTA^{4-}$	$Ni(EDTA)^{2-}$	25
Ca^{2+}	$EDTA^{4-}$	$Ca(EDTA)^{2-}$	25
Zn^{2+}	$EDTA^{4-}$	$Zn(EDTA)^{2-}$	25
Co^{2+}	$EDTA^{4-}$	$Co(EDTA)^{2-}$	25
Mg^{2+}	$EDTA^{4-}$	$Mg(EDTA)^{2-}$	25
BeF_2	NH_4F	$NH_4[BeF_3]$; $(NH_4)_2[BeF_4]$, $(NH_4)_3[BeF_5]$; $(NH_4)_4[BeF_6]$	41
$UO_2(NO_3)_2$	Na_2CO_3	$Na_4UO_2(CO_3)_3$ $Na_2UO_2(CO_3)_2$	42
$FeCl_3$	H_3PO_4	$Fe(HPO_4)^+$ $Fe(HPO_4)_2^-$	43
$Na_4P_2O_7$	$BeSO_4$	$Be(P_2O_7)^{2-}$ $Be(P_2O_7)_2^{6-}$	44
Pb^{2+}	$C_2H_3O_2^-$	$Pb(C_2H_3O_2)^+$	45
$CuSO_4$	$Na_2S_2O_3$	$Cu(S_2O_3)_5^{9-}$ and others	46
Zn^{2+}	$(NH_4)_2Hb(SCN)_4$	$ZnHg(SCN)_4$	47
$AgNO_3$	$Na_2S_2O_3$	$Na_3Ag(S_2O_3)_2$ and others	48
$Hg(CN)_2$	KCN	$K_2[Hg(CN)_2]$	35
Ni^{2+}	Ethylenediamine	$Ni(en)_3^{2+}$ and others	49
Cu^{2+}	Ethylenediamine	$Cu(en)_2^{2+}$ and others	49
$HgCl_2$	KI	K_2HgI_4	39
$Zn(NO_3)_2$	KCN	$K_2Zn(CN)_4$	39
$NiSO_4$	KCN	$K_2Ni(CN)_4$	39
$Co(NO_3)_2$	KCN	$K_2Co(CN)_4$	39
$CdSO_4$	$NaOH$	$CdSO_4 \cdot 3CdO$ $CdSO_4 \cdot CdO$	11
$CuSO_4$	$NaOH$	$CuSO_4 \cdot 3CuO$ $CuSO_4 \cdot CuO$	11
$K_4Fe(CN)_6$	$CuSO_4$	$K_2CuFe(CN)_6$	12
$CdSO_4$	$K_4Fe(CN)_6$	$K_2CdFe(CN)_6$ and others	13
$FeCl_3$	$K_3Fe(CN)_6$	$Fe[Fe(CN)_6]$	14

TABLE VIII.4 (*continued*)

Titrate	Titrant	Complex formed	Ref.
$FeCl_2$	$K_3Fe(CN)_6$	$Fe_3[Fe(CN)_6]_2$	15
Cd^{2+}	I^-	$CdI_4{}^{2-}$	19
$RbNO_3$	$Pb(NO_3)_2$	$RbNO_3 \cdot Pb(NO_3)_2$ and others	50
Zn^{++}	Na_2 tartrate (T)	ZnT, $[ZnT_2]^{2-}$	51
Cd^{++}	Na_2T	CdT	51
Cu^{++}	Na_2T	CuT	51
Zn^{++}	Na_3 citrate (Cit)	$ZnCit^-$	51
Cd^{++}	Na_3Cit	$CdCit^-$	51
Cu^{++}	Na_3Cit	$CuCit^-$	51

dilution, stirring, time constant of the temperature detection device, and others. With the advent of the modern automatic recording titrator, much more reliable data can certainly be obtained.

Because of the wide use of ethylenediaminetetraacetic acid (EDTA) and its derivatives in analytical chemistry, the application of this technique to EDTA titrations was of particular interest. Jordan and Alleman (25) found that the stoichiometry of the reaction corresponded to

$$Me^{++}(aq) + Y^{4-}(aq) \rightleftharpoons [MeY]^{--}(aq) + xH_2O$$

where Me^{++} is a divalent metal ion and Y^{4-} is the quadridentate EDTA anion. Side reactions which could take place were limited under the experimental conditions employed. Typical titration curves are shown in Figure VIII.11. The method was applicable to metal ion concentrations as low as $5 \times 10^{-4}M$ with an accuracy of from $\pm 3\%$ for the former concentration to $\pm 1\%$ for $1 \times 10^{-2}M$ solutions.

A summary of the various complexation reactions that have been investigated by thermometric titrations is given in Table VIII.4.

4. OXIDATION–REDUCTION REACTIONS

Compared to the amount of work done on precipitation or complexation reactions, little work has been done on redox reactions. The reason for this is not known because the method appears to be satisfactory on the examples that have been studied. Certainly most redox reactions could be followed and the end points detected by thermometric titrations.

A summary of various redox reactions that have been studied by this technique is given in Table VIII.5.

TABLE VIII.5

Some Redox Reactions That Have Been Investigated by Thermometric Titrations

Titrate	Titrant	Precision and accuracy, $\pm\%$	Ref.
Fe^{2+}	MnO_4^-		10
$H_2C_2O_4$	MnO_4^-		10
$Fe(CN)_6^{4-}$	MnO_4^-		10
$KBrO_3$	H_3AsO_3		10
$NaOCl$	H_3AsO_3		10
Fe^{2+}	Ce^{4+}	1	18
Fe^{2+}	$Cr_2O_7^{2-}$	0.5	18, 5
$Fe(CN)_6^{4-}$	Ce^{4+}	1	18, 27
Ti^{3+}	Ce^{4+}	2	18
H_2O_2	Ce^{4+}	3.7	27
$(-CH_2NH_3)_2SO_4FeSO_4 \cdot 4H_2O$	Ce^{4+}	1	27

5. REACTIONS IN NON-AQUEOUS SOLVENTS

The determination of acetic anhydride in glacial acetic acid has been the subject of a number of studies (52). The heat of reaction caused by the reaction of acetic anhydride with aniline, in toluene, was measured without the use of a catalyst. However, the procedures could not be strictly classified as thermometric titrations. Somiya (53–55), however, proposed the use of thermometric titration in place of the calorimetric procedure. Water in acetic acid has been determined by titration with acetic anhydride in the presence of perchloric acid as a catalyst (56). Mixtures of sulfuric acid, acetic anhydride, and acetic acid have been analyzed by Somiya (57,58). The reaction of dioxane and ethyl acetate with aluminum chloride, in benzene, was studied by Trambouze (59). The method is said to give a $\pm 3\%$ accuracy.

The neutralization of sodium acetate with perchloric acid in glacial acetic acid has been determined by a thermometric titration (31). Using the initial slope method, the heat of reaction for

$$\text{Na}^+\text{C}_2\text{H}_3\text{O}_2{}^- + \text{H}^+\text{ClO}_4{}^- \xrightarrow{\text{HOAc}} \text{HC}_2\text{H}_3\text{O}_2 + \text{Na}^+\text{ClO}_4{}^-$$

was found to be -5.7 ± 0.2 kcal/mole compared to a literature value of -5.7 kcal/mole (60).

Zenchelsky et al. (61) titrated tin(IV) chloride with dioxane in benzene, carbon tetrachloride, nitrobenzene, and chloroform. A SnCl_4:dioxane complex with a 1:1 stoichiometry was formed. However, only in benzene and carbon tetrachloride could an accuracy of $\pm 1\%$ be attained in the titration. Nitrobenzene as a solvent gave an accuracy of within $\pm 5\%$, while chloroform was a poor solvent because of the very small heat evolution. Apparently the reaction in chloroform is more complicated than in the other solvents in that a slow reaction appeared to be superimposed on a more rapid one. The former reaction was probably due to the crystallization of the product since on standing, a precipitate gradually appeared. Cioffi and Zenchelsky (62) studied the complexes between tin(IV) chloride and the Lewis bases tetrahydrofuran, tetrahydropyran, 2-methyltetrahydrofuran, 2,5-dimethyltetrahydrofuran, and 4-methyltetrahydropyran in benzene. The reaction studied was

$$\text{SnCl}_{4(C=0)} + 2\text{Base}_{(C=0)} \rightarrow \text{SnCl}_4\cdot 2\text{Base}_{(C=0)}$$

Taking α, the degree of dissociation of the complex, and M as the analytical molar concentration of tin(IV) chloride, at the equivalence point

$$K = \frac{1 - \alpha}{4\alpha^3 M^2} \tag{VIII.14}$$

From K and the ΔH^0 of the reaction, the various thermodynamic quantities, ΔF^0 and ΔS^0 could be calculated. The quantity, α, was calculated from the thermometric titration curve by an extrapolation procedure. From the values of K so obtained, the strengths of the bases were in the order: tetrahydrofuran $>$ tetrahydropyran $>$ 4-methyltetrahydropyran $>$ 2-methyltetrahydrofuran $>$ 2,5-dimethyltetrahydrofuran.

The titration of a number of amines with hydrobromic acid in acetonitrile was studied by Forman and Hume (63). The heats

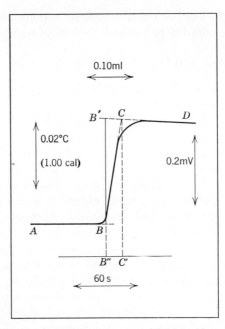

Fig. VIII.12. Thermometric titration curve of 0.86×10^{-3}m KCl with 1.40 m AgNO₃ in fused LiNO₃–KNO₃ at 158°C (28). *A-B*, Temperature–time blank; *B*, start of titration; *B-B*, corrected temperature change corresponding to reaction enthalpy; *B″-C′*, stoichiometric measure of titrant required; *C*, end point; *C-D*, excess reagent line.

of neutralization were calculated by the initial slope, dT/dV, method (31).

Little work has been done on the use of this titration technique in fused salts at elevated temperatures. Judging from the results found in aqueous and non-aqueous systems at room temperature, thermometric titrations in fused salts should provide a rapid and accurate means for a number of analytical determinations involving precipitation, oxidation–reduction, and complexation reactions.

A beginning in this solvent media was made by Jordan et al. (28), who studied the titration of potassium chloride with silver nitrate at 158°C in a lithium nitrate–potassium nitrate melt. A typical titration curve is illustrated in Figure VIII.12. The distance $B''\text{-}C'$ was taken as the measure of the volume of titrant corresponding to the end point, while the temperature change, ΔT, was taken as distance B-B'. Extrapolation to B' along the excess reagent line, C-D, was used to correct adequately for such extraneous effects as temperature differences between titrant and titrate and heats of dilution.

The results of five titrations for the reaction:

$$Ag^+ + Cl^- \rightarrow AgCl(s)$$

with potassium chloride concentrations ranging from 8×10^{-4} to 2×10^{-2}m and silver nitrate concentrations of 1m gave a mole $Ag^+/$mole Cl^- ratio of 0.99 ± 0.02. The heat of precipitation was -18.9 ± 0.3 kcal/mole. The latter value is compared to -18.30 kcal/mole obtained previously by an electrochemical method (64).

Much more work is to be expected in this interesting solvent media.

References

1. Hume, D. N., and J. Jordan, *Anal. Chem.*, **30**, 2064 (1958).
2. Dean, P. M., and O. O. Watts, *J. Am. Chem. Soc.*, **46**, 855 (1924).
3. Dean, P. M., and E. Newcombe, *J. Am. Chem. Soc.*, **47**, 64 (1925).
4. Jordan, J., and T. G. Alleman, *Anal. Chem.*, **29**, 9 (1957).
5. Ewing, G. W., *Instrumental Methods of Analysis*, McGraw-Hill, New York, 1954, pp. 311-13.
6. Chatterji, K. K., and A. K. Ghosh, *J. Indian Chem. Soc.*, **34**, 407 (1957).
7. Hallett, L. T., R. P. Graham, N. H. Furman, H. C. Diehl, S. E. Q. Ashley, and H. V. Churchill, *Anal. Chem.*, **24**, 1348 (1952).
8. Bell, J. M., and C. F. Cowell, *J. Am. Chem. Soc.*, **35**, 49 (1913).
9. Duboit, P., and E. Grobet, *J. Chim. Phys.*, **19**, 324 (1922).
10. Mayr, C., and J. Fisch, *Z. Anal. Chem.*, **76**, 718 (1929).
11. Haldar, B. C., *J. Indian Chem. Soc.*, **23**, 147 (1946).
12. Bhattacharya, A. B., and H. C. Gaur, *J. Indian Chem. Soc.*, **24**, 487 (1947).
13. Bhattacharya, A. B., and H. C. Gaur, *J. Indian Chem. Soc.*, **25**, 185 (1948).
14. Bhattacharya, A. B., and R. S. Saxena, *J. Indian Chem. Soc.*, **29**, 263 (1952).
15. Bhattacharya, A. B., and R. S. Saxena, *J. Indian Chem. Soc.*, **29**, 529 (1952).
16. Zenchelsky, S. T., *Anal. Chem.*, **32**, 289R (1960).
17. Jordan, J., *J. Chem. Ed.*, **40**, A5 (1963).
18. Jordan, J., *Handbook of Analytical Chemistry*, L. Meites, ed., McGraw-Hill, New York, 1963, Sec. 8-3.
19. Chatterji, K. K., *J. Indian Chem. Soc.*, **35**, 709 (1958).
20. Nayar, M. R., and C. S. Pande, *J. Indian Chem. Soc.*, **28**, 112 (1951).
21. Linde, H. W., L. B. Rogers, and D. N. Hume, *Anal. Chem.*, **25**, 404 (1953).
22. Schlyter, K., and L. G. Sillen, *Acta Chem. Scand.*, **13**, 385 (1959).
23. Schlyter, K., *Trans. Roy. Inst. Technol. Stockholm*, **132**, 1 (1959).
24. Lingane, J. J., *Anal. Chem.*, **20**, 285 (1948).

25. Jordan, J., and T. G. Alleman, *Anal. Chem.*, **29**, 9 (1957).
26. Muller, R. H., and H. J. Stolten, *Anal. Chem.*, **25**, 1103 (1953).
27. Tyson, B. C., W. H. McCurdy, and C. E. Bricker, *Anal. Chem.*, **32**, 1640 (1961).
28. Jordan, J., J. Meier, E. J. Billingham, and J. Pendergast, *Anal. Chem.*, **31**, 1439 (1959).
29. Jordan, J., J Meier, E. J. Billingham, and J. Pendergast, *Anal. Chem.*, **32**, 651 (1960).
30. Zenchelsky, S. T., and P. R. Segatto, *Anal. Chem.*, **29**, 1856 (1957).
31. Keily, H. J., and D. N. Hume, *Anal. Chem.*, **28**, 1294 (1956).
32. Jordan, J., and W. H. Dumbaugh, *Anal. Chem.*, **31**, 210 (1959).
33. Miller, F. J., and P. F. Thomason, *Talanta*, **2**, 109 (1959).
34. Chatterjee, K. K., and A. K. Ghosh, *J. Indian Chem. Soc.*, **34**, 407 (1957).
35. Mondain-Monval, P., and R. Paris, *Bull. Chim. Soc. France*, **5**, 1641 (1938).
36. Mondain-Monval, P., and R. Paris, *Compt. Rend.*, **207**, 338 (1938).
37. Paris, R., and J. Robert, *Compt. Rend.*, **223**, 1135 (1946).
38. Paris, R., and P. Tardy, *Compt. Rend.*, **223**, 1001 (1946).
39. Mondain-Monval, P., and R. Paris, *Compt. Rend.*, **198**, 1154 (1934).
40. Jordan, J., and E. J. Billingham, *U. S. At. Energy Comm.*, **1960**, NYO-2215.
41. Purkayastha, B. C., *J. Indian Chem. Soc.*, **24**, 257 (1947).
42. Haldar, B. C., *J. Indian Chem. Soc.*, **24**, 503 (1947).
43. Banerjee, S., *J. Indian Chem. Soc.*, **27**, 417 (1950).
44. Haldar, B. C., *J. Indian Chem. Soc.*, **27**, 484 (1950).
45. Purkayastha, B. C., and R. N. Sen-Sarma, *J. Indian Chem. Soc.*, **23**, 31 (1946).
46. Chatterjee, K. K., *J. Indian Chem. Soc.*, **35**, 883 (1958).
47. Chatterjee, K. K., *J. Indian Chem. Soc.*, **35**, 57 (1958).
48. Gaur, J. N., and M. S. Bhadraver, *J. Indian Chem. Soc.*, **36**, 108 (1959).
49. Poulsen, I., and J. Bjerrum, *Acta Chem. Scand.*, **9**, 1407 (1955).
50. Nayar, M. R., and C. S. Pande, *J. Indian Chem. Soc.*, **28**, 112 (1951).
51. Jordan, J., and M. P. Ben-Yair, *Arkiv Kemi*, **11**, 239 (1956).
52. Richmond, H. D., and J. A. Eggleston, *Analyst*, **51**, 281 (1926).
53. Somiya, T., *J. Soc. Chem. Ind.* (*Japan*), **32**, 490 (1929).
54. Somiya, T., *Proc. Imp. Acad.* (*Tokyo*), **3**, 79 (1927).
55. Somiya, T., *Proc. Imp. Acad.* (*Tokyo*), **5**, 34 (1929).
56. Greathouse, L. H., H. J. Janssen, and C. H. Haydel, *Anal. Chem.*, **28**, 357 (1956).
57. Somiya, T., *J. Soc. Chem. Ind.* (*Japan*), **31**, 306 (1928).
58. Somiya, T., *J. Soc. Chem. Ind.* (*Japan*), **32**, 490 (1929).
59. Trambouze, Y., *Compt. Rend.*, **233**, 648 (1951).
60. Jolly, W. L., *J. Am. Chem. Soc.*, **74**, 6199 (1952).
61. Zenchelsky, S. T., J. Periale, and J. C. Cobb, *Anal. Chem.*, **28**, 67 (1956).
62. Coiffi, F. J., and S. T. Zenchelsky, *J. Phys. Chem.*, **67**, 357 (1963).
63. Forman, E. J., and D. N. Hume, *J. Phys. Chem.*, **63**, 1949 (1959).
64. Flengas, S. N., and E. Rideal, *Proc. Roy. Soc.* (*London*), **A233**, 443 (1956).
65. Jordan, J., *Record Chem. Progr.* (*Kresge-Hooker Sci. Lib.*), **19**, 4 (1958).
66. Jordan, J., *Chimia* (*Aarau*), **17**, 101 (1963).

CHAPTER IX
PYROLYTIC TECHNIQUES

A. Introduction

Although the term "pyrolysis" can be applied to most of the other thermal techniques discussed in this book, in this chapter it will be used to describe techniques in which the sample is thermally decomposed and the decomposition products analyzed by some physical or chemical means. The pyrolyzates can be analyzed by mass spectrometry, vapor phase gas chromatography, or infrared spectroscopy. The pyrolysis chamber is usually connected directly to the analytical instrument, although in many cases the pyrolyzates are condensed to liquids at a low temperature, or collected as a gas in a glass bulb, and then analyzed. For more rapid analyses, the first method is preferred.

The pyrolytic techniques discussed here fall into several classifications. The first involves the detection of the pyrolysis products, usually gases, by a thermal conductivity detector. In this manner, the progress of the pyrolysis reaction can be followed as a function of temperature. The temperatures at which the peaks begin, the peak maxima temperatures, and the number of peaks present, are used for identification of the sample. Each peak may be due to the evolution of a single gas or a mixture of gases, the exact composition of which is relatively unimportant in most cases. The second classification concerns the pyrolysis of a sample under isothermal conditions and analysis of the pyrolyzate by some technique. In this case, the composition of the pyrolyzate is of prime importance. If the pyrolyzates from a series of decomposition reactions at different temperatures are taken, the relative abundance of dissociation species can then be plotted as a function of temperature. In this manner then, this technique becomes similar to the method involved in the first classification.

B. Gas Evolution Analysis (GEA)

The wide variation in weight-loss curves obtained by thermogravimetry, due mainly to variables in the furnace, sample holder

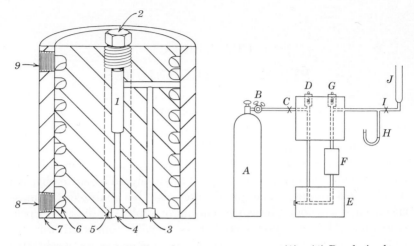

Fig. IX.1. Pyrolysis block and accessory apparatus (1). (1) Pyrolysis chamber; (2) nickel plug; (3) carrier gas inlet; (4) carrier gas outlet; (5) cartridge heater wells (2); (6) helical threads cut in inner body of block; (7) outer shell of block; (8) cooling jacket inlet; (9) cooling jacket outlet. (A) Carrier gas supply; (B) pressure regulator; (C) flow-control needle valve; (D) reference thermal conductivity; (E) pyrolysis chamber; (F) combustion tube; (G) active cell; (H) manometer· (I) pressure-control needle valve; (J) rotameter.

design, furnace atmosphere, heating rate, etc., prompted Rogers et al. (1) to construct a gas evolution apparatus. With this apparatus, a small amount of sample is pyrolyzed in a dynamic helium gas or air stream at a constant heating rate. The evolved pyrolysis gases are detected, as a function of temperature or time, by a thermal conductivity detector. A schematic illustration of the pyrolysis block and accessory apparatus is given in Figure IX.1. The thermal conductivity detector employed model airplane glow plugs as detectors and a bridge circuit designed by Felton and Buehler (2).

For a purely volatile compound, the gas evolution analysis (GEA) curves showed a gradual rise with increasing temperature, and then dropped off suddenly at a temperature designated by T_x (1). If it is assumed that the helium stream above the sample becomes saturated with vapor, the rate of disappearance of the sample is

$$-dN/dt = pv/RT \tag{IX.1}$$

where p is the vapor pressure and v the flow rate in ml/s. If N_0

moles of sample are present originally, and if the vapor pressure is related to the Clausius–Clapeyron equation.

$$N_0 = \frac{p_0 v \exp{(\Delta H/RT_0)}}{R_r} \int_0^{T_x} \frac{\exp{(-\Delta H/RT)}}{T} \, dt \quad (IX.2)$$

This integral can be evaluated approximately, and leads to the expression

$$p(T_x) \cong 3 \times 10^4 \left(N_0 \frac{r}{v}\right) \frac{\Delta H}{T_x} \quad (IX.3)$$

where $p(T_x)$ is the vapor pressure at T_x, expressed in millimeters. A similar expression was derived for the case of a nonvolatile compound, assuming that a first-order rate law is obeyed. This assumption is generally valid for a large number of commercial explosives. The expression obtained is

$$\frac{E}{R}\left(\frac{1}{T^{1/4}} - \frac{1}{T_m}\right) = 1 + \ln 4 \frac{ZR}{rE} T_{1/4}{}^2 \exp{(-E/RT_{1/4})} \quad (IX.4)$$

where $r = -dN/dt$, T_m is the temperature for which p is a maximum, E is the activation energy in kcal/mole, and $T_{1/4}$ is the temperature at which $p = 1/4 P_{max}$. Excellent agreement was found between the theoretical and experiment GEA curves for PETN (pentaerythritol tetranitrate) as is illustrated in Figure IX.2.

The qualitative effects of operating variables such as flow rate, heating rate, sample weight, thermal conductivity cell sensitivity, pressure, and type of carrier gas on the GEA curves of volatile and nonvolatile compounds were determined. These variables with the exception of the variation in thermal conductivity cell sensitivity affected the peak maximum temperatures and peak heights. In this case, only the peak heights were affected. The variation in GEA curves with sample weight is illustrated in Figure IX.3. The peak maximum temperatures varied from 160°C for a 1.4 mg sample to 178°C for a 20.5 mg sample. The effect was even more pronounced with the GEA curve of TNT (trinitrotoluene). A 1.5 mg sample had a peak maximum temperature of 153°C, while a 20.9 mg sample shifted the peak maximum to 197°C. Thus, judicious control of the sample size appears to be necessary for reproducibility of peak temperatures.

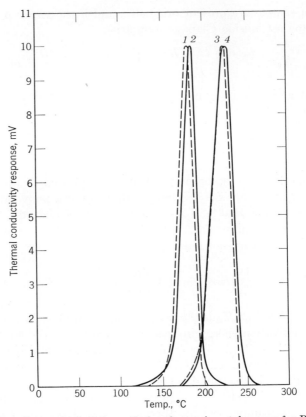

Fig. IX.2. Comparison of theoretical and experimental curves for PETN (1). (1) Theoretical curve for PETN; (2) experimental curve for PETN, uncorrected for gas flow time lag; (3) theoretical curve for RDX; (4) experimental curve for RDX, uucorrected for gas flow time lag.

In the case of a mixture of compounds with similar boiling points, resolution of the peaks was not affected. Melting points were, of course, not detected by this technique unless decomposition occurred at the same time. Quantitative as well as qualitative results can be obtained by this technique if, under identical conditions of pyrolysis, the areas under the GEA peaks are compared with standard substances.

A similar GEA apparatus was described by Vassallo (3) for the pyrolysis of various polymeric materials. The detection system

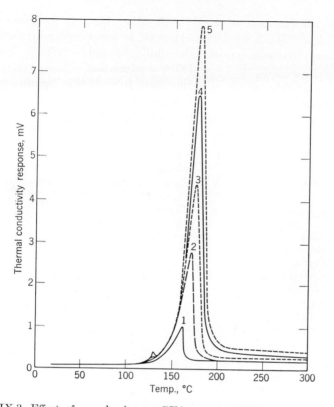

Fig. IX.3. Effect of sample size on GEA curve of PETN (1). (1) 1.4 mg PETN; maximum at 160°C; (2) 5.0 mg PETN; maximum at 167°C; (3) 9.7 mg PETN; maximum at 177°C; (4) 15.0 mg PETN; maximum at 178°C; (5) 20.5 mg PETN; maximum at 178°C.

consisted of a thermistor thermal conductivity cell employing 100 000 Ω thermistors and operated at a bridge current of 10 mA. Located between the pyrolysis chamber and the detector cell was an 800°C CuO combustion chamber, similar to that previously described (1). An X–Y recorder was used to record the GEA curves instead of a strip-chart recorder. Contrary to previous comments (1), it was stated (4) that GEA cannot replace TGA; however, for comparing polymers of similar structure, GEA has more discrimination and is more rapid. A weight loss of 2 mg can be detected at much faster heating rates then those used in TGA.

The combination of GEA with other thermal techniques such as DTA and TGA would be expected to yield especially significant results as the advantages of each technique could be utilized. Such has been the case with the GEA–DTA combination. Measurements are made on a single sample at an identical furnace heating rate, furnace atmosphere, sample particle size, and other variable conditions. A summary of GEA and DTA reactions for a specific chemical or physical change is given in Table IX.1 (4).

TABLE IX.1

GEA and DTA Effects During a Chemical or Physical Change (4)

Chemical or physical change	DTA endotherm	GEA	
		Yes	No
Decomposition	x^a	x	x
Fusion	x		x
Crystal transition	x^a		x
Desorption	x	x	x
Vaporization			
Desolvation	x	x	
Ebullition	x	x^b	
Sublimation	x	x^b	

[a] May also be an exothermic reaction.

[b] Possible condensation before reaching gas detector.

The first apparatus for simultaneous DTA–GEA was the Pyrex glass system of Ayres and Bens (4), although it was probably envisioned by Stone (5) with his dynamic gas flow DTA system (see Chap. VI). The system was used to study the thermal dissociation of various explosives and propellants. An interesting compound that was pyrolyzed was nitroglycerine, the GEA–DTA curves of which appear in Figure IX.4. The endothermic peaks in the 141–206°C temperature range are the result of vaporization of the nitroglycerin, boiling point 143°C, with some decomposition, as indicated by the GEA curve. A slight inflection corresponding to the maximum rate of vaporization (endothermic peak at 191°C) showed a change in rate of the decomposition gas reaching the detector, with a maximum rate of evolution being reached at 202°C. As the temperature was increased, more of the nitroglycerin previously distilled into the cool exit tube was decomposed, giving rise

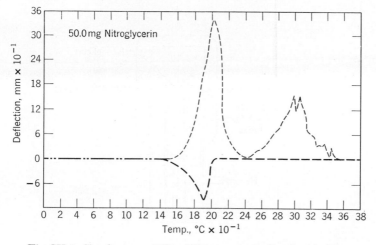

Fig. IX.4. Simultaneous DTA–GEA curves of nitroglycerin (4).

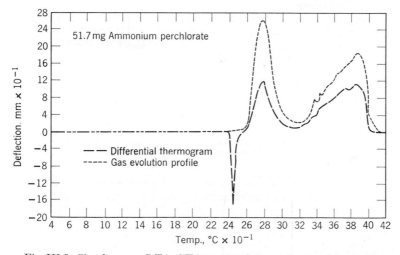

Fig. IX.5. Simultaneous DTA–GEA curves of ammonium perchlorate (4).

to the further peaks in the GEA curve. The curves showed no deviation in this region since all of the nitroglycerin had distilled away from the differential temperature probes.

Another application of this technique illustrating a phase transition and also a decomposition reaction is the thermal dissociation of am-

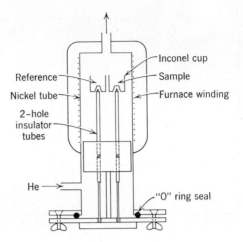

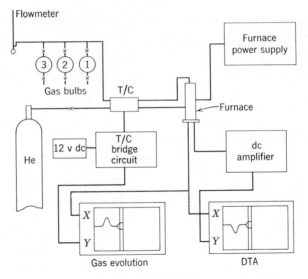

Fig. IX.6. Combined DTA–GEA apparatus (7).

monium perchlorate, as illustrated in Figure IX.5. Ammonium perchlorate, a typical propellant oxidizer (4), had an endothermic phase transition at a peak maximum temperature of 204°C. This was due to the *orthorhombic* → *cubic* crystalline transition and gave

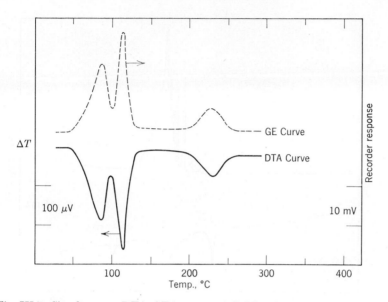

Fig. IX.7. Simultaneous DTA–GEA curves of $CuSO_4 \cdot 5H_2O$ (35.7 mg of sample)
(7).

little gas evolution as seen on the GEA curve. The subsequent
exothermic peak and resultant GEA peak at 258°C were attributed
to the initial decomposition of NH_4ClO_4, with final decomposition
beginning at 320°C. The results of this study were not in agreement
with other DTA data (5,6) due probably to differences in heating
rate and diluents employed.

Ayres and Bens (4) pointed out that difficulties were observed
in their system by increased vaporization of the sample due to the
gas flow and the occasional condensation of this vapor in the cool
part of the exit tube. The vaporization of the sample below the
boiling point made boiling-point determinations difficult, while the
condensation of sample before passage through the gas detector
presented difficulties, as later the gas stream may become hot enough
to decompose the condensate.

Wendlandt (7) has described a similar DTA–GEA apparatus,
which was of a more robust construction than that previously described (4), and did not necessitate the use of a glass beads diluent.
The apparatus is illustrated schematically in Figure IX.6.

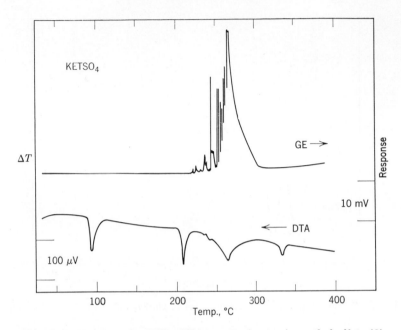

Fig. IX.8. Simultaneous DTA–GEA curves of potassium ethylsulfate (8).

The sample and reference materials were placed in small Inconel cups of 0.27 ml capacity which seated directly onto the differential thermocouple junctions. Helium was used as the carrier gas; the evolved decomposition gases were detected with a thermistor thermal conductivity cell of conventional design. The thermistor bridge output and the ΔT amplified voltages were recorded on the Y-axes of two different X–Y recorders; the furnace temperature was recorded simultaneously on the two X-axes.

The DTA–GEA curves for the dehydration of $CuSO_4 \cdot 5H_2O$ are illustrated in Figure IX.7. The origin of the various peaks was due to the following reactions:

85°C peak: $CuSO_4 \cdot 5H_2O(s) \rightarrow CuSO_4 \cdot 3H_2O(s) + 2H_2O(l)$

$2H_2O(l) \rightarrow 2H_2O(g)$ (from saturated solution)

115°C peak: $CuSO_4 \cdot 3H_2O(s) \rightarrow CuSO_4 \cdot H_2O(s) + 2H_2O(g)$

230°C peak: $CuSO_4 \cdot H_2O(s) \rightarrow CuSO_4(s) + H_2O(g)$

From the GEA curve it can be seen that each of the DTA peaks was matched by a corresponding GEA peak showing that a volatile decomposition product, water vapor, was evolved.

Similarly, for the thermal dissociation of potassium ethylsulfate, as shown in Figure IX.8, a crystalline phase transition indicated by the DTA curve did not give a peak in the GEA curve (8). The transition from $\alpha \rightarrow \beta$ $KC_2H_5SO_4$ resulted in a DTA peak at 93°C. Further heating of the compound gave the fusion peaks, at 207°C, which again did not result in a GEA curve peak. The fusion peak was followed by the decomposition endothermic peak which did give a corresponding GEA curve. The decomposition reaction was:

$$\beta\text{-}KC_2H_5SO_4(s) \rightarrow K_2S_2O_7(s) + C_2H_4(g) + H_2O(v)$$

A similar DTA–GEA set of curves was obtained for potassium methylsulfate.

A combined DTA–gas sampling technique has been described by Murphy et al. (9). The evolved gases were collected in a glass sampling bulb, from a system initially under a vacuum. Composition of the evolved gases was then determined by use of a mass spectrometer. This type of system would be useful if only one peak were involved in the DTA curve.

The potentialities of the combined DTA–GEA apparatus are readily apparent. The presence of a crystalline or other phase transition is easily detected, thus aiding in the interpretation of the DTA curve. By analysis of the evolved gases by some physical means, the stoichiometry of the reaction responsible for the peaks can be determined. It is also possible to study the thermal behavior of the sample under isothermal conditions as well as under various gaseous atmospheres and pressures.

As previously stated (4), the small amount of modification necessary to install a GEA to a regular DTA apparatus and the inexpensive equipment needed are far outweighed by the amount of additional information obtained from one sample. Several commercial firms, the R. L. Stone Co., the Technical Equipment Corporation (Deltatherm), and the Perkin-Elmer Corporation now include this feature on certain types of their instruments.

C. Analysis of Pyrolyzates by Gas Chromatography

In the case of large organic molecules or polymeric materials, it is more convenient to dissociate them into smaller fragments by pyrolysis and then analyze the pyrolyzate by use of a suitable column in a gas chromatograph. In many cases, the pyrolyzate peaks need not be identified since the resulting chromatogram is used only for qualitative purposes (13). Conversely, by a careful analysis of the decomposition fragments, the mechanism or mode of degradation of the complex substance can often be deduced (14–16).

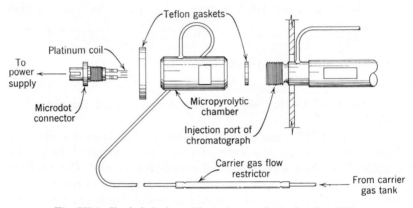

Fig. IX.9. Exploded view of hot-wire pyrolysis chamber (25).

Essentially, the technique consists of a pyrolysis chamber connected directly to the inlet port of the gas chromatograph. The sample is injected into the pyrolysis chamber, which is either at a fixed elevated temperature or can be heated to an elevated temperature in a matter of seconds, and the pyrolyzate introduced into the column of the instrument. One sample at a time is pyrolyzed and the pyrolytic fragments separated by the column into their component parts. A number of pyrolysis chambers have been described in the literature. The designs include a heated tube or microreactor (10–12,17–21); a heated platinum or other wire filament (3,11,13,16,22–25); and a small metal or Vycor crucible heated by a wire coil (24,26).

A typical hot-wire type pyrolysis chamber is illustrated in Figure IX.9. It consists of a small stainless steel fitting threaded at one end for attachment to the injector port of the gas chromatograph, and a $1/4$-in. diameter electrical connector containing a platinum wire coil at the other end. The coil was constructed of No. 26 B & S wire, 2.8 cm long, coiled on a $1/16$-in. mandrel to give four turns and fitted to the connector with brass connector pins. The pyrolysis chamber was continuously swept by carrier gas and was maintained at 100 ± 5°C by conduction of heat from the injector block. The temperature of the coil was determined by using a color temperature vs. electrical current graph, such as is illustrated in Table IX.2.

TABLE IX.2
Color Temperature vs. Coil Temperature (25)

Color	Temp., °C	Coil current, A		
		New	20 Runs	40 runs
Incipient red	550	4.4	6.5	8.7
Dark red	770	4.8	7.2	9.6
Bright red	900	5.4	8.1	10.8
Yellowish-red	1100	6.0	8.8	11.8

Samples were placed on the coil in the form of a solution in phosphoric acid or an organic solvent. The acid aided in the fission of certain compounds by providing hydrogen and oxygen. After placing the solution on the coil, the water or solvent was evaporated by bringing the coil temperature to 100°C for a short time, or samples could be placed on the coil as small fragments of solids.

More accurate temperature control of the pyrolysis reaction was obtained by the Vycor sample boat-wire coil heater method (24). The boat temperature was detected by a Chromel–Alumel thermocouple placed in a small indentation in the bottom of the boat. This thermocouple was calibrated against a second thermocouple placed with the sample inside the boat. During the pyrolysis runs this second thermocouple was removed to prevent any catalytic effects on the polymer degradation due to the metals in the thermocouple. Temperature measurements were considered to be accurate to within ±10°C.

Because quantitative measurements are not possible, or at least difficult with hot-wire pyrolysis chambers, the hot-tube or microreactor chamber is at times more useful (21). Providing that a

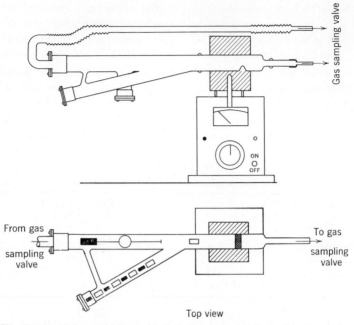

Fig. IX.10. Schematic diagram of a tube-type pyrolysis chamber (21).

metal tube is not employed, there are no catalytic effects to complicate the pyrolysis as there may be with hot-wire units. Also, it is not possible to measure the temperature of the glowing wire with any exactness since this is evaluated by observing its color. A serious objection to the sample boat-wire coil method is the fairly long heat-up time required, usually 20–40 s. This means that the sample itself goes through the whole temperature range before reaching the desired temperature, and therefore the composition of the breakdown products reflects the pyrolysis not at a certain temperature but up to a certain temperature. The products of the lower temperature pyrolysis may also react further; thus a combination of primary and secondary pyrolysis products may appear on the chromatogram.

To circumvent these difficulties, a pyrolysis apparatus which allowed degradation of the sample under careful control of temperature and operating conditions, has been described (21) and is illustrated in Figure IX.10.

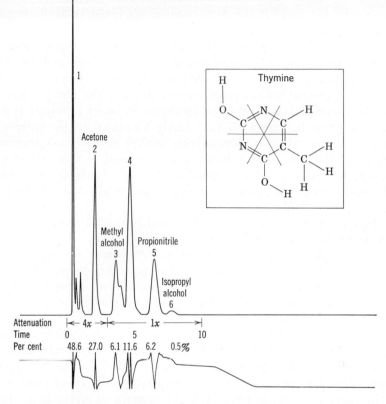

Fig. IX.11. Pyrolysis of thymine. Sample sizes: 20–124 μg; temperature of 1100–1300°C for 5 s (25).

The apparatus was composed of two parts: the pyrolysis chamber and the furnace with the electrical control unit. The chamber was connected directly to the gas sampling valve on the gas chromatograph. Provision was made for the introduction of multiple samples into the pyrolysis hot zone without dismantling the apparatus. The samples were placed in small porcelain boats and introduced rapidly into the hot zone by means of a plunger. The spent sample boat was then removed and pushed into the vertical storage zone. A new sample was then pushed into the pyrolysis zone and the process repeated. In this way, from six to eight measurements were performed under identical conditions without disconnecting the pyrolysis chamber. Pyrolysis measurements could be made in the 300–950°C temperature range.

The gas chromatograph–pyrolysis technique has been applied to a large number of organic compounds. Jennings and Dimick (25) studied the pyrolysis of thymine, cytosine, isocytosine, 2,6-dichloro-7-methyl purine, guanine, and others. The chromatogram of the thymine (2,4-dihydroxy-5-methylpyrimidine) pyrolysis products is given in Figure IX.11. Easily identified in the products were isopropyl alcohol, propionitrile, methyl alcohol, and acetone. Many of the pyrolysis products, such as carbon dioxide and water vapor, were not detected because of the use of a hydrogen flame detector. In general, the compound gave 169 to 170 counts per mg of sample.

In a comprehensive study, Nelson and Kirk (26) used this technique to identify 27 substituted barbituric acids. The pyrolysis sample holder consisted of a shallow platinum cup, 1.5 × 3 mm in size, welded at its ends to two 18-gage platinum wires. The pyrolyzates produced a series of peaks which were reproducible in retention time and relative size so long as conditions were kept constant.

By far the most widely studied compounds by this technique have been polymeric materials. Polymers studied include polystyrene and poly(methylmethacrylate) (19,24); methyl methacrylate copolymers and polymer mixtures containing methyl acrylate and ethyl acrylate, acrylic acid, ethyl methacrylate, and others (16); nitrocellulose, poly(n-butylmethacrylate), and polyvinyl alcohol (21,27); polybutene (20); poly(ethylene-ethylacrylate) and poly-(ethylene vinyl acetate)(28); poly(methyl acrylate)(15); poly(vinyl acetate) (11,19); and poly(n-butyl acrylate) and propylene oxide–ethylene oxide polymer (19).

Chromatograms obtained by pyrolysis of polystyrene at 425, 825, and 1025°C (24) are shown in Figure IX.12. At 425°C, only the styrene monomer was eluted from the column; at 825°C, additional products were obtained such as toluene, ethylbenzene, benzene, and ethylene + acetylene; and at a still higher temperature,

1025°C, the intensities of these peaks increased indicating that reactions leading to their formation became more prominent. There was no further change in the composition of the pyrolyzate on in-

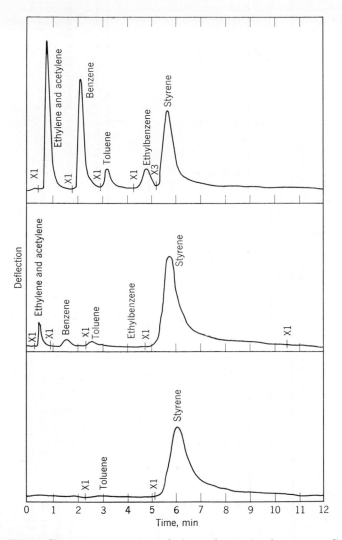

Fig. IX.12. Chromatograms of pyrolysis products of polystyrene. Column, Apiezon L; column temperature, 140°C; middle curve, 825°C; bottom curve, 425°C. Attenuations indicated (24).

TABLE IX.3

Composition of Pyrolyzates of Polystyrene in Weight Per Cent [a]

Product	Pyrolysis temperature, °C							
	425	525	625	725	825	1025	1025	1125
Carbon dioxide	—	—	—	—	—	Trace	Trace[b]	—
Ethylene	—	—	—	Trace[b]	4.1[b]	6.9[b]	6.9[b]	6.8[b]
Acetylene	—	—	—	Trace[b]	4.1[b]	6.9[b]	6.7[b]	6.8[b]
Benzene	—	—	—	Trace	8.1	13.4	12.0[b]	13.0
Toluene	Trace[d]	Trace[d]	Trace[d]	0.9[d]	2.5[d]	5.6[d]	2.7[c]	5.8
Ethylbenzene							3.7[c]	
Styrene	64.3	67.5	74.4	83.9	73.7	62.8	63.8	64.3
Material retained in column	35.7	32.5	25.6	14.4	7.5	4.3	4.3	3.3

[a] Average of two or more analyses. Column: 30% (wt.) Chlorowax 70 on ground firebrick, 30–60 mesh (except where indicated otherwise); col. temp., 140°C.

[b] Column: silica gel 30–200 mesh; col. temp, 100° C. Values obtained by resolving total percentage of gaseous products with Chlorowax 70 and Apiezon L column, respectively.

[c] Column: 30% (wt.) Apiezon L on ground firebrick, 30–60 mesh; col. temp., 140° C.

[d] Weight per cent of toluene and ethylbenzene.

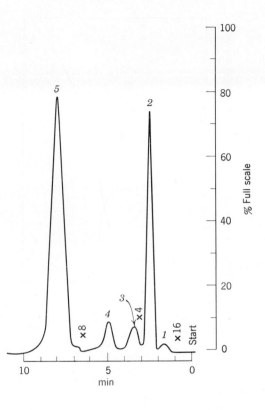

Fig. IX.13. Chromatogram obtained brom the pyrolysis of poly(vinyl alcohol) at 500°C. (1) Light gases; (2) acetaldehyde; (3) methyl acetate; (4) ethanol; (5) water (21).

creasing the temperature to 1125°C. The composition of the pyrolyzates of polystyrene (24) is given in Table IX.3. The table shows that the amount of styrene increased from 64.3% at 425°C to 83.9% at 725°C and then dropped off to 63.8% at 1025°C. Although a detailed explanation of the complex degradation reactions cannot be given without kinetics studies, the C_6H_5—C bond is probably most susceptible to cleavage. The resulting radicals may then undergo a variety of reactions such as disproportionation, further cleavage of bonds, or recombination of other fragments.

The chromatogram (21) of the pyrolyzate of poly(vinyl alcohol) is given in Figure IX.13. At lower temperatures, poly(vinyl alco-

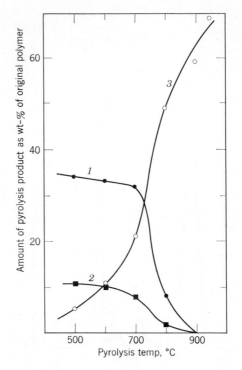

Fig. IX.14. Amount of characteristic breakdown products of poly(vinyl alcohol) as a function of pyrolysis temperature. (*1*) acetaldehyde; (*2*) acetic acid; (*3*) carbon monoxide + carbon dioxide (21).

hol) pyrolyzed mainly to water, acetaldehyde, and acetic acid. The inorganic and light organic gases represented only a small percentage of the total products. However, between 700 and 800°C, there was a sudden change in concentration of nearly all of the major components. The amount of gases abruptly increased while the amount of acetaldehyde and acetic acid sharply decreased. Such changes in concentration of the pyrolysis products are given in Table IX.4. A plot of changes in concentration of acetaldehyde, acetic acid, and carbon monoxide + carbon dioxide is given in Figure IX.14. The water, ethanol, and methyl acetate concentrations did not change significantly between 700 and 800°C. The amounts of water and ethanol gradually decreased with increasing temperature, while the methyl acetate concentration increased slightly up to 800°C, then disappeared suddenly. Water and ethanol disappeared above 900°C. Above this temperature, the pyrolysis products consisted only of gases.

TABLE IX.4

Composition of Breakdown Products of Poly(vinyl Alcohol) (21)

	Temperature, °C					
	500	600	700	800	900	950
	Weight per cent of original polymer					
Carbon dioxide	1.3	2.4	3.5	9.0	11.0	13.5
Carbon monoxide	4.0	8.8	17.6	40.0	48.0	55.0
Methane	2.0	3.0	4.8	14.0	19.0	23.5
Ethane	0.2	0.4	0.6	1.0	1.0	0.8
Ethylene	0.2	0.3	0.6	4.0	6.0	6.5
Acetaldehyde	34.0	33.0	32.0	8.0	—	—
Acetic acid	10.5	10.0	8.0	2.0	—	—
Ethanol	5.0	5.2	5.0	4.8	4.4	—
Methyl acetate	1.5	1.8	2.4	2.6	—	—
Unidentified	11.5	10.0	6.0	—	—	—
Water	24.5	24.0	19.0	14.0	10.0	—
Residue	5.0	—	—	—	—	—

D. Analysis of Pyrolyzates by Mass Spectrometry

Although requiring much more elaborate instrumentation techniques, the mass spectrometer has been employed to analyze the pyrolysis products of various large molecular weight organic compounds. In the case of mass spectroscopy, the only requirement is that the pyrolyzate be capable of being ionized in the gas phase. With many nonvolatile materials, it merely becomes a matter of heating them to increase their vapor pressure. With such compounds as polymers and biological materials, which cannot exist intact in the gas phase at high temperatures, they dissociate into smaller fragments. Such substances can be analyzed on the mass spectrometer if they decompose in a characteristic fashion to give volatile decomposition products. The identity and relative amounts of the pyrolyzate compounds from a given material should always be the same, just as the identity and relative peak heights of the ions together are the fragmentation pattern of a compound in a mass spectrometer.

An excellent discussion of the application of the mass spectrometer to the analysis of the pyrolysis products of complex organic materials was given by Zemany (29). The principle is that complex compounds will decompose in a reproducible fashion when they are heated. Provided that all operating conditions are as carefully controlled as possible, the same products will be formed in duplicate runs despite uncontrollable variations in the conditions of pyrolysis. The products from the pyrolysis should be sufficiently specific for the original material. If the only volatile products are carbon monoxide and hydrogen, the method would not be very good for distinguishing among various materials. Ideally, each different substance should decompose to a distinctly different set of products.

Using a filament type heater from a standard vacuum electron tube, Zemany (29) pyrolyzed a number of compounds and examined their pyrolyzates with the mass spectrometer. Solid samples in solution were prepared for pyrolysis by first coating the filament with the solution and then evaporating off the solvent. Some solid samples could be placed directly inside the coils of the heater, while others were placed inside a nickel tube which was then inserted inside the filament coil. Slight differences in the products were obtained when the same sample was heated in different ways so that in a comparison of the pyrolysis patterns, the exact method of pyrolysis had to be considered. A suitable sample size for the spectrometer was 0.1 mg of material. Too large a sample gave a greater proportion of decomposition products characteristic of lower temperatures. For reproducible results, it was recommended that the sample size be limited to a few milligrams.

A number of homopolymers, copolymers, alkyls, and other compounds were studied by Zemany (29) and others (30–34). Major products obtained from the pyrolysis of several homopolymers are given in Table IX.5. A convenient punched card filing system for the pyrolysis patterns of various materials has been described (29). More complete discussion of the degradation of polymers by pyrolysis has been given by Wall (35).

In conjunction with DTA studies, Wendlandt et al. (36) studied the pyrolysis of some metal chelates of cupferron (N-nitrosophenyl-hydroxylamine, ammonium salt) (36) and salicylaldehyde, salicyl-aldimine, and salicylaldehydeethylenediimine (37) with the mass spectrometer. The mass spectra of the pyrolysis products of cup-

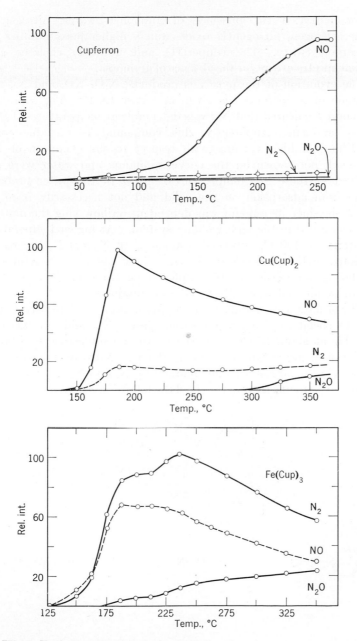

Fig. IX.15. Evolution of pyrolysis products as a function of temperature (36).

ferron indicated the presence of ammonia, water, nitrogen(II) oxide, nitrogen, nitrogen(I) oxide, and a higher mass number hydrocarbon entity. The copper(II) and iron(III) chelates gave similar spectra except for the absence of ammonia.

The evolution of the pyrolysis products, N_2O, NO, and N_2, as a function of temperature, is given in Figure IX.15. For cupferron, the curves indicated that NO was detectable at temperatures slightly above ambient. Apparently this compound is unstable under conditions of high vacuum with respect to the evolution of NO. Although not shown on the curve, ammonia and water were also evolved at these low temperatures. Most of the water probably came from adsorption on the solid and not necessarily from the pyrolysis, since its amount was dependent on how long the material was contained in the high vacuum system. At higher temperatures greater than 100°C, appreciable amounts of N_2 and N_2O were also detected in the pyrolysis products. These gases could result from further decomposition of the cupferron or from hot-tube reactions involving nitrosobenzene, NO, and other products.

The situation was similar for the pyrolysis of the copper(II) cupferrate chelate. The decomposition gases, NO and N_2, were detectable at about 250°C with the maximum intensities for the gas evolution being obtained at about 185°C. Nitrogen(II) oxide was present in the largest amount followed by N_2 and N_2O. A proposed decomposition mechanism involved the following reaction:

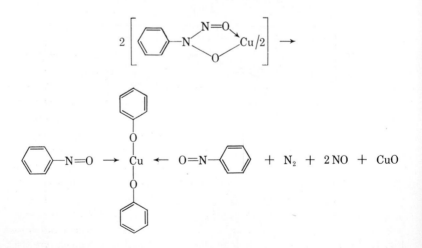

TABLE IX.5

Major Products in Pyrolyzates of Several Homopolymers (29)

Polymer	Monomer	Product
Rubber	Isoprene	Isoprene
Neoprene	Chloroprene	Chloroprene
Kel-F	$CF_2 = CFCl$	$CF_2 = CFCl$
Polystyrene	Styrene	Styrene
Poly(vinyl alcohol)	Vinyl alcohol	Acetaldehyde
Polyethylene	Ethylene	C_nH_{2n}
Teflon	$CF_2 = CF_2$	C_nF_{2n}
Poly(vinyl chloride)	$CH_2 = CHCl$	HCl + benzene

At still higher temperatures, additional NO was evolved as well as a hydrocarbon entity and CuO.

The mass spectra of the pyrolysis products of iron(III) cupferrate contained an interesting feature. The evolution of N_2 and NO began at about 125°C, giving a curve break at about 185°C. Then, at slightly higher temperatures, above 210°C, additional N_2 and NO were evolved. This behavior correlated nicely with an endothermic DTA peak obtained under identical conditions. The greater amount of N_2 than NO in the pyrolysis gases may be due to the greater stability of iron(III) oxide compared to copper(II) oxide. Thus, the C—N and N—O bonds would be broken more easily than the Fe—O bonds.

E. Analysis of Pyrolyzates by Infrared Spectroscopy

According to Harms (38), there is a serious limitation in the characterization of polymers by their infrared spectra. Because of the intractable physical state of many polymers, the procedures such as casting and melting, customarily used for the preparation of samples are difficult, if not impossible. Such substances are the cured, infusible, insoluble, and largely non-extractable synthetic resins and elastomers. These materials are too resilient to be dispersed by mulling in Nujol or other substances, or contain fillers, particularly carbon black, which is opaque to infrared radiation. Harms found that an ideal solution for these problems was by pyrolysis of the polymer and an examination of the pyrolyzates by infrared spectroscopy. By this method a difficult situation is not circumvented entirely, but is nevertheless achieved. Other investigators have studied the effect of elevated temperatures on thin films or sheets of polymers and have followed the degradation by the change in their infrared spectra (39–41).

As in the case of the pyrolyzate analyses by gas chromatography and mass spectrometry, if all of the pyrolysis products from the substance are examined, the infrared spectrum should always be the same from the standpoint of both band position and intensity ratios. It might be expected that the pyrolysis products from a given substance would give a spectrum which is poorly defined and featureless (38); however, remarkably discrete spectra are the rule rather than the exception. In a few cases the spectrum of the pyrolyzate closely resembles the unformulated and uncured or low molecular weight monomer of the polymer. This behavior is probably due to the tendency of the polymers to pyrolyze into simple monomeric or low molecular weight species.

The pyrolyzate spectra from asbestos-filled molded phenolic resin, butylated urea-formaldehyde resin, an epoxy resin, fluorolube oil, nylon 66, Saran, Mylar, Dacron, Terylene, Orlon, Dynel, natural rubber gum, vulcanized natural rubber, GR-S 65 SP rubber gum and vulcanized mixture, butyl rubber gum, Buna N rubber, neoprene, methyl silicone oil, Hycar PA rubber, 9825 Formex enamel, tung oil wire enamel, Hycar phenolic resin, and Nyform were obtained by Harms (38).

The pyrolyzate spectrum of nylon 66 is given in Figure IX.16. The spectrum is similar to that of the original material, also given in Figure IX.16, up to about 7μ. Bands occurring at about 3.07 (N–H stretching), at 6.4–6.6 (N–H bending of N-substituted amides), and at 3.28μ appear in the pyrolyzate spectrum as well. A band due to C≡N triple bond stretching (nitrile) made its appearance at approximately 4.5μ in the pyrolyzate spectrum. Absorptions at about 10.1 and 11.0 μ were of further use in identifying nylon as the parent material.

In a study by Beachell et al. (40), a thin film of polyvinyl formal was heated on a NaCl plate at 150°C for 20 h. The heated product and the original sample spectra are shown in Figure IX.17. The primary changes in the spectrum were a large increase in the intensity of the carbonyl band, a decrease in the carbon–hydrogen bands, and a decrease in the formal bands from 8 to 10 μ. A new band appeared at 6.1–6.2 μ which had been assumed to be the ethylenic bond

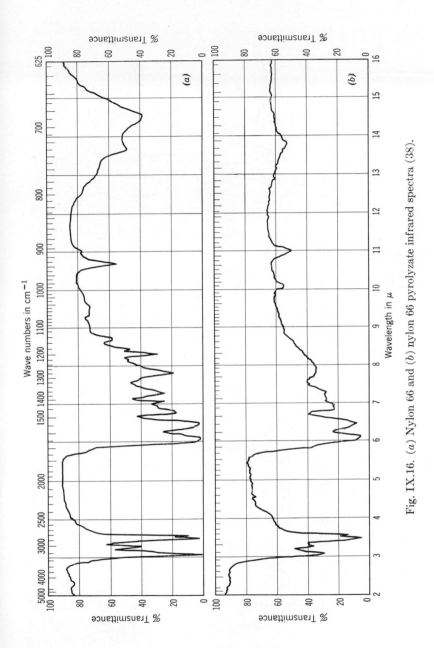

Fig. IX.16. (*a*) Nylon 66 and (*b*) nylon 66 pyrolyzate infrared spectra (38).

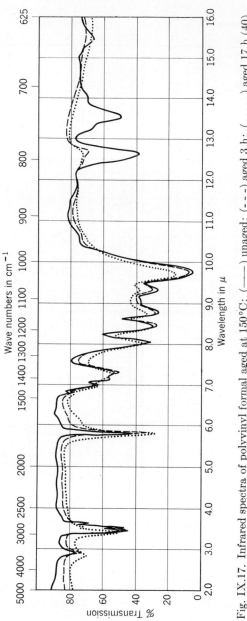

Fig. IX.17. Infrared spectra of polyvinyl formal aged at 150°C; (——) unaged; (- - -) aged 3 h; (. . . . .) aged 17 h (40).

vibration. The hydroxyl band appeared fairly constant, so that it must be concluded that carbonyl groups are not formed primarily by the oxidation of hydroxyl groups in the chain, unless a balance between consumption and production of hydroxyl groups is assumed, which is rather unlikely. Pronounced degradation from 20 to 500 h was apparent from the loss of most of the characteristic bands of the spectrum and the appearance of several new bands.

F. Miscellaneous Methods

1. Linear Pyrolysis Rates of Solids

The linear pyrolysis technique has been used to investigate the kinetics of decomposition of a number of solid compounds, both inorganic and organic. This technique was first suggested by Wilfong et al. (42). They showed that the burning rate of a solid substance was equal to the linear decomposition rate of the solid at a temperature equal to the steady-state temperature of the burning surface. Under these conditions the kinetics of the decomposition could be handled by the Arrhenius equation.

Various methods have been employed for measuring the decomposition rates of solids (43–45). The most rapid and accurate method for these studies is the hot-plate pyrolysis method (46) and its modification as described by Barsh et al. (45). The decomposition rate was determined by following the motion of a reference point on the sample strand either with a cathetometer or a linear potentiometer. The temperature was measured with a thermocouple which was interposed between the sample and the heated surface of the hot-plate.

A schematic diagram of the linear pyrolysis apparatus is shown in Figure IX.18. A sample is clamped in the sample holder and adjusted so that the center of the surface to be pyrolyzed will coincide with the position of the thermocouple on the surface of the heating element. After heating the pyrolysis surface to the desired temperature, the sample is allowed to decompose by contact with the heated surface. The rate of decomposition at that temperature is recorded automatically. The procedure is then repeated at other temperatures.

In general, only certain types of compounds can be studied by this technique. Substances which cannot be studied are: (a) materials which do not decompose at an appreciable rate below 700°C; (b)

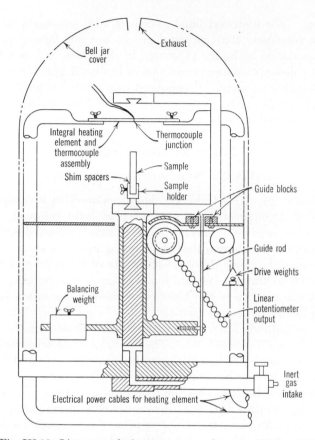

Fig. IX.18. Linear pyrolysis apparatus—schematic diagram (45).

materials which leave solid residues during pyrolysis; and (c) materials which contain macroscopic inhomogeneities. Compounds which have been studied, many in a preliminary manner only, include NH_4X ($X^- = $ Cl, Br, ClO_4, NO_3, F, HF_2, and N_3), hydrazinium azide, ice, carbon dioxide (solid), naphthalene, paraldehyde, polymethylmethacrylate, polystyrene, polyethylene, nylon, and other polymeric materials (45).

This apparatus has proven to be a useful tool with which to investigate the kinetics of sublimation and decomposition of solid materials. It has led to the development of new mechanisms of the corrosion of solids, the sublimation of ammonium chloride, and the pyrolytic decomposition of Plexiglas.

2. Pyrolysis of Airborne Solids

A rather novel use of a pyrolysis technique was developed by Thomas and Baker (47) to study the concentration of proteins and other organic substances, such as pollen, in the air. The pyrolysis of the proteins was carried out to yield cyanide ion as one of the products, the concentration of which was determined by an electro-chemical method.

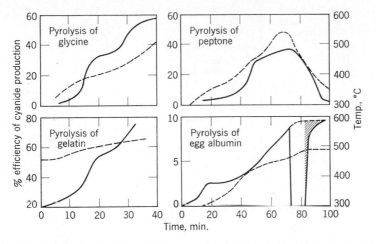

Fig. IX.19. Production of cyanide ion by pyrolysis of several protein materials (47). (———) Cyanide; (- - -) temperature.

The pyrolysis chamber consisted of a borosilicate glass tube, 5 cm long and 2 mm in inside diameter, wound with a Nichrome wire heater. The protein was passed through the column in the form of an aerosol. Results of the pyrolysis of several proteins are given in Figure IX.19 in which the pyrolysis temperature was varied over a period of several hours, with a maximum temperature of about 500°C. The pyrolysis technique, coupled with the subsequent electrochemical detection of hydrogen cyanide, appears to offer a sensitive and versatile technique for the detection of protein in the atmosphere.

3. THERMAL STABILITY DETERMINATIONS

The evaluation of the thermal stability, or resistance to thermal breakdown or pyrolysis, of many materials used for high-temperature applications has become an important problem in materials research. The usual technique employed to measure this parameter for certain materials has been the isoteniscope (48). Various modifications of this apparatus have been made in the past few years, but all of them suffer from the tedious and time-consuming nature of the determinations.

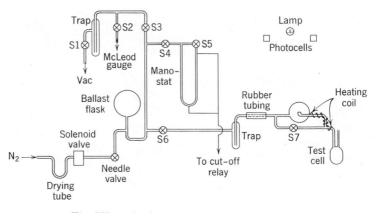

Fig. IX.20. Bodenstein gage and test cell (49).

Fisch and Verderame (49) have eliminated these drawbacks by the use of an automatic apparatus containing a Bodenstein quartz spiral manometer. The arrangement of the apparatus is illustrated in Figure IX.20. A mirror was attached to the top of the gage spiral and by means of a light source, lens, and two photocells, the pressure change in the system could be detected. The amplified current from one of the photocells activated a solenoid valve which controlled the admittance of nitrogen into the system. When the light beam contacted the second photocell, the solenoid valve was deactivated, closing the nitrogen supply. The distance between the photocells corresponded to a definite time or pressure increment which was measured with a recording timer. All measurements in the test cell were made in the temperature range of 0–1000°F.

The decomposition rates of bis(2-ethylhexyl)sebacate, tetra(2-ethylhexyl)silicate, and other compounds were determined (49). Good agreement was found between the values obtained with the automatic apparatus and the conventional manual isoteniscope method.

4. FLASH PYROLYSIS

In contrast to the use of normal pyrolytic methods in gas chromatography where the sample is pyrolyzed in a matter of several seconds, flash pyrolysis of a sample by an intense radiant energy source takes place in milliseconds. Momentary temperatures in

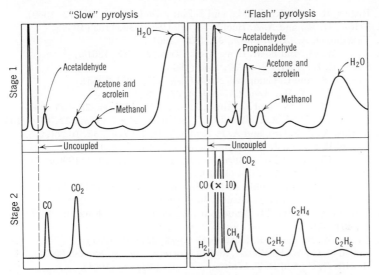

Fig. IX.21. Chromatograms of cellulose pyrolysis products (50).

excess of 600°C can be obtained in the sample. Martin and Ramstad (50) have constructed a compact, two-stage chromatography system to be used in conjunction with flash pyrolysis. The unique feature of this system was that the pyrolysis reaction was carried out directly in the helium carrier gas stream just prior to its entering the first of two initially coupled stages. Products of the reaction went directly onto the liquid partition column of the first stage, and then passed onto the adsorption column of the second stage. The two stages were then uncoupled; the first stage analyzed the higher molecular weight products while the second stage simultaneously analyzed the fixed gases.

The chromatograms of the products obtained by the flash pyrolysis of cellulose are given in Figure IX.21. The curves compare the low molecular weight products formed during a flash pyrolysis with those produced by a relatively slow pyrolysis. The flash pyrolysis heated the sample to about 600°C, while the slower pyrolysis took place between 250 and 350°C.

References

1. Rogers, R. N., S. K. Yasuda, and J. Zinn, *Anal. Chem.*, **32**, 672 (1960).
2. Felton, H. R., and A. A. Buehler, *Anal. Chem.*, **30**, 1163 (1958).
3. Vassallo, O. A., *Anal. Chem.*, **33**, 1823 (1961).
4. Ayres, W. M., and E. M. Bens, *Anal. Chem.*, **33**, 568 (1961).
5. Stone, R. L., *Anal. Chem.*, **32**, 1582 (1960).
6. Gordon, S., and C. Campbell, *Anal. Chem.*, **27**, 1102 (1955).
7. Wendlandt, W. W., *Anal. Chim. Acta*, **27**, 309 (1962).
8. Wendlandt, W. W., and E. Sturm, *J. Inorg. Nucl. Chem.*, **25**, 535 (1963).
9. Murphy, C. B., J. A. Hill, and G. P. Schacher, *Anal. Chem.*, **32**, 1374 (1960).
10. Zlatkis, A., J. F. Oro, and A. P. Kimball, *Anal. Chem.*, **32**, 162 (1960).
11. Lehrle, R. S., and J. C. Robb, *Nature*, **183**, 1671 (1959).
12. Legate, C. E., and H. D. Burnham, *Anal. Chem.*, **32**, 1042 (1960).
13. Janak, J., *Nature*, **185**, 684 (1960).
14. de Angelis, G., P. Ippoliti, and N. Spina, *Ric. Sci.*, **28**, 1444 (1958).
15. Radell, E. A., and H. C. Strutz, *Anal. Chem.*, **31**, 1890 (1959).
16. Strassburger, J., G. M. Brauer, M. Tryon, and A. F. Forziati, *Anal. Chem.*, **32**, 454 (1960).
17. Swann, W. B., and J. P. Dux, *Anal. Chem.*, **33**, 654 (1961).
18. Smith, G. G., W. H. Wetzel, and B. Kosters, *Analyst*, **86**, 480 (1961).
19. Hewitt, G. C., and B. T. Whitham, *Analyst*, **86**, 643 (1961).
20. Porter, R. S., A. S. Hoffman and J. F. Johnson, *Anal. Chem.*, **34**, 1179 (1962).
21. Ettre, K., and P. F. Varadi, *Anal. Chem.*, **35**, 69 (1963).
22. Barlow, A., R. S. Lehrle, and J. C. Robb, *Polymer*, **2**, 27 (1961).
23. Cleverly, B., and R. Hermann, *J. Appl. Chem.*, **10**, 192 (1960).
24. Lehmann, F. A., and G. M. Brauer, *Anal. Chem.*, **33**, 673 (1961).
25. Jennings, E. C., and K. P. Dimick, *Anal. Chem.*, **34**, 1543 (1962).
26. Nelson, D. F., and P. L. Kirk, *Anal. Chem.*, **34**, 899 (1962).
27. Ettre, K., and P. F. Varadi, *Anal. Chem.* **34**, 752 (1962).
28. Barrall, E. M., R. S. Porter, and J. F. Johnson, *Anal. Chem.*, **35**, 73 (1963).
29. Zemany, P. D., *Anal. Chem.*, **24**, 1709 (1952).
30. Madorsky, S. L., and S. Strauss, *Ind. Eng. Chem.*, **40**, 848 (1948).
31. Wall, L. A., *J. Res. Natl. Bur. Std. U.S.*, **41**, 315 (1948).

32. Achhammer, B. G., M. J. Reiney, L. A. Wall, and F. W. Reinhart, *J. Polymer Sci.*, **8**, 555 (1952).
33. Bradt, P., and F. L. Mohler, *Anal. Chem.*, **27**, 875 (1955).
34. Madorsky, S. L., S. Strauss, D. Thompson, and L. Willamson, *J. Res. Natl. Bur. Std., U.S.*, **42**, 499 (1949).
35. Wall, L. A., in *Analytical Chemistry of Polymers*, G. M. Kline, ed., Interscience, New York, 1962, Part II, Chapter V.
36. Wendlandt, W. W., S. I. Ali, and C. H. Stembridge, *Anal. Chim. Acta*, in press.
37. Wendlandt, W. W., S. I. Ali, and C. H. Stembridge, *Anal. Chim. Acta*, **30**, 84 (1964).
38. Harms, D. L., *Anal. Chem.*, **25**, 1140 (1953).
39. Achhammer, B. G., M. J. Reiney, and F. W. Reinhart, *J. Res. Natl. Bur. Std. U.S.*, **47**, 116 (1951).
40. Beachell, H. C., P. Fotis and J. Hucks, *J. Polymer Sci.*, **7**, 353 (1951).
41. Kmetko, E. A., *Phys. Rev.*, **82**, 456 (1951).
42. Wilfong, R. E., S. S. Penner, and F. Daniels, *J. Phys. Colloid Chem.*, **54**, 863 (1950).
43. Melville, H. W., and N. Grassie, *Proc. Roy. Soc. (London)*, **A119**, 1, 14 (1949).
44. Spingler, K., *Z. Physik. Chem.*, **B52**, 90 (1942).
45. Barsh, M. K., H. W. Andersen, K. W. Bills, G. Moe, and R. D. Schultz, *Rev. Sci. Instr.*, **29**, 392 (1958).
46. Schultz, R. D., and A. O. Dekker, in *Fifth International Symposium on Combustion*, Reinhold, New York, 1955, p. 260.
47. Thomas, C. O., and B. B. Baker, *Anal. Chem.*, **31**, 1391 (1959).
48. Smith, A., and A. W. C. Menzies, *J. Am. Chem. Soc.*, **32**, 891, 907, 1412 (1910).
49. Fisch, K. R., and F. D. Verderame, *J. Chem. Eng. Data*, **6**, 131 (1961).
50. Martin, S. B., and R. W. Ramstad, *Anal. Chem.*, **33**, 982 (1961).

CHAPTER X

DYNAMIC REFLECTANCE SPECTROSCOPY

A. Introduction

Although the absorption spectroscopy of solutions in the ultraviolet, visible, and infrared regions of the spectrum has been widely studied, relatively little work has been done on the reflectance (or reflection) spectroscopy of solids. Outside of studies on single crystals of various compounds and of manufactured products such as paper, textiles, plastics, and paint pigments, there is a dearth of investigations on the application of reflectance spectroscopy to problems of interest in analytical chemistry. The reasons for this are not clear. Certainly, commercial instruments are available for this technique; a conventional spectrophotometer can be converted to a reflectometer merely by the addition of an attachment. The spectra are as easily obtainable as those of transmittance spectra of solutions and generally in the same wavelength regions. Perhaps the main difficulty has been the nonreproducibility of the sample surface since the reflectance spectrum of a sample is a function of particle size and the nature of the reflecting surface. Various techniques have been employed to obtain a reproducible surface such as the use of a matrix substance in the form of finely divided powder or filter paper (1,2).

Most of the studies on the reflectance spectra of various substances have been conducted at ambient or low temperatures. Few studies of interest in analytical chemistry have been carried out at elevated temperatures either under isothermal or dynamic temperature conditions. It is not the object of this discussion to report on reflectance studies at ambient temperatures, but rather to elaborate on studies carried out at elevated temperatures. However, basic studies on the determination of emissivities of substances at very high temperatures will not be included.

B. Theory

The theoretical treatment of the nature of the radiation reflected from a surface of a substance has been discussed by Kubelka and

Munk (3), Schreyer (4), and Kortum and Vogel (5). The radiation reflected by a finely divided, powdered substance consists of two components, called the diffuse and regular components, respectively. The diffuse component consists of the radiation penetrating into the interior of the sample layer and re-emerging to the surface after being scattered many times (6). The regular component consists of the radiation resulting from reflection at the surface of the single crystallites of the sample. If the sample exhibits selective absorption, the spectral intensity distribution of both components deviates from the spectral distribution of the primary radiation in a different manner. For the diffuse part, the reflectance at a given wavelength is given by the relationship

$$R_{\text{diff}(\infty)} \equiv \left(\frac{I}{I_0}\right)_1 = \frac{1 - \sqrt{\kappa/(\kappa + 2s)}}{1 + \sqrt{\kappa/(\kappa + 2s)}} \tag{X.1}$$

In this equation, κ is the absorption coefficient and s the scattering coefficient. This relationship is valid for infinite thickness of a layer which in general practice is about 2–3 mm (3). For the regular part, according to Fresnel's law, the reflectance at the same wavelength is

$$R_{\text{reg}} \equiv \left(\frac{I}{I_0}\right)_2 = \frac{(n - 1)^2 + n^2 k^2}{(n + 1)^2 + n^2 k^2} \tag{X.2}$$

where n is the refractive index of the substance, and $k = \kappa\lambda_0/4\pi n$, the absorption index. From the above expression, it can be seen that R_{reg} approaches the limiting value of one for large values of k, or, that highly absorbing substances possess high reflectivity, such as is illustrated by metals. Thus, the diffuse and regular reflectance components counteract and determine together the spectral intensity of the reflected radiation.

Kortum (6) has shown that the measured reflectance of a sample is a function of particle size. The apparent absorbance,

$$E_{1+2} \equiv \log \left(\frac{I_0}{I}\right)_{1+2} \tag{X.3}$$

is very dependent on particle size as shown by the reflectance spectra of $K_3[\text{Fe(CN)}_6]$ in Figure X.1. For coarse particles, 200–500 μ in diameter, the regular reflectance is dominant due to the strong damping of the oscillations of electrons. With decreasing particle size and, therefore, decreasing contribution of the regular reflectance, the structure of the spectrum is greatly improved. Simultaneously, the apparent absorbance decreases because the average thickness of

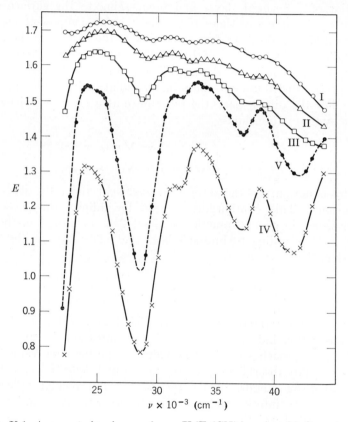

Fig. X.1. Apparent absorbance of pure $K_3[Fe(CN)_6]$ against MgO as standard by reflectance measurements (6). Average diameter of crystallites: (I) d = 500 to 200 μ; (II) d = 100 to 60 μ; (III) d = 40 μ; (IV) d = 2 to 1 μ.

the layer penetrated is reduced. However, for very small particles, with a mean diameter less than 1 μ, the apparent absorbance begins to rise again, since the regular reflectance drops sharply as the sample particle size approaches the dimension of the wavelength of the incident radiation.

Since the regular part of the reflected radiation interferes with the measurement of the intrinsic absorption spectrum, it must be eliminated as far as possible. Kortum and Vogel (7) reduced the regular reflectance component by examination of the sample and reference reflected radiation with crossed polarizing prisms. They also found that dilution of the sample with the same substance used as reference would reduce the regular component. In the case of the latter technique, the regular reflectance was essentially the same in both cases and was therefore eliminated; hence, the pure diffuse reflectance spectrum was obtained.

The reflectance spectrum curve of a powdered solid substance is identical to that of the absorption spectrum of the substance if use is made of the Kubelka–Munk function, $F(R_\infty)$ (3). This function is obtained by transformation of equation (X.1), or

$$F(R_\infty) \equiv \frac{(1 - R_\infty)^2}{2R_\infty} = \frac{K}{S} \qquad (X.4)$$

Since the scattering coefficient, s, is nearly independent of the wavelength, equation (X.4) can be rearranged to give

$$\log F(R_\infty) = \log K + \text{const}$$
$$= \log \epsilon + \log c + \text{const} \qquad (X.5)$$

Thus, a plot of $\log F(R_\infty)$ of a substance vs. wavelength gives a curve identical to the true absorption spectrum except for an additive constant. Or, if the dilution matrix method is employed, a plot of $\log F(R_\infty)/c$, where c is the concentration of the sample, vs. wavelength will give the same results. This latter expression has been used to describe the reflectance spectrum of anthraquinone diluted with sodium chloride, measured against pure sodium chloride (6).

C. Instrumentation

Instruments for the measurement of total, diffuse, and specular reflectance spectra in the ultraviolet, visible, and infrared spectral regions have been described by a number of investigators (8–16). There are also a number of reflectance attachments for standard spectrophotometers manufactured by such commercial firms as Beckman Instruments, Inc., Fullerton, California; the Perkin-Elmer Corporation, Norwalk, Connecticut; Bausch and Lomb, Inc., Roch-

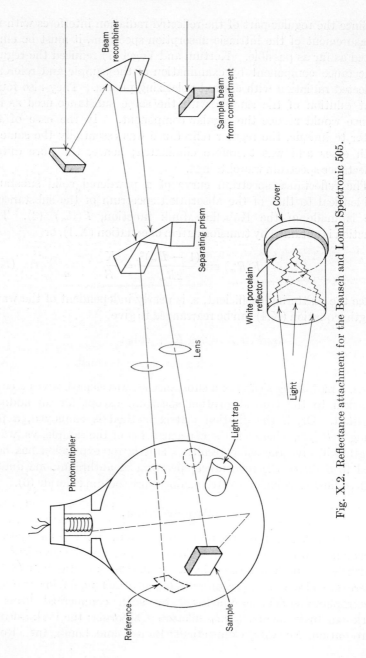

Fig. X.2. Reflectance attachment for the Bausch and Lomb Spectronic 505.

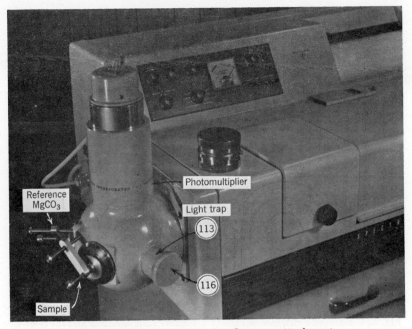

Fig. X.3. Bausch and Lomb reflectance attachment.

ester, New York; Carey Instruments, Applied Physics Corp., Monrovia, California; and Carl Zeiss, Inc., New York, New York.

To illustrate the experimental techniques involved in reflectance spectra measurements, the Bausch and Lomb Spectronic 505 spectrophotometer, equipped with a reflectance attachment, will be described. A schematic view of the reflectance attachment is given in Figure X.2. Radiation from the monochromator is recombined, separated, and then focused into two beams by means of a prism and lens arrangement. The two light beams pass into an integrating sphere where they strike the sample and reference materials, placed on the outside surface of the sphere. The radiation is then reflected from the sample and reference back into the sphere which is coated with a white, reflecting material, such as magnesium oxide. By means of the two light traps located on the sphere, the specular component of the reflected radiation can be absorbed or reflected back into the sphere. If the former case is taken, the total reflectance of the sample and reference will be recorded; if the latter case, only the

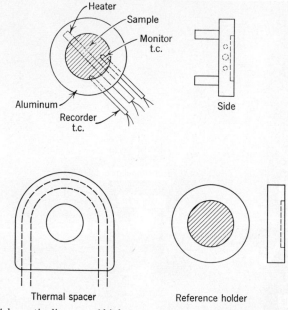

Fig. X.4. Schematic diagram of high-temperature sample holder and the reference sample holder.

diffuse reflectance will be obtained. Radiation reflected from the inside surface of the sphere is then detected by a photomultiplier tube, located at the top of the sphere, amplified, and recorded as a function of wavelength. A photograph of the attachment is given in Figure X.3.

Normally, the reflectance spectrum of a sample is taken at ambient temperature. However, Wendlandt et al. (17) introduced a heated sample holder which was used in conjunction with the Bausch and Lomb Spectronic 505 spectrophotometer. In Figures X.4 and X.5 are illustrated the heated sample holder and apparatus arrangement. This apparatus is a modification of the technique previously described (17).

The main body of the heated sample holder was about 6.0 cm in diameter by 1.1 cm thick and was machined from aluminum. The sample was contained in a circular indentation, 2.5 cm in diameter by 0.1 cm deep, cut out on the external face of the metal block. Two circular ridges were cut at regular intervals on the indentation to

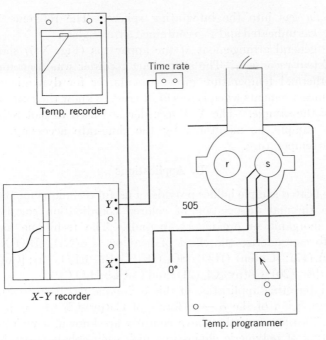

Fig. X.5. Schematic diagram of reflectance apparatus.

increase the surface area and to prevent the powdered sample from falling out of the holder when it is in a vertical position.

The sample holder was heated by a 0.25-in.-diam by 2.0-in.-long stainless steel sheathed heater cartridge having a rating of 100 W at 120 V. Two thermocouples were employed to measure the temperature of the holder. One thermocouple, which was held in place by a two-holed ceramic insulator tube, was in intimate contact with the powdered sample and measured the sample temperature; the other thermocouple, also contained in an insulator tube, was used to monitor the metal block temperature and to control the temperature programmer. The holder could be programmed at heating rates from 0.5 to 30°C/min, or the temperature held at a fixed point, through use of the temperature programmer-controller.

In the case of metal salt hydrates or amine complexes, a 1-mm-thick cover glass of Pyrex glass or quartz enclosed the sample indentation. The cover glass prevented the entrance of water or ammonia gas into the integrating sphere. The reference sample holder was unheated and also contained a cover glass.

The general arrangement of the apparatus (Fig. X.5) shows the use of two recorders. The strip-chart recorder was used for static or isothermal temperature measurements, or for dynamic temperature measurements when it was of interest to know the exact heating rate of the sample. The $X-Y$ recorder was used to plot reflectance of the sample, as monitored by the time-rate accessory, against sample temperature.

D. Applications

The heated sample holder provides a useful technique for the study of the thermal dissociation of colored coordination complexes or other inorganic or organic compounds. The technique has been used to characterize the effect of heat on $[Co(NH_3)_5H_2O]X_3(X =$ Cl, Br) (17); $[Cu(en) (H_2O)_2]SO_4$ (18); $CoBr_2 \cdot 6H_2O$ (19); $[Co(NH_3)_4-(H_2O)_2]Br_3$ (20); $Co(py)_2Cl_2$ (21); and $CoCl_2 \cdot nH_2O$ (22).

An interesting application of this technique has been to study the transformation of the $\alpha \rightarrow \beta$ forms of $Co(py)_2Cl_2$ (py = pyridine) (21). Two forms of the above complex are known, a violet α-form consisting of polymeric chains in which each cobalt is octahedrally surrounded by four chlorine atoms and two nitrogen atoms, while the β-form consists of a tetrahedral structure in which each cobalt is surrounded by two chlorine atoms and two nitrogen atoms. It is known that the blue β-form of the compound can be obtained by heating the violet α-form in a sealed tube at 110–120°C for several hours. This transformation is easily seen by use of the high-temperature reflectance spectra technique, as shown in Figure X.6.

The 25°C curve contained peak maximas at 530 and 630 mμ with a possible shoulder peak at about 550 mμ. On heating, the intensities of these peaks increased slightly until, at 125°C, the curve had changed completely, giving the spectrum of the blue or β-form of the compound. Further increases in intensity took place at higher temperatures until, at 155°C, peak maximas or shoulder peaks were found at 420, 435, 580, and 650 mμ, respectively.

The thermal dehydration of $CoBr_2 \cdot 6H_2O$ was also observed by use of this technique (19). The reflectance curves of a 30% $CoBr_2 \cdot 6H_2O$ mixture with aluminum oxide, at various temperatures, are given in Figure X.7. At room temperature, 25°C, the curve had

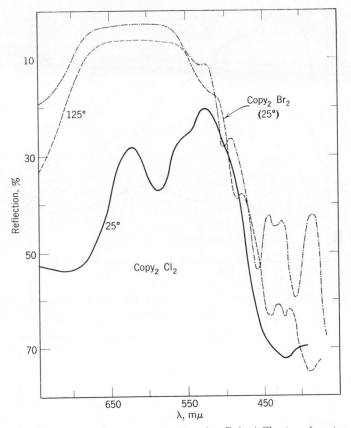

Fig. X.6. Diffuse reflectance-spectra curves of α-Co(py)$_2$Cl$_2$ at various temperatures (21).

peak maximas at 550, 640, 665, 695, and 725 mμ. When heated to 50°C, all of the peaks increased in intensity, with the most pronounced increases in the 640, 665, 695, and 725 mμ peaks. At 100°C, these peak maxima decreased in intensity, while the peak at 550 mμ increased. The change in intensities of these peaks with temperature is due to the formation of intermediate hydrates, the exact structure of which is not known. On continued heating, the curves changed little. From 150 to 250°C, peaks with peak maxima at about 400, 640, and 570 mμ were observed. It was concluded that the curve at 150°C represented that of anhydrous CoBr$_2$.

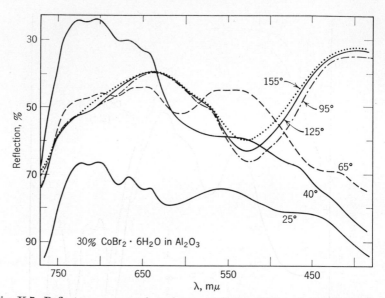

Fig. X.7. Reflectance curves of a mixture of CoBr₂·6H₂O and Al₂O₃ at elevated temperatures (19).

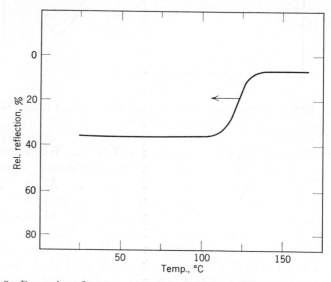

Fig. X.8. Dynamic reflectance spectrum of Co(py)₂Cl₂ at a heating rate of 2°C/min

The color changes of heated and unheated milk were determined by changes in their reflectance spectra by Burton (23). The reflectance spectrum of milk, before and after heating at a known temperature, was determined with a Beckman DU spectrophotometer or an Evans Electroselenium Ltd. reflectance spectrophotometer. It was found that the color changes involved the nonfat constituents of milk since the reflectance spectrum of cream changed little on heating. The fat phase was little affected by heating, and its presence, even in small amounts, tended to mask the changes taking place in the other constituents.

In the previous discussion of high-temperature reflectance spectroscopy, essentially static or isothermal temperature conditions were employed. The temperature of the sample was maintained at a fixed point while the reflectance spectrum was scanned over the wavelength range of the instrument. If, however, the spectrophotometer is set on a wavelength at which a peak in the reflectance curve either decreases or increases with change in temperature, and the reflectance of the sample is measured as a function of increasing sample temperature, the technique becomes a "dynamic" one. The term dynamic refers to the change in reflectance of the sample with change in temperature. Because of the dynamic nature of this measurement, this technique is called "dynamic reflectance spectroscopy" (DRS) (21).

The DRS curve of $Co(py)_2Cl_2$ at a wavelength of 625 mμ is shown in Figure X.8. The curve shows that the $\alpha \rightarrow \beta$ transition began at about 100°C and was completed at about 135°C. This was in good agreement with the data found by DTA measurements.

Likewise, the DRS curves for $CoBr_2 \cdot 6H_2O-Al_2O_3$ mixtures, at different wavelengths, show the formation and dissociation of various intermediate hydrates (19).

The technique of dynamic reflectance spectroscopy appears to be a promising technique, in conjunction with other thermal methods, to study the thermal dissociation of colored compounds. Other applications include the study of solid-state reactions at elevated temperatures in which there is a colored reactant or product, the determination of thermochromic transition temperatures, and possible kinetics studies of the formation and decomposition of colored compounds. Unlike TGA and DTA, dynamic reflectance spectroscopy can be used to monitor only a single reaction at a time, thus eliminating the effect of reactions occurring simultaneously.

References

1. Lermond, C. A., and L. B. Rogers, *Anal. Chem.*, **27**, 340 (1955).
2. Fischer, R. B., and F. Vratny, *Anal. Chim. Acta*, **13**, 588 (1955).
3. Kubelka, P., *J. Opt. Soc. Am.*, **38**, 448, 1067 (1948); P. Kubelka and F. Munk, *Z. Tech. Physik*, **12**, 593 (1931).
4. Schreyer, G., *Z. Physik. Chem. (Frankfurt)*, **17**, 359 (1957); **18**, 123 (1958).
5. Kortum, G., and J. Vogel, *Z. Physik. Chem. (Frankfurt)*, **18**, 110 (1958).
6. Kortum, G., *Trans. Faraday Soc.*, **58**, 1624 (1962).
7. Kortum, G., and J. Vogel, *Z. Physik. Chem. (Frankfurt)*, **18**, 230 (1958).
8. Dearth, L. R., W. M. Shillcox, and J. A. Van der Akker, *Tappi*, **34**, 126 (1951).
9. Oldham, M. S., *J. Opt. Soc. Am.*, **41**, 673 (1951).
10. Clark, C., R. Vinejar, and J. D. Hardy, *J. Opt. Soc. Am.*, **43**, 993 (1953).
11. Jacquez, J. A., W. McKeehan, J. Huss, J. M. Dimtroff, and H. F. Kuppenheim, *J. Opt. Soc. Am.*, **45**, 971 (1955).
12. Shulman, J. H., and C. C. Klick, *J. Opt. Soc. Am.*, **43**, 516 (1953).
13. Blair, G. R., *J. Am. Ceram. Soc.*, **43**, 197 (1960).
14. Kropotkin, M. A., and B. P. Kozyrev, *Izv. Leningrad Elecktrotekh. Inst.* **1960**, No. 44, 87.
15. Sanderson, J. A., *J. Opt. Soc. Am.*, **37**, 771 (1947).
16. Oster, G., *Anal. Chem.*, **25**, 1165 (1953).
17. Wendlandt, W. W., P. H. Franke, and J. P. Smith, *Anal. Chem.*, **35**, 105 (1963).
18. Wendlandt, W. W., *J. Inorg. Nucl. Chem.*, **25**, 833 (1963).
19. Wendlandt, W. W., *Science*, **140**, 1085 (1963).
20. Wendlandt, W. W., W. R. Robinson, and W. Y. Yang, *J. Inorg. Nucl. Chem.*, **25**, 1495 (1963).
21. Wendlandt, W. W., *Chemist-Analyst*, **53**, 71(1964).
22. Wendlandt, W. W., unpublished.
23. Burton, H., *J. Dairy Res.* **21**, 194 (1954).

CHAPTER XI

THERMAL ANALYSIS

A. Introduction

The purity of organic and inorganic compounds can be determined by a number of techniques ranging from simple physical methods of boiling and melting point determinations to more sophisticated instrumental methods such as absorption or emission spectroscopy. An attempt is made to summarize the principal instrumental techniques for purity (or impurity) determinations in Table XI.1. The figures cited are not very accurate and may vary widely, depending on the main component as well as the impurities present. The first six methods may each show a number of contaminants in one single experiment and permit the determination of each of them. Electrical conductance permits the estimation of ions in aqueous or non-aqueous solutions as well as the ionic components in semiconductors. Although the latter is a rather limited technique, it does approach the optimum purity-control method for group contaminants.

The method offering the widest potential for the determination of the purity of a substance is thermal analysis (1). It is applicable

TABLE XI.1

Methods of Impurity Determination of Chemical Compounds (1)

Method	Sensitivity[a]	Substance	
		Organic	Inorganic
Emission and x-ray spectroscopy	10^{-4}–10^{-5}		X
Activation analysis	10^{-1}–10^{-8}	X	X
Polarography	10^{-6}	X	X
Mass spectroscopy	10^{-3}–10^{-5}	X	X
Chromatography	10^{-5}	X	X
Absorption spectroscopy	10^{-3}	X	
Electrical conductance	10^{-8}		X
Thermal analysis	10^{-5}	X	X

[a] Smallest fraction of impurity still detectable.

345

to all substances which are sufficiently stable at their melting points and permits the determination of the total quantity of contaminant not soluble in the solid phase. Thermal analysis may be defined as a method for the determination of the amount of contaminants (s) in a substance from an analysis of the temperature–time or temperature–heat content of the material covering its melting range.

Various methods have been used to determine the temperature–time or temperature–heat content curves of a substance. They include the following:

(a) Static or calorimetric methods in which an adiabatic calorimeter is employed.

(b) Dynamic or thermometric methods (not to be confused with thermometric titrations) in which heat evolution or absorption occurs continuously and preferably at a constant rate. The amount of heat supplied per unit time is not measured directly but may be calculated as a fraction of the total heat of melting of the substance. A dynamic apparatus must be calibrated with some standard material having a known heat of fusion.

(c) Dilatometric method; a method which is rather limited and will not be discussed here.

Various reviews on the subject of thermal analysis as a means of determination of the purity of organic compounds have been published by Sturtevant (2), Cines (3), Mathieu (4), and Smit (1), and also a recent book by Smit (5).

B. Theory

The treatment of temperature–heat content curves from a theoretical viewpoint has been carried out by a number of investigators, starting with White (6) in 1920. Other early papers on the subject are by Andrews et al. (7), Skau (8), Mair et al. (9), Glasgow et al. (10), Malotaux and Straub (11), and Thomas and Parks (12). More recent treatments have been given by Rossini (13), Mastrangelo and Dornte (14), Badley (15), and Smit (1). The reader is referred to the above for a more comprehensive presentation than that given here.

To analyze the temperature vs. time curve, the curves in Figure XI.1 will be discussed. The basic analysis of this curve has been described by White (6) and modified by Carleton (16). The re-

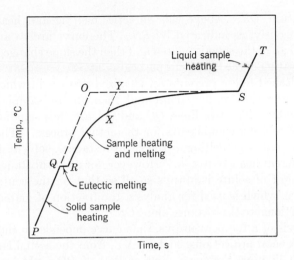

Fig. XI.1. Melting-temperature curve for two component system. (——)Actual
equilibrium curve; (- - - -) idealized process; (– – – –) heating without melting
(specific heat component) (16).

sulting temperature vs. time curve is based on the linear relationship
of heat input to time and to the equation

$$N_2 = \frac{\Delta H}{RT^2}(T_0 - T) = A(T_0 - T) \qquad (XI.1)$$

where N_2 is the mole fraction of solute, ΔH is the heat of fusion of
the solvent, T_0 is the freezing point of pure solvent, and T is the equilibrium temperature. This equation is restricted to those examples
which are nearly pure and in which, on freezing, the pure major
component solidifies, leaving the impurity in solution.

The linear relationship of heat input to time follows from the
maintenance of a constant temperature interval between the sample
and the bath. During melting, this heat input has two components:
a specific-heat component which raises the temperature of the sample
and the thermometer bulb, and a melting component. The separation of these two components on a time scale is illustrated in Figure
XI.1. The initial straight line portion, PQ, represents the heating
of the solid sample and thermometer bulb. In the case of a two
component system, there is a flattening of the curve at the eutectic

temperature, QR. Above this eutectic, melting and heating occur simultaneously, as indicated by RS. The curve arches and flattens out until all of the solid is melted and then the slope changes abruptly, where heating of the liquid sample begins, at ST.

The dashed line represents an idealized process in which all solid is heated to the freezing point and then all the sample is melted isothermally. The two lines, QO and OS, are thus separate specific-heat and melting components for the actual process. The flat line, OS, represents the melting of the two substances, solvent and solute, with different heats of fusion. However, for most substances studied, the amount of solute is always small so that on the central part of the curve, which is used for analysis, the fraction of material melted is proportional to the distance along OS.

Analysis of a temperature vs. time curve depends on the construction of several projections, such as XY, from the actual curve to the ideal flat line, or, the same slope as that of PQ could be used with negligible error. However, a run usually begins at a temperature at which some melting is already under way, so that the slope of the separate specific heat component is not known. When the properties of the sample are known, a slope for XY may be approximated from the dimensions of the apparatus, the specific heat, the heat of fusion of the sample, and a rough estimate of the impurity, assuming ideal solution behavior. Usually, however, these properties will not be known, but either the properties or the slope may be estimated with sufficient accuracy to be useful.

If x represents the mole fraction of impurity in the original sample and T_1 the freezing point of the impure sample (temperature at point S), then equation (XI.1) gives

$$N_2 = A(T_0 - T) \tag{XI.2}$$

$$x = A(T_0 - T_1) \tag{XI.3}$$

whence

$$N_2 = x + A(T_1 - T) \tag{XI.4}$$

If f is the mole fraction of the solvent frozen at temperature T,

$$f = \frac{N_2 - x}{N_2} = \frac{A(T_1 - T)}{x + A(T_1 - T)} = \frac{A \Delta T}{x + A \Delta T} \tag{XI.5}$$

If Δt represents the time difference from the point of complete melting, YS, and Δt_1 the total time represented by the ideal-melting flat line, OS, then

$$f = \frac{\Delta t}{\Delta t_1} \tag{XI.6}$$

Equations (XI.5) and (XI.6) are rearranged to

$$\Delta t = \Delta t_1 - \frac{x}{A}\left(\frac{\Delta t}{\Delta T}\right) \tag{XI.7}$$

Thus, the theory predicts that a plot of Δt against $\Delta t/\Delta T$ will give a straight line whose slope is $-x/A$. The term A is equal to

$$A = \frac{\Delta H}{RT^2} \tag{XI.8}$$

and is a characteristic property of the major component in the sample. When ΔH is not known, A may be determined from an additional run on the sample containing a known mole fraction of added solute. Alternatively, ΔH may be estimated by comparing the curve for the sample with a curve for a reference substance of known heat of fusion, obtained in the same apparatus. Then x is the product of A and x/A determined from the slope of the curve.

For the temperature–heat content curves, a similar expression can be derived. Rossini (13) has shown that the thermodynamic relation for equilibrium between a liquid phase, of the major and minor components, and a crystalline phase of the major component alone is given by

$$\ln N_1 = \ln (1 - N_2) = -A(T_0 - T)$$
$$[1 + B(T_0 - T) + \ldots] \tag{XI.9}$$

where N_1 and N_2 are the mole fractions of the major and minor components, respectively, in the liquid phase. The temperature, T_0, is the freezing point of the pure major component ($N_1 = 1$) and T is the equilibrium temperature for the mixture. The quantity A is given by equation (IX.8), while B is the other cryoscopic constant

$$B = \left(\frac{1}{T_0}\right) - \left(\frac{\Delta C_p}{2\Delta H}\right) \tag{XI.10}$$

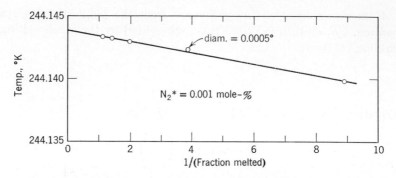

Fig. XI.2. The melting curve of benzotrifluoride (17).

where C_p is the molar heat capacity of the liquid less that of the solid. For highly purified samples, T approaches T_0 and N_2 approaches zero so that equation (XI.9) can be written as

$$N_2 = A(T_0 - T) \qquad (XI.11)$$

If N_2 is the mole fraction of impurity in the liquid phase for a fraction F of the sample liquid, then

$$N_2 = N_2^* \, (1/F) \qquad (XI.12)$$

where N_2^* is the mole fraction of impurity in the sample. Combining equations (XI.11) and (XI.12) gives

$$T = T_0 - \left(\frac{N_2^*}{A}\right)\left(\frac{1}{F}\right) \qquad (XI.13)$$

A plot of T vs. $(1/F)$ will give a straight line of slope $-(N_2^*/A)$ and the intercept at $(1/F) = 0$ will be T_0. Thus, from the slope of the line, the purity of the sample can be determined. Such a curve of $(1/F)$ vs. temperature for benzotrifluoride is given in Figure XI.2.

The above procedure is based upon the assumptions that (17): (a) the values of T are thermodynamic equilibrium temperatures; (b) an ideal solution is formed in the liquid phase; (c) the impurity is insoluble in the solid phase; and (d) N_2^* is very much less than one. Departure from linearity in a plot of T vs. $(1/F)$ may be taken as an indication that one or more of these basic assumptions is not met fully.

Gunn (37) has proposed for quantitative purity determination another method, which can also be used for the estimation of heat capacities and heats of fusion of the sample.

Assuming Newton's law, the heat transfer to the sample is

$$dH/dt = k(T_b - T_s) \qquad (XI.14)$$

where T_b is the temperature of the block, T_s is the temperature of the sample, and k is the heat-transfer coefficient. The rate of temperature change of the sample is

$$dT_s/dt = k(T_b - T_s)/(nC_s + C_g) \qquad (XI.15)$$

where n is the number of moles of sample, C_s is its molar heat capacity, and C_g is the heat capacity of the glass bulb, sample well packing, and part of the thermocouple. If T_b is increased at a constant rate, r, T_s will approach asymptotically and follow a parallel time vs. temperature line such that

$$dT_s/dt = dT_b/dt = r \qquad (XI.16)$$

displaced in temperature at a given time by a thermal heat, h:

$$h = T_b - T_s = r(nC_s + C_g)/k \qquad (XI.17)$$

and displaced in time at a given temperature by a lag, l:

$$l = (T_b - T_s)/r = (nC_s - C_g)/k \qquad (XI.18)$$

Thus, l is a function only of the heat capacity and k, but h is also a function of heating rate, r:

$$h = rl \qquad (XI.19)$$

The treatment for purity determinations used by Gunn (37) assumes that k is a constant, but that its value need not be known; likewise, the values of n, C_s, and C_g need not be known.

In Figure XI.3 is illustrated an idealized melting curve to be described by this treatment. Curve AB represents the block temperature, increasing at an approximately constant rate, r. Curve CGF represents the sample temperature, t, being selected before this temperature departs from a line parallel to AB and T_f after the temperature has returned to a line parallel to AB. From equation

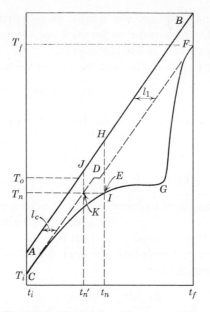

Fig. XI.3. Idealized melting curve (37).

(XI.14), it follows that the heat transferred to the sample in warming it from T_i to T_f is

$$H_f - H_i = k \int_{t_i}^{t_f} (T_b - T_s)dt = k(ABFGC) \qquad \text{(XI.20)}$$

If no latent heat were associated with the fusion, the sample would warm along path $CDEF$, where T_0 is the melting point and the curves CD and EF are separated from AB by the different lags, l_c and l_1, which reflect the different heat capacities of the solid and liquid, that of the solid generally being lower. The absorption of heat would be $k(ABFEDC)$, hence, the molar heat of fusion, ΔH, of the sample is

$$n\Delta H = k(ABFGC) - k(ABFEDC) = k(CDEFG) \qquad \text{(XI.21)}$$

The area, $CDEFG$, will be called Z; in practice, it is evaluated by graphical integration, that is, by dividing the area into several easily measured triangles which cover an area judged visually to be equal.

The heat transferred to the sample to warm it from T_i to T_n is $k(AHIC)$, and is denoted as W. The heat required to warm the solid from T_i to T_n in the absence of melting would be $k(AJKC)$, and is denoted as X. Instead of integrating X graphically, it is noted that

$$X = rl_c(t_n' - t_i) = h_c(t_n' - t_i) \qquad (XI.22)$$

The amount of heat which has been used to melt part of the sample at time t_n is $k(W - X)$; the quantity $W - X$ is denoted as Y. The reciprocal of the fraction of the sample melted, F^{-1}, is

$$F^{-1} = Z/Y \qquad (XI.23)$$

where F^{-1} may be calculated for as many points as desired on the melting curve.

For ideal or sufficiently dilute solutions, the van't Hoff law of freezing point lowering has the form

$$T = T_0 - N_2 F^{-1} RT_0^2/\Delta H \qquad (XI.24)$$

where T_0 is the melting point of the pure material and N_2 is the mole fraction of impurity. Hence, the values of T_n plotted against F^{-1} should lie on a straight line whose slope multiplied by the cryoscopic constant, $RT^2/\Delta H$, is equal to N_2.

C. Experimental Techniques

For thermal analyses by the static method, a precision, adiabatic calorimeter is required. Although many adiabatic calorimeters have been described in the literature, Glasgow et al. (18) have described a calorimeter which was used to determine the purity of benzene and other substances in the temperature range from 10 to 300°K. The calorimeter is illustrated schematically in Figure XI.4.

The sample container, suspended in the calorimeter by a small tube, was constructed of copper and had a capacity of about 106 ml. Tinned copper vanes were arranged radially from the central re-entrant well, containing a heater and a platinum resistance thermometer, to the outer wall of the container. The vanes were held in place by means of a thin coating of tin. A thin-copper thermal shell was attached to the upper periphery of the container to obtain a nearly isothermal surface. The outer surface of the container, the

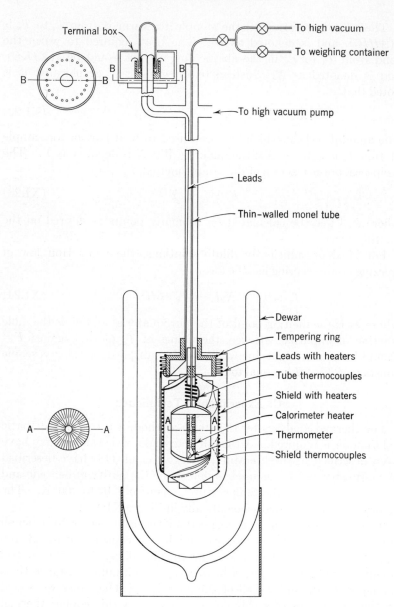

Fig. XI.4. Adiabatic calorimeter for volatile compounds (18).

inner and outer surfaces of the shell, and the inner surface of the adiabatic shield were gold plated and polished to minimize heat transfer by radiation. A high vacuum, 10^{-6} mm Hg, was maintained in the space surrounding the sample container and the adiabatic shield.

The resistance of the platinum thermometer was measured by means of a Mueller bridge. The electrical input energy was determined from the measurements of the current and potential across a 100 Ω Constantan wire heater and the time interval of heating. The heater current and potential were measured by means of a Wenner potentiometer in conjunction with a resistor and a volt box. The time interval of heating was measured by means of a precision interval timer.

The calculations involved in the determination of the specific heat of a sample have been described by Stull (19). During a heat input, an electric current of I amperes flowed through the sample heater because of a voltage e impressed on the heater terminals for t seconds. The heat in calories, H, is then

$$H = \frac{Iet}{4.1840} \tag{XI.25}$$

This heat input caused the temperature of the sample to go from its initial state, T_i, before the heat was applied, to T_f, the final temperature of the sample after the sample had reached a constant temperature. Thus, $T_f - T_i = \Delta T$, the rise in temperature due to H, and

$$\frac{T_f - T_i}{2} = T_a, \text{ the average temperature of the space heat input}$$

Now heat was absorbed by the sample container of weight w grams and specific heat C_{pc} at T_a, as well as by the sample of W grams and specific heat C_{ps} at T_a. Expressed mathematically,

$$H = [wC_{pc} + WC_{ps}] \Delta T \tag{XI.26}$$

and combining equations (XI.14) and (XI.15),

$$\frac{Iet}{4.1840 \, W\Delta T} - \frac{W}{W} C_{vc} = C_{ps} \tag{XI.27}$$

Equation (XI.27) is the basic equation used to calculate the heat capacity of the sample. By slight modification of the equation, the calculations can be made by an electronic digital computer.

Other calorimeters that have been used for melting determinations have been described by Clarke et al. (20), Aston and Fink (21), Pilcher (22), Mazee (23), and Ruehrwein and Huffman (24).

In the case of the dynamic method, the constant heat supply to the sample is obtained by maintaining a constant thermal head between the sample and its surroundings. This may be done by two different methods: (a) by a constant wall apparatus, and (b) by an adapted wall apparatus (1). A constant wall apparatus maintains a constant temperature between the wall of the sample container and the sample. In an adapted wall apparatus, a constant heat supply to the sample is also maintained when the sample is surrounded by a mantle and its temperature is continuously adapted to the temperature of the sample in such a way that the difference between both temperatures remains constant.

The various constant and adapted wall apparatuses have been summarized by Smit (1). The former type have been built by White (6) and Rossini and co-workers (9,10). Instruments of the latter type have been described by Thomas and Parks (12), Malotaux and Straub (11), Carleton (16), Smit and Kateman (25), Smit (26,27), Glasgow and Tenenbaum (28), Glasgow et al. (18), Handley (29), and Barnard-Smith and White (30).

The applications of the constant wall instruments are mainly for the determination of cooling or freezing curves, and not for heating or melting curves. This is probably due to the fact that when heat must be transported to the sample, the outer wall of the apparatus, and thus the isolating mantle, must be at a temperature much higher than when heat must be transported from the sample (1). Since due to radiation the isolating power of a vacuum jacket decreases rapidly at increasing temperatures, it is clear that the thermal head for heating a sample at a permissible rate will be lower than the opposite thermal head for cooling the sample at the same rate.

Depending upon the temperature range to be covered, the wall of the adapted wall instruments consists of a glass bulb immersed in a liquid bath or a thick cylindrical mantle made of metal. The temperature of the bath or of the metal mantle is adapted to the

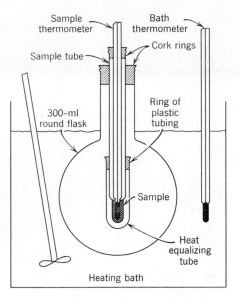

Fig. XI.5. Apparatus for determination of melting temperatures (16).

temperature of the sample so that the difference of the two temperatures remains constant. Between the wall and the measuring vessel containing the sample, there is an air space which provides the necessary insulation. The thermal gradient or difference usually amounts to about 2°C and the rate of heating of the sample is quite low, about 0.1–0.3 of a °C/min. This type of apparatus is not stirred.

A simple apparatus of the adapted wall type has been described by Carleton (16) and is a modification of the apparatus described by Smit (26). The apparatus is schematically illustrated in Figure XI.5.

The enclosure of the sample is in the form of a thin, uniform film surrounding the bulb of a 0.1°C graduated mercury thermometer. The thermometer was positioned by means of a bored cork in a glass sample tube drawn to the proper dimensions in the portion surrounding the thermometer bulb. To reduce the effects of temperature fluctuations, the sample tube was jacketed with a slightly larger tube retained by a plastic ring. The entire sample assembly was placed in a 300 ml round-bottomed flask, in such a position that

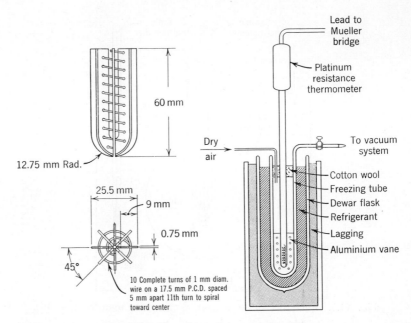

Fig. XI.6. Freezing-point apparatus (30).

the thermometer bulb was at the approximate center of the flask.
The flask was immersed to the neck in a suitable heating bath which
was provided with a stirrer, thermostat, and thermometer.   The volume of sample required for a determination was about 0.3 ml.   The
outside bath was heated at a rate of 0.3°C per 100 s or per minute.
A plot of sample temperature vs. time was started at 15 to 20°C.
below the melting point of the substance.

Another apparatus which was similar to that described previously
by Glasgow et al. (10), and modified by Barnard-Smith and White
(30), is schematically illustrated in Figure XI.6.   The sample,
usually about 25 ml, was frozen and melted in a double walled tube,
the rate of heat transfer from the refrigerant or heating bath to the
sample being controlled by the vacuum between the walls of the
tube.   A rotating stirrer was used and, for smaller samples, an
aluminum tube was inserted to reduce the volume of the sample
chamber.   The temperature of the sample was measured by a
platinum resistance thermometer and a Mueller bridge.   The

instrument could also be used for heat of fusion measurements by insertion of a series of aluminum vanes. These vanes assisted in the even distribution of heat throughout the sample.

D. Errors, Limitations, and Other Factors Affecting Results

The errors in the determination of temperature vs. heat content or time curves have been discussed in detail by Smit (31) and Mc-Cullough and Waddington (17). The former discussed the qualitative consideration concerning the rates of phase transitions, the rates of diffusion, and the temperature differences occurring with the "thin-film" method. The latter were concerned with the limitations of the calorimetric method based on the results of more than 125 melting-point studies.

1. LIMITATIONS OF THE DYNAMIC METHOD

a. *Solid–Liquid Transitions*

When heat is supplied to a system, its temperature will increase until the net rate of melting equals the rate of heat supply. When heat is withdrawn from the system, its temperature will decrease until the rate of heat production by crystallization equals the rate of cooling. This is only possible below a temperature, T_m, the temperature at which thermodynamic equilibrium exists. However, in this region, the rate of heat production may be low and may increase only slightly at decreasing temperatures. Consequently, the temperature obtained may differ appreciably from the equilibrium temperature. The temperature finally obtained remains constant so long as the rate of heat production of the system equals the rate of cooling. This is illustrated by the heating and cooling curves of antipyrine containing 9.1 mole-% acetanilide, as shown in Figure XI.7. The heating curve of pure antipyrine showed a range of constant temperature at 110.45°C, which appeared to be independent of the rate of heating. The cooling curve determined at a comparable rate of cooling showed a small undercooling peak and then the temperature raised to a maximum at about 109°C. The height of the maximum was dependent on the rate of cooling. The curves obtained by heating and cooling the antipyrine and 0.1 mole-% acetanilide mixture were comparable to those obtained with the pure antipyrine.

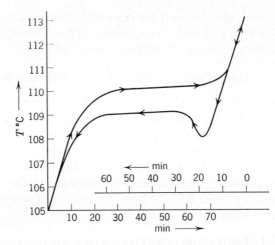

Fig. XI.7. Heating and cooling curves of a sample of antipyrine containing 0.1 mole-% acetanilide. Upper curve is the heating curve (31).

Similar analogous behavior has been observed with azobenzene, benzyl benzoate, and *p*-xylene, and slight differences with naphthalene.

b. Solid Phase Transitions

A heating curve usually shows the existence of *solid* → *solid* or enantiotropic transitions. When melting occurs before the *solid* → *solid* transition is completed, the melting curve will obviously be unreliable. Smit (31) recommended that the sample be stored for a period of time at a temperature above the transition temperature before determination of the melting curve.

c. Rates of Diffusion

When the solid and liquid of a multicomponent system are in thermodynamic equilibrium, the composition of the solid will usually differ from that of the liquid. When the system is submitted to further melting or crystallization, the composition of at least one of the phases will change in the vicinity of the contact surface. Diffusion tends to equalize the concentration differences occurring both in the solid and in the liquid phase and should, therefore, be promoted.

d. Effect of Stirring

Stirring promotes the homogeneity of the liquid phase only and does not affect the inhomogeneities occurring in the solid phase. Thus, even when stirring is applied, thick layers may be disadvantageous. Stirring is an advantage at times in that it may cause disintegration of solid particles which may promote the bulk rate of crystallization. The advantage is rather dubious, according to Smit (31), because stirring can only be applied over a limited range of solid–liquid ratios.

e. Rate of Heat Transport

When heat is supplied or withdrawn from a calorimeter, temperature differences will occur throughout all parts of the calorimetric system, including the wall, the sample, and even the thermometer. These differences constitute a source of errors, the magnitude of which depend on the rate of heating, the sizes of the system components, and the heat conductivities of the construction materials. The magnitude of these errors has been calculated by Smit (31).

f. Temperature Differences during Melting

Melting, of course, starts at the inner wall of the sample container and subsequently proceeds to the thermometer bulb. As soon as melting starts, the flow of heat to the thermometer decreases appreciably. It is not reduced to zero, however, because the temperature of the thermometer is below the temperature of the melting zone. The difference between the temperature indicated by the thermometer and the temperature of the melting zone constitutes an error which gradually decreases with time. The deviations will be large at the start of the melting process and gradually approach zero as the curve is continued. It is important to know within what time this error has decreased to a value not exceeding the limit of accuracy of the determination. An attempt has been made by Smit (31) to calculate this exact time.

g. Influence of Contact between Layers

Contact is never perfect between the glass wall, the sample, and the thermometer bulb. This imperfect contact can give rise to extra temperature differences. Heat can flow from the environment along the stem to the bulb of the thermometer and subsequently to the sample. The temperature of the thermometer will be high when imperfect contact exists between the sample and the bulb.

2. LIMITATIONS OF THE STATIC METHOD

The limitations of the static method undoubtedly apply to a greater or lesser extent to any melting-point method. These limitations are as follows (17):

a. Uncertainty of Impurity Values

Inhomogeneous distribution of impurity in the liquid phase may result in low values of N_2^* because the slope of the melting curve is usually decreased by this effect. A more important source of error, however, is the fairly common formation of a solid solution. The formation of solid solutions has long been recognized as a possible limitation of all melting-point purity methods, but it has not been realized that the phenomenon is so common.

b. Evidence of Solid-Solution Formation

It is not unreasonable to expect that solid solutions may be formed in highly purified samples, for the impurities may often be isomeric with the main component. About one-half of the melting curves observed by McCullough and Waddington (17) showed moderate to pronounced deviation from linearity of the T vs. $1/F$ plots, indicative of solid-solution formation. In fact, linear melting curves over the entire range of fractions melted are rare. Both the formation of solid solutions and inhomogeneous distribution of impurity will usually cause impurity values calculated from melting-point studies to be too low. The calculation of impurity values from the slope of the melting curve at high fractions melted will minimize errors in most cases.

c. Application of Solid-Solution Theory

If a melting curve shows evidence of appreciable solid-solution formation, it may require application of a solid-solution treatment (14,15) to give an accurate impurity value, although Smit (1) has criticized one of the treatments (14). Unfortunately, the method often has failed to give an adequate representation of observed melting curves. In some instances, the solid-solution treatment has given an excellent representation of experimental data, but the high sensitivity of the method to small thermometric errors makes the calculated impurity values unreliable. For example, the difference in temperatures observed with 70 and 90% of a sample melted may easily be in error by ±0.0005°C. For the solid-solution treatment, such an error would correspond to an uncertainty of 500% in the impurity value for very pure compounds with normal cryoscopic constants, whereas the same 0.0005°C error corresponds of 150% uncertainty if solid insolubility is assumed.

3. Comparison of Results Obtained by the Static and Dynamic Methods

It is rather interesting to note that the impurity values determined by static methods are systematically lower than those determined on the same sample by dynamic methods (3,4). However, an extremely careful study by Glasgow et al. (18) on a sample of

TABLE XI.2
Comparison of the Results from Dynamic and Static Methods (18)

| | Purity, mole-% | | |
Sample	Computed from contamination	Dynamic	Static
A	100[a]	$99.99_4 \pm 0.002$	99.9937 ± 0.0010
B	99.9964	$99.97_0 \pm 0.004$	99.958 ± 0.005
C	99.9610	$99.94_0 \pm 0.002$	99.947 ± 0.005

[a] The "pure" sample was assumed to be pure beyond the sensitivity of the methods of analysis employed.

very pure benzene contaminated by known amounts of n-heptane showed that the divergence between the two methods of determination was not as large as was formerly obtained. The results of this study are given in Table XI.2. It is suggested that the difference in values may be due to chemi-sorbed water as a source of contamination.

4. RECOMMENDATIONS

The following recommendations have been suggested by Smit (31) for thermal analysis:

(1) When a static method is used, each period of heat supply to the substance should be followed by a period of "adiabatic conditions" of sufficient length so as to approach equilibrium to a desired extent.

(2) For the dynamic method, heating curves are preferred to cooling curves.

(3) Before starting a measurement of a heating curve, the sample should be kept at a temperature slightly below the initial melting point for at least one hour.

(4) The stirring method for determining heating curves is not recommended.

(5) The rate of heating of samples with small heats of fusion should be decreased as far as practical.

(6) Subject each curve to an internal check and also select a reliable part of the curve for purity determination. Besides experimental checks on the technique, the curve should be checked to see if it obeys the equation (31):

$$T_y = T_a - \frac{C_f C_m}{C_f + Y(C_m - C_f)} \cdot p \qquad \text{(XI.28)}$$

where T_y is the temperature at which a fraction Y of the sample has melted, T_a is the melting point of the absolutely pure substance, C_f and C_m are constants, and p is the mole-% of contamination present in the sample.

Equations (XI.17) can be rearranged to give

$$T_y = C_1 - \frac{C_2}{C_3 + Y} \qquad \text{(XI.29)}$$

where C_1, C_2, and C_3 are constants which can be resolved algebraically by selecting three pairs of corresponding values of T_y and Y. If the T_y values of the melting curve are plotted as a function of $1/(C_3 + Y)$, the plot should be a straight line with slope C_2.

With all of the above distressing sources of error and limitations, thermal analysis has several incomparable advantages (1). Being a physical method, it may be applied without any knowledge concerning the chemical properties of the main component or the contaminants of the sample. It is sensitive, although not equally sensitive, to all types of contaminants. When the sample may be considered as a binary system, it certainly permits quantitative determination of its content of contaminants.

E. Applications to Impurity Determinations and Other Problems

The impurities in synthetic mixtures of naphthalene with anthracene or diphenyl were determined by the melting curve method of

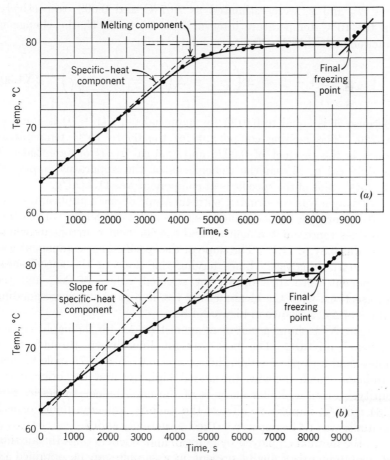

Fig. XI.8. (*a*) Melting curve of pure naphthalene; (*b*) melting curve of naphthalene containing 1.45 mole-% diphenyl (16).

Carleton (16).   Melting curves for pure naphthalene alone and for naphthalene containing 1.45 mole-% diphenyl are given in Figure XI.8.   The ideal-melting flat lines extend across from T_0, and diagonal lines representing heating without melting (specific heat effect) are drawn in at selected values of ΔT.   Slopes of these lines were obtained by resolving the slope of the equilibrium curve at 70°C into separate specific-heat and melting components, calculated from the dimensions of the apparatus and the properties of naphthalene.

The calculation was as follows for pure naphthalene: the quantities, T_0 and x, were estimated as 79.7°C and 0.003, respectively. In the 10°C temperature interval from 65 to 75°C, the change in fraction melted, $\Delta(1-f)$ was calculated from

$$\Delta(1-f) = \Delta\left(\frac{x}{N_2}\right) = \Delta\left(\frac{x}{x+A(T_0-T)}\right) \qquad (XI.30)$$

Because A is equal to 0.0184 for naphthalene, $\Delta(1-f)$ is equal to 0.0226.   The melting component for the 65 to 75°C temperature range is the product of 0.0226 and 35.6 cal/g(ΔH of naphthalene), or 0.81 cal/g.   From the dimensions of the apparatus employed, the total value of the specific heat component was 11.1 cal/g.

A triangle was constructed with the slope of the equilibrium curve at 70°C forming the long side as shown in Figure XI.8a.   The other two sides represent the melting and specific-heat components whose ratio was 0.81 to 11.1.   The slope of the specific-heat component was used in the analysis.   Lines having the slope of the specific-heat component were then drawn for selected values of ΔT, and the intersections with the ideal-melting flat line gave the corresponding values of ΔT, as shown in Figure XI.8b.

Figure XI.9 shows a plot of Δt against $\Delta t/\Delta T$ for the naphthalene–biphenyl mixture.   The best straight line drawn through these points had a slope of -0.95; hence $x = 0.0175 = 1.75$ mole-% contaminant which includes the added biphenyl and the original impurity.   From a similar analysis of the naphthalene by itself, $x = 0.34$ mole-% impurities.   Thus, the mole-% biphenyl found experimentally was 1.41 compared to the 1.45 actually added.

In the method employed by Schwab and Wichers (32), the amount of contaminant originally present in a sample can be obtained by determining the freezing curve of the original sample and also the

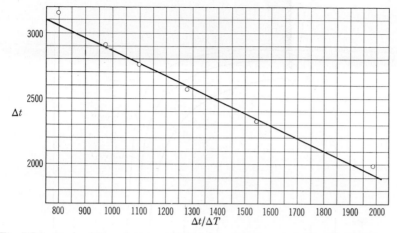

Fig. XI.9. Derived line of Δt vs. $\Delta t/\Delta T$ for naphthalene + 1.45 mole-% dipheny (16).

curve of the original sample plus a known amount of contaminant. The above comparative method is said to be applicable even if the fraction frozen does not vary linearly with time. Herington (33) has also described the use of this method using a similar experimental apparatus as previously described above.

A set of freezing curves used in the comparative method is given in Figure XI.10. The difference, ΔT, between the initial freezing temperature and the temperature at a time equal to half that required for complete freezing is found, as shown in curve *1*. A known amount of impurity, x_1 mole-%, is then added and another freezing curve is obtained using the same rate of cooling as previously employed. A value, ΔT_1, for the difference between the new initial freezing temperature and the temperature at a time equal to half that required for complete freezing is thus obtained. The same procedure is carried out after the addition of a second amount of impurity, x_2, and another ΔT_2 value obtained.

From the following relationship

$$(\Delta T_1 - \Delta T)/x_1 = (\Delta T_2 - \Delta T)/x_2 \qquad (XI.31)$$

the amount of contaminant originally present, x, can be given by

$$x = \frac{x_1 \, \Delta T}{\Delta T_1 - \Delta T} \qquad (XI.32)$$

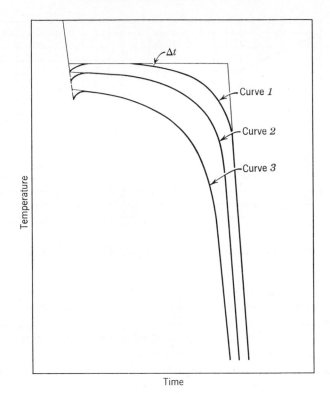

Fig. XI.10. Temperature-time curves obtained in freezing experiments (33).

The experiments are carried out in duplicate or triplicate and the standard error computed. The standard error was found to vary from sample to sample but the mean of several results indicated a value of approximately $\pm x/8$ for this quantity.

If this technique is used, it is important to choose a suitable substance to add to the system. In general, the melting point of this material should not be higher than the melting point of the main material and should have a lower melting point. The chosen material should not form solid solutions nor should it form a compound with the main component.

When a freezing curve is obtained, the values may vary at times, due to the nonlineasity of the temperature in the entire system, defects in the temperature detection, and so on. The determination of an actual curve to fit the experimental data presents a difficult problem. Various techniques, such as the use of a flexible spline, have been employed to draw this curve. An optical method, using a lantern projector, has been employed successfully by Saylor (34).

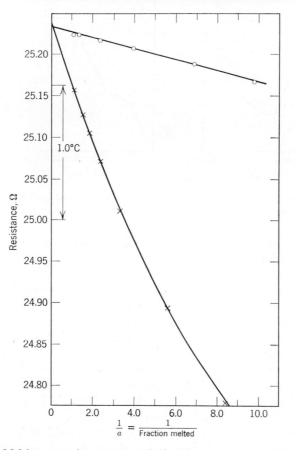

Fig. XI.11. Melting curve for n-pentane (20). (O), n-pentane, 99.80% pure; (×) same + 2.26 mole-% iso-octane.

Another method that has been suggested is that given by Kienitz (35). A hyperbola is constructed from certain values of time and temperature which best represent the measured curve. In this way, the freezing point of a sample is better obtained than with the

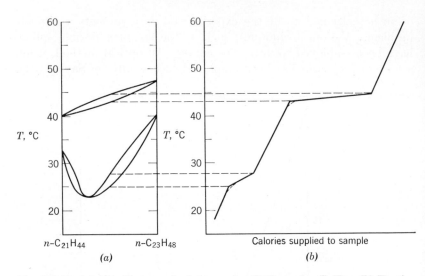

Fig. XI.12. (a) T-x diagram of mixtures of n-$C_{21}H_{44}$ and n-$C_{23}H_{48}$; (b) Heating curve for 50 mole-% n-$C_{21}H_{44}$ and 50 mole-% n-$C_{23}H_{48}$ (23).

analytical or geometrical methods of evaluation via three points on the equilibrium curve.

The purity of a n-pentane sample was determined by a calorimetric method by Clarke et al. (20). The results obtained for pure n-pentane and for a synthetic n-pentane–iso-octane mixture are given in the resistance (temperature) vs. time curve in Figure XI.11. For purity determination, these data have been converted to fraction melted after each equilibration period by allowing for the heat necessary to raise the temperature of the solid and liquid and for the amount of heat leak from radiation and conduction. The heat of fusion determined from this work was 2090 calories per mole which gave a purity of 99.79 mole-% for the n-pentane.

To the sample of pure n-pentane, 2.40 mole-% of iso-octane was added. The melting curve so obtained showed considerable curvature, while that for the pure n-pentane was a straight line. From the slope of the line, a purity of 97.58 mole-% was obtained compared to a theoretical value of 97.53 mole-%.

The purity of two samples of pentaborane was also determined with this instrument. Sample I was 99.99 mole-% pure, while Sample II analyzed as 99.91 mole-%. On mixing the two samples together to obtain a sample purity of 99.94 mole-%, the experimental calorimetric purity was 99.949 mole-%.

The purity of several highly reactive substances, such as titanium-(IV) chloride, was obtained in a special freezing point apparatus developed by Glasgow and Tenenbaum (28). The freezing point of titanium(IV) tetrachloride under saturation pressure with zero impurity was calculated to be $-24.10 \pm 0.01 °C$.

The thermal analysis of a number of normal alkanes was studied by Mazee (23). In the case of a binary mixture in which the components are completely miscible both in the liquid and solid states, the curves in Figure XI.12 were obtained. Curve (a) is the temperature–composition phase diagram while (b) is the heating curve so obtained on a 50 mole-% $n\text{-}C_{21}H_{24}$–50 mole-% $n\text{-}C_{23}H_{48}$ synthetic mixture. The heating curve is simple and easy to interpret and leaves no room for uncertainties. The amount of "impurity," in this case the amount of the second component, can be calculated with sufficient accuracy.

When certain organic salts, such as cyclohexylamine stearate, cyclohexylamine palmitate, and others, are melted, they undergo the probable double decomposition reaction

$$CS + DP \rightleftharpoons DS + CP$$

where CS and DP are the amine salts. The system consisting of these four substances is a ternary system of the reciprocal or metathetical type. Systems of this type have been investigated by thermal analysis by Skau et al. (36).

References

1. Smit, W. M., Z. Elektrochem., 66, 779 (1962).
2. Sturtevant, J. M., "Calorimetry," in Techniques of Organic Chemistry, 2nd ed., Vol. I, A. Weissberger, ed., Interscience, New York, 1949, Part 1, p. 731.
3. Cines, M. R., "Solid–Liquid Equilibria of Hydrocarbons," in Physical Chemistry of Hydrocarbons, Vol. I., A. Farkas, ed., Academic Press, New York, 1950, Chapter 8.
4. Mathieu, M. P., Acad. Roy. Belg. Classe Sci. Mem., 28, No. 2 (1953).
5. Smit, W. M., Thermal Analysis, Elsevier Press, Amsterdam, 1959.
6. White, W. P., J. Phys. Chem., 24, 393 (1920).
7. Andrews, D. H., G. T. Kohmann, and J. Johnston, J. Phys. Chem., 29, 914 (1925).
8. Skau, E. L., J. Am. Chem. Soc., 57, 243 (1935).

9. Mair, B. J., A. R. Glasgow, and F. D. Rossini, *J. Res. Natl. Bur. Std.* (*U.S.*), **26**, 591 (1941).
10. Glasgow, A. R., A. J. Streiff, and F. D. Rossini, *J. Res. Natl. Bur. Std.* (*U.S.*), **35**, 355 (1945).
11. Malotaux, R. N. M. A., and J. Straub, *Rec. Trav. Chim.*, **52**, 275 (1933).
12. Thomas, S. B., and C . S. Parks, *J. Phys. Chem.*, **35**, 2091 (1931).
13. Rossini, F. D., *Chemical Thermodynamics*, Wiley, New York, 1950.
14. Mastrangelo, S. V. R., and R. W. Dornte, *J. Am. Chem. Soc.*, **77**, 6200 (1955).
15. Badley, J. H., *J. Phys. Chem.*, **63**, 1991 (1959).
16. Carleton, L. T., *Anal. Chem.*, **27**, 845 (1955).
17. McCullough, J. P., and G. Waddington, *Anal. Chim. Acta*, **17**, 80 (1957).
18. Glasgow, A. R., G. S. Ross, A. T. Horton, D. Enagonio, H. D. Dixon, C. P. Saylor, G. T. Furukawa, M. L. Reilly, and J. M. Henning, *Anal. Chim. Acta*, **17**, 54 (1957).
19. Stull, D. R., *Anal. Chim. Acta*, **17**, 133 (1957).
20. Clarke, J. T., H. L. Johnston, and W. De Sorbo, *Anal. Chem.*, **25**, 1156 (1953).
21. Aston, J. G., and H. L. Fink, *Anal. Chem.*, **19**, 218 (1947).
22. Pilcher, G., *Anal. Chim. Acta*, **17**, 144 (1957).
23. Mazee, W. M., *Anal. Chim. Acta*, **17**, 97 (1957).
24. Ruehrwein, R. A., and H. M. Huffman, *J. Am. Chem. Soc.*, **65**, 1620 (1943).
25. Smit, W. M., and G. Kateman, *Anal. Chim. Acta*, **17**, 161 (1957).
26. Smit, W. M., *Chem. Weekblad*, **36**, 750 (1939).
27. Smit, W. M., *Rec. Trav. Chim.*, **75**, 1309 (1956).
28. Glasgow, A. R., and M. Tenenbaum, *Anal. Chem.*, **28**, 1907 (1956).
29. Handley, R., *Anal. Chim. Acta*, **17**, 115 (1957).
30. Barnard-Smith, E. G., and P. T. White, *Anal. Chim. Acta*, **17**, 125 (1957).
31. Smit, W. M., *Anal. Chim. Acta*, **17**, 23 (1957).
32. Schwab, F. W., and E. Wichers, *Temperature—Its Measurement and Control in Science and Industry*, Reinhold, New York, 1941, p. 256.
33. Herington, E. F. G., *Anal. Chim. Acta*, **17**, 15 (1957).
34. Saylor, C. P., *Anal. Chim. Acta*, **17**, 36 (1957).
35. Kienitz, H., *Anal. Chim. Acta*, **17**, 43 (1957).
36. Skau, E. L., F. C. Magne, and R. R. Mod, *Anal. Chim. Acta*, **17**, 107 (1957).
37. Gunn, S. R., *Anal. Chem.*, **34**, 1292 (1962).

CHAPTER XII

MISCELLANEOUS THERMAL METHODS

There are a number of other thermal methods which are not as widely employed as those previously discussed. These methods may find extensive use in analytical chemistry at some future date, hence, they are included in this chapter. The techniques discussed here include thermoluminescence, oxyluminescence, dilatometry, electrical conductivity, high-temperature x-ray diffraction, and others. There are other miscellaneous methods, such as thermomanometry and thermomagnetic analysis, which will not be included here.

A. Thermoluminescence

The technique of thermoluminescence involves the measurement of the emitted light energy of a sample as a function of temperature as it is heated to elevated temperatures at a slow, constant rate, below that of incandescence. The curve so obtained, called a "glow curve," consists of a series of peaks or maximas which are caused by the emission of light energy at various elevated temperatures. The intensity and temperatures at which the peaks appear may be used to characterize or identify the sample or may by used for the evaluation of catalysts, radiation damage to sample, dosimetry, or for geological age determination of geological materials. Indeed, the technique has been found to be extremely useful for geochemical investigations of limestone and dolomite rock deposits.

The early applications of thermoluminescence to the analysis and identification of rocks have been made by Deribere (1), Garlick (2), Kohler and Leitmeier (3), Royer (4), Saurin (5), and Northrup and Lee (6); the more recent applications include those by Saunders (7), Parks (8), Daniels et al. (9), Lewis (10), and Bose et al. (11). The applications of thermoluminescence to problems of geological thermometry and age determination have been discussed by Ingerson (12) and Zeller (13). Excellent reviews on the general subject of thermoluminescence include those by Daniels et al. (9), Bose et al.

(11), Mott and Gurney (14), Fonda and Seitz (15), Kroger (16), Leverenz (17), and Pringsheim (18).

The property of thermoluminescence is exhibited by crystalline substances, for example, the metal salt halides, which have been exposed to radioactivity of various types or to x-rays. The radiation causes the dislocation of electrons in the crystal which may result in an F-center; the release of these various F-centers or electron traps to lower energy states is brought about by increasing the crystal temperature and is accompanied by the emission of light energy. The emission of light energy is dependent upon changes in crystalline structure, concentration of impurities in the crystal, and to past physical treatment.

The mechanism of electron-trap formation in the crystals is beyond the scope of this discussion. In general, an electron trap may be caused by (9): (a) imperfections and vacancies in the crystal lattice produced at the time the crystal was formed, or created later by mechanical pressure or thermal treatment; (b) statistical imperfections that are due to kinetic motions and that increase at higher temperatures; (c) distortions caused by impurity ions of larger or smaller size than those comprising the crystal lattice; and (d) ion dislocations, or holes, produced by radioactive bombardment. The latter type of electron-trap formation is by far the most common and can be produced by bombardment of the crystal with hard or soft x-rays, γ-rays, α-particles, and β-rays. An energy of about 10 eV is sufficient to remove electrons from ions in most crystal lattices and to provide them with enough energy to move about in the crystal. However, unless there are traps into which the electrons can go, there is no mechanism to provide for thermoluminescence.

The kinetics of the isothermal decay of the thermoluminescence of single crystals of lithium fluoride has been determined by Boyd (19). Using a model analogous to the theory of absolute reaction rates for chemical reactions, the intensity of thermoluminescence, I, as a function of time, was shown to be

$$I = \frac{\bar{E}_1 k_3 \left[K/(K+1)\right]}{\left[k_3 \left[(K/(K+1)\right]t + 1/n_3^0\right]^2} \qquad \text{(XII.1)}$$

where $\bar{E}_1$ is the average energy involved in the transition; k_3 is the rate constant; and $K = n_2/n_1$, where n_1, n_2, and n_3 are the number of molecules in the initial, activated, and final states, respectively.

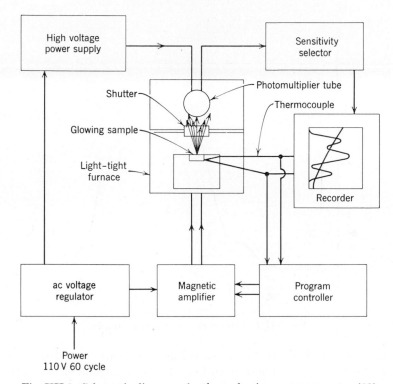

Fig. XII.1. Schematic diagram of a thermoluminescence apparatus (10).

Various instruments have been described for the measurement of the thermoluminescence of solid samples. Instrumental arrangements have been described by Urbach (20), Randall and Wilkins (21), Boyd (19), Daniels et al. (9), Saunders (7), Parks (8), and Lewis (10). Basically, the apparatus consists of the following components: (a) a heated sample block, (b) a sample temperature programmer or power supply, (c) a photomultiplier tube and power supply, and (d) a recorder, either of the two-pen strip-chart or X-Y function type. Such an apparatus, as described by Lewis (10), is illustrated in Figure XII.1.

The glow curves are normally obtained at a heating rate of 1°C/min. As the sample temperature is increased, the sample emits light which is detected by the photomultiplier tube whose output current varies linearly with the intensity of the emitted light. This

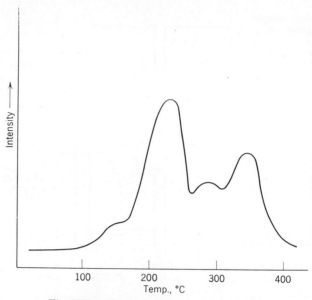

Fig. XII.2. Typical glow curve of a sample.

output current is converted into a voltage signal and recorded on one channel of the strip-chart recorder. The other channel of the recorder is connected to a thermocouple imbedded in the sample chamber and hence records the sample temperature. Thus, both light intensity emitted and temperature of the sample are recorded as a function of time. The temperature range of the apparatus is from ambient to 500°C. Glow curves can be obtained on 50 mg of finely powdered sample.

A typical glow curve is illustrated in Figure XII.2. The intensity of the emitted light is measured in arbitrary units (but can be converted into microlamberts or lumens, if necessary), while the temperature is recorded in °C.

The types of substances which are thermoluminescent, either in their natural state or after radiation bombardment, include (9): the alkali metal halides, calcite, dolomite, fluorite, aluminum oxide, magnesium oxide, gypsum, quartz, glass, feldspars, feldspathoids, certain dried clays, and ceramic materials. Of over 3000 rock samples examined for thermoluminescence, some 75% of them showed visible

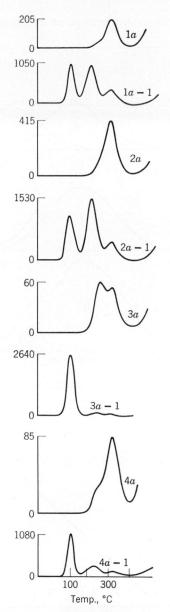

Fig. XII.3. Natural and γ-ray activated glow curves of some calcite-dolomite samples. The -1 indicates γ-ray irradiated (10).

Sample	Dolomite, %	Calcite, %	Carbonate, %
1a	89.7	10.3	100.0
2a	92.2	7.9	92.5
3a	0.0	100.0	100.0
4a	48.6	51.4	100.0

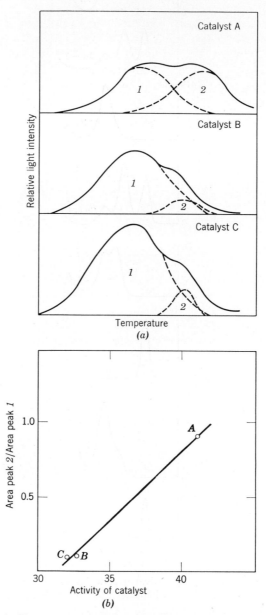

Fig. XII.4. (a) Glow curves of catalysts (9). (b) Thermoluminescence and catalytic activity.

light emission (9). Nearly all limestones and acid igneous rocks are naturally thermoluminescent, due mainly to the presence of trace elements of uranium, thorium, and so on. Calcium and magnesium carbonates show light-yellow to orange colored light emission, while potassium and sodium feldspars exhibit white to blue-violet light emission.

The glow curves obtained are characteristic of a specific sample or substance and yield information concerning specific impurities present or that the sample has had certain heat treatments or physical histories. However, glow curves are not suitable for the analysis of chemical compounds but are useful for identification and control purposes only. This is illustrated by the glow curves for several dolomite and calcite samples in Figure XII.3. The curves definitely show differences based upon the composition of the sample but could hardly be used for the analysis of, say, magnesium or calcium contents.

Saunders (7) has shown that the intensities of the peaks in the glow curves increased with increase in depth in a Niagara limestone deposit. The glow curves were useful for studying the various strata of the deposit. Parks (8) reported a similar study relating glow curves of the samples with the identification and characterization of a formation, identification of the top and bottom of limestone formations, and the characterization of erosion or nondeposition of zones.

Garino-Canina and Cohen (22) used glow curves to characterize germanium oxide–aluminum oxide mixtures. It was found that after excitation by ultraviolet radiation, the peak positions, between 50 and 70°C, and the peak intensities of the curves varied with a change in alumina content introduced into the germanium oxide glass. The amount of alumina varied from 0 to 5%.

A rather interesting application of this technique is in the evaluation of the efficiency of surface catalysis (9,23). The glow curves for three commercial alumina catalysts are given in Figure XII.4; the relationship between glow curve peak area and catalyst activity are given in Figure XII.4 b. The total glow curve is composed of two peaks, the areas under peak number 2 were related to catalytic activity. As can be seen from Figure XII.4 b, an excellent correlation exists between the peak areas and the activity of the catalysts. It should be noted that many catalysts do not give any thermoluminescence and in other cases there is no apparent correlation. A number of catalysts that have been examined do exhibit such a correlation and hence suggest thermoluminescence as a useful tool for catalyst evaluation.

Thermoluminescence has been used to study radiation damage (24) and also the radioactivity of certain minerals (3,8,25,26).

B. Oxyluminescence

Closely related to thermoluminescence is the technique of oxyluminescence. This term was adopted by Ashby (27) to describe the emission of light when certain polymers are heated in air or oxygen to 150–200°C. Oxygen must be present for light emission to take

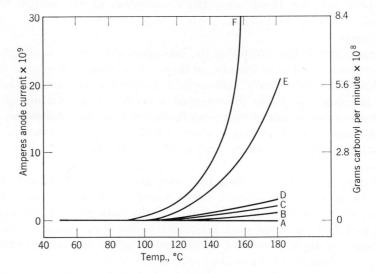

Fig. XII.5. Effect of oxygen concentration in the intensity of oxyluminescence of polypropylene. (A) Argon; (B) 2.6% oxygen in nitrogen; (C) 6.4% oxygen in nitrogen; (D) 11.0% oxygen in nitrogen; (E) air; and (F) oxygen (27).

place; the intensity of the light is proportional to the concentration of the oxygen in contact with the polymer surface. Experimentally, the same type of apparatus is used as was described for thermoluminescence studies. The amount of light emitted is quite weak and varies from 10^{-10}–10^{-8} lumens on the polymer samples studied.

With nylon, the strongest emitter thus far examined, the emitted light at 200°C was just bright enough to be seen by the human eye. Preliminary studies on polypropylene showed that one-half of the emitted light was in the 4200–5150 Å wavelength range and the other half in the 3000–4200 Å wavelength range.

The intensity of the oxyluminescence is affected by the concentration of the oxygen in the gas in contact with the sample surface, as is shown with polypropylene in Figure XII.5. The temperature of the polymer was increased from ambient to 180°C at a heating rate of 6°C/min.

Since the presence of antioxidants decreases the intensity of the emitted light, the technique is useful for the screening of compounds for anti-oxidant action. Any substance which decreases the initial light emission is a potential antioxidant.

C. Dilatometry

The thermal expansion of a metallic or ceramic substance is a physical parameter of utmost importance to the development of new alloys and ceramic materials. The determination of the volume change of a substance, usually as a function of temperature, is called dilatometry, or more precisely, thermodilatometric analysis (TDA). The technique involves the continuous measurement of the sample length as it is heated or cooled at a constant known rate. Temperature ranges employed vary from −200 to 2200°C. Pronounced changes in sample volume occur during most *solid* → *solid* phase transitions, hence, TDA is a valuable tool for the detection of such phenomena.

Two experimental methods have been employed to determine the TDA curves of a solid substance, they are: (*a*) normal or standard TDA in which the change in length of a single sample is determined as a function of temperature; and (*b*) differential TDA in which the thermal expansion of the sample is compared to that of a standard sample and the difference in thermal expansion between the two substances is determined as a function of temperature. The differential method is, of course, more sensitive and probably more accurate because instrumental environmental conditions (room temperature changes, electronic component stability, and so on) cancel out. Various transducers have been employed to detect the change in specimen length, among then are: (*a*) light-beam optical lever

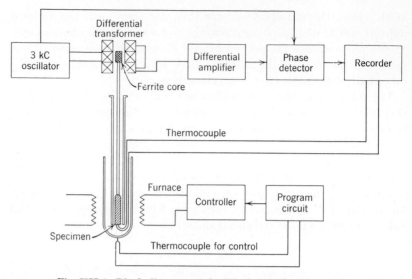

Fig. XII.6. Block diagram of the Rigaku Denki dilatometer.

(28,29); (b) variable inductance transformer (30); (c) strain gage (31); (d) dial indicator (57); (e) interferometry (32); (f) microformer (variable differential transformer) (33); and others.

A block diagram of a standard automatic recording dilatometer is given in Figure XII.6. This apparatus is manufactured by the Rigaku Denki Co. Ltd. (8, Kanda-Daidokorocho, Chiyoda-Ku, Tokyo, Japan). The sample, contained in the furnace assembly, is connected to a differential transformer by a silica push rod. Movement of the ferrite core in the transformer provides an output voltage which is proportional to the linear movement of the core. This output voltage is then amplified, demodulated, and recorded on the Y-axis of a X–Y recorder. The temperature of the sample, as detected by a thermocouple, is recorded on the X-axis of the recorder. Thus, a plot of sample thermal expansion vs. temperature is obtained. A detailed diagram of the standard sample holder assembly is given in Figure XII.7, while the differential arrangement is illustrated in Figure XII.8.

A rapid quenching type of dilatometer which is designed to study phase transformation characteristics of steels during rapid quenching from high to low temperatures is also available (Rigaku Denki

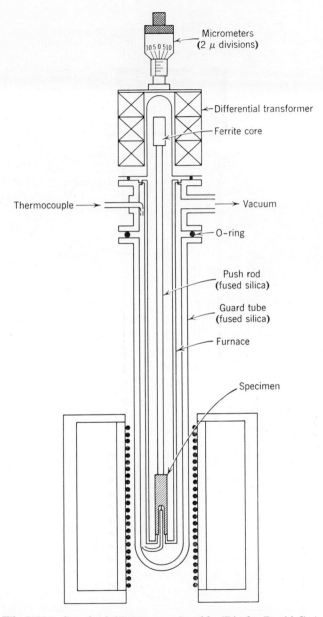

Fib. XII.7. Standard dilatometer assembly (Rigaku Denki Co.).

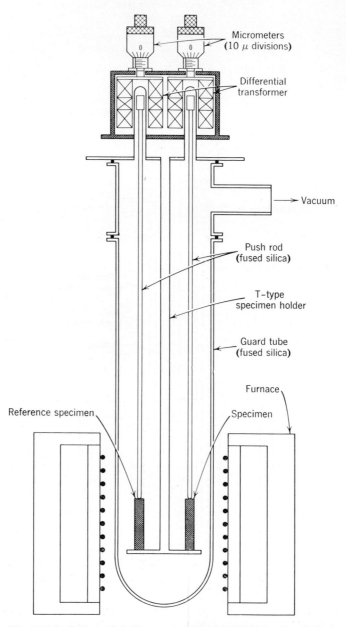

Fig. XII.8. Differential dilatometer assembly (Rigaku Denki Co.).

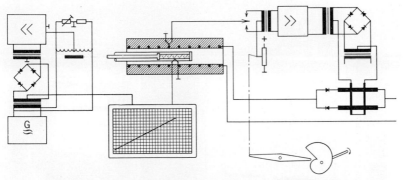

Fig. XII.9. Linseis dilatometer (William J. Hacker & Co. Inc.).

Co.). The sample is heated to quenching temperature in an upper furnace, the detecting assembly attached to it, and the sample and detecting assembly rapidly immersed in the quenching medium (oil or water), which is contained below the furnace. Provision is made for the rapid recording of the differential transformer voltage output, such as a recording oscillograph or high speed potentiometric recorder.

A schematic diagram of the Linseis dilatometer (sold in the U.S.A. by William J. Hacker & Co., Inc., P.O. Box 646, West Caldwell, New Jersey) is given in Figure XII.9.

The instrument consists of the same basic components as discussed for previous instruments. An iron core in an induction coil is used to detect changes in volume of the sample. By use of a unique amplification potentiometer, an amplification of up to 10 000 times may be obtained for the linear displacement signal. Furnaces may be obtained for operation up to 2200°C, as well as a low temperature unit which can be used over the temperature range from ambient to −200°C. A special quenching type of dilatometer is also available. Various furnace atmospheres, from high vacuum to gases at atmospheric pressure, may be employed.

A recording dilatometer is also manufactured and sold by the Harrop Precision Furnace Co. (3470 East Fifth Avenue, Columbus 19, Ohio).

The Harrop dilatometer is shown in Figure XII.10. The sensitivity of the apparatus is 0.0001 in. or less with an accuracy (3 in. sample) of ±0.05% from 0–950°C, and ±0.1% from 950–

Fig. XII.10. Harrop Direct-Reading Dilatometer.

1500°C. The difference between the two is attributed to the different push rods employed; silica to 950°C and alumina from 950 to 1500°C.

The dilatometer curves can be obtained either as a function of temperature (TDA) curve), as is illustrated in Figure XII.11a, or as a function of time, at constant temperature, as shown in Figure XII.11b. In the case of the former, the TDA curves provide information concerning phase transformations and so on, while in the latter, the kinetics of the transformation may be obtained.

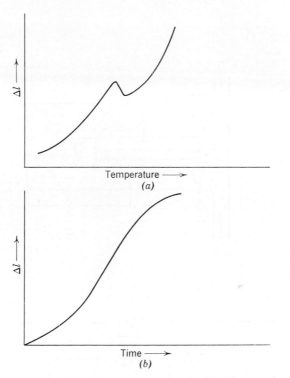

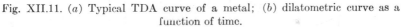

Fig. XII.11. (a) Typical TDA curve of a metal; (b) dilatometric curve as a function of time.

D. Electrical Conductivity

The continuous measurement of the change of electrical resistance or conductivity of a sample as a function of temperature is a useful technique for the study of polymorphic phase transformation temperatures. This method may be used to supplement other thermal methods such as differential thermal analysis or calorimetry and may be more useful than the above methods in certain cases. In general, the instrumentation is more elementary than DTA, but the applicability is not as great as in the latter. A combined DTA–electrical conductivity apparatus has previously been described in Chapter VI by Berg and Burmistrova (34).

The thermal coefficient of electrical resistance of a sample changes during a phase transformation because of a change in ionic mobility

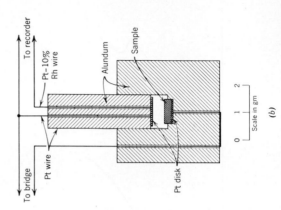

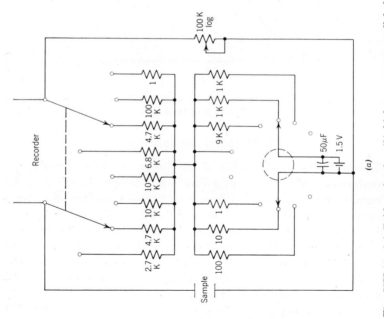

Fig. XII.12. (a) Bridge circuit; (b) high-temperature cell holder for electrical resistance measurements (35).

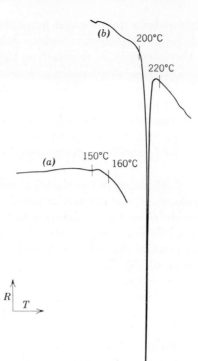

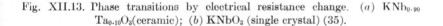

Fig. XII.13. Phase transitions by electrical resistance change. (*a*) KNb$_{0.90}$
Ta$_{0.10}$O$_3$(ceramic); (*b*) KNbO$_3$ (single crystal) (35).

within the lattice (i.e., fusion) or because of a change in the electronic
energy levels (35).   This change in resistance as a function of temperature may be easily measured by use of a dc or ac bridge circuit
and appropriate recording equipment.

Instruments capable of measuring the change in electrical conductivity of a solid sample as a function of temperature have been described by Garn and Flaschen (35), Glaser and Moskowitz (36),
Reisman et al. (37), Colner and Zmeskal (38), Shimizu (39), and
Berg and Burmistrova (34).

The bridge circuit and high temperature sample holder described
by Garn and Flaschen (35) are illustrated in Figure XII.12. The
bridge circuit is rather standard in that bridge potentials from
0.0015 to 1.5 V can be obtained from a single cell.   The output from

the bridge is amplified by a dc microvolt amplifier and recorded on one channel of a $X_1 - X_2$ strip-chart recorder. Sample temperature, as detected by a thermocouple, is recorded on the other channel of the recorder.

The sample is placed between two disk-shaped platinum electrodes. These electrodes are 9 and 12 mm in diameter, respectively, by 10 mil thick and retain the sample by a weight-loaded contact for good electrical connections. Sample temperature was measured by a platinum–platinum–10% rhodium thermocouple welded to the upper disk.

There is a marked difference in the electrical resistance curves for pure crystalline potassium niobate and a powdered $KNb_{0.90} Ta_{0.10}$-O_3 mixture. These differences are illustrated in Figure XII.13 (35). The pure $KNbO_3$ exhibits a sharp crystalline phase transition between 200 and 220°C while the mixture showed a gradual resistance change beginning at about 150°C.

The change in electrical conductivity of a sample, coupled with DTA, is a useful combination of techniques to study *solid–solid* reactions, as was shown by Berg and Burmistrova (34). There was a sharp increase in electrical conductivity at the onset of the solid state reactions. Electrical conductivity was also used to study the fusion of pure substances and eutectic mixtures, and to detect polymorphic transitions of salts. The electrical conductivity of the fused salt can also be used to determine its purity (34).

E. Miscellaneous Thermal Methods

1. AUTOMATIC MELTING POINT DETERMINATION

With all of the sources of error inherent with the determination of melting points by the capillary tube method (40), it is surprising that so few automatic melting point instruments have been developed and described in the literature. The first automatic apparatus was described by Muller and Zenchelsky (41) in 1952, followed by an instrument developed by Furst and Shapiro (42) in 1954. Both units employ a photoelectric device for detection of the fusion point of the substance.

The apparatus of Muller and Zenchelsky (41) is illustrated schematically in Figure XII.14. The sensing and control circuit employed makes use of the fact that polycrystalline substances scatter

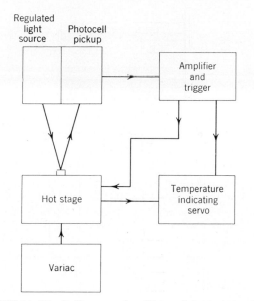

Fig. XII.14. Block diagram of melting-point apparatus (41).

light while shiny metallic surfaces give specular reflection. If a beam of light is incident upon a polished metal surface, it will be reflected in a beam at an angle that is equal to the angle of incidence. If a thin film of powdered sample is placed on the metallic surface, the light intensity at the photocell will diminish because the incident light is now scattered in many directions. On melting, the metal surface is again visible beneath the transparent liquid film, thus giving rise to specular reflection once again, causing the photocell to register maximum intensity.

The sample is heated in the hot stage assembly, illustrated in Figure XII.15, at heating rates of less than 5°C/min. The sample temperature, detected by a thermocouple located in the metal block, is indicated by a Helipot Duodial connected to a servo motor and servo amplifier. On fusion of the sample, as detected by the photocell pick-up, the servomotor is automatically interrupted by a Schmitt trigger circuit and relay, thus indicating the sample fusion temperature. The fusion temperatures, in the range from 68 to 215°C, can be read to ± 0.25°C with an accuracy and precision well within those required for practical organic chemistry.

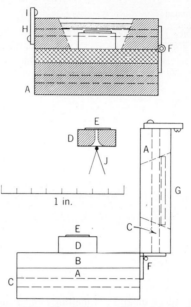

Fig. XII.15. Hot stage assembly (41). A, Brass block; B, transite insulation spacer; C, heater wells (to contain heater wires); D, transite platform (to support disk); E, platinum disk (fastened as a rivet); F, hinge; G, window; H, transite (insulator for heating wire binding post); I, binding post (for heater wire); J, thermocouple junction.

The Meltometer, described by Furst and Shapiro (42), is similar to the above except that the light beam is passed through the sample, not incident to it. Any increase or decrease in transmittance of unfiltered, polarized, or monochromatic light through the heated sample indicates that a thermal-phase transition has occurred. This information may be used to lock the pyrometer indicator at a fixed value, thus indicating the temperature at which the phase transition took place. The apparatus may be used to measure melting points, decomposition points, softening points, melting ranges, and arbitrary melting points as represented by amorphous waxes, asphalts, and plastics.

A schematic diagram of the Meltometer and a detail of the furnace assembly are given in Figure XII.16. The changes in intensity of the transmitted light are detected by the phototube. The resulting electrical signal can either be recorded or used to trigger the locking circuit of the pyrometer, thus indicating the fusion of the sample. A typical optical transmittance curve of a sample is given in Figure XII.17. As can be seen, the curve definitely indicates the temperature at which the sample undergoes fusion. For substances that show only softening or decomposition points, the transmittance curve would indicate a more gradual change than that indicated above.

The reproducibility and accuracy of the instrument are $\pm 1\%$ of full scale with a maximum temperature limit of 500°C.

2. HEATED INFRARED GAS CELL

A simple, inexpensive, heated infrared gas cell has been described by Burns (43) which was used for the investigation of the infrared-active gases evolved on thermal decomposition of various propellants and explosives. The cell is simple to construct, as can be seen in Figure XII.18. The temperature of the cell can be controlled by varying the input voltage into the heater coils with a variable transformer or with a thermistor temperature regulator, also described by Burns (43).

A novel use of the cell was to determine the heat of vaporization of nitrobenzene by use of the relationship:

$$\log p = - \frac{\Delta H}{2.3RT} + C \qquad (XII.2)$$

where p is the vapor pressure of the substance, ΔH is the latent heat of vaporization, R is the gas constant, and T is absolute temperature. From Beer's law

$$A = apl \qquad (XII.3)$$

where A is the absorbance at a particular wavelength, a is the absorbancy index, p is the pressure of the absorbing species, and l is the optical path length. By combination with equation (XII.2), the relationship

$$\log A = - \frac{\Delta H}{2.3RT} + k \qquad (XII.4)$$

is obtained.

For nitrobenzene, plots of base-line absorbance of the peak near 1540 cm^{-1} as a function of $1/T$ gave a straight line from whose slope a ΔH of 11.36 kcal mole^{-1} was calculated (11.72 kcal mole^{-1} literature value). Although the method is an expensive one for vapor pressure studies, it has one major advantage over manometric methods in that the sample need not be pure, provided that the impurity does not absorb at the same frequency as the major component. It is also conceivable that the heat of vaporization of several compounds could be determined simultaneously by measurement at different wavelengths.

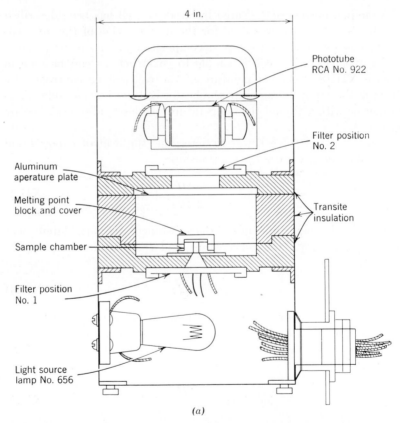

Fig. XII.16. (a) Schematic diagram of furnace; (b) schematic diagram of Meltometer (42).

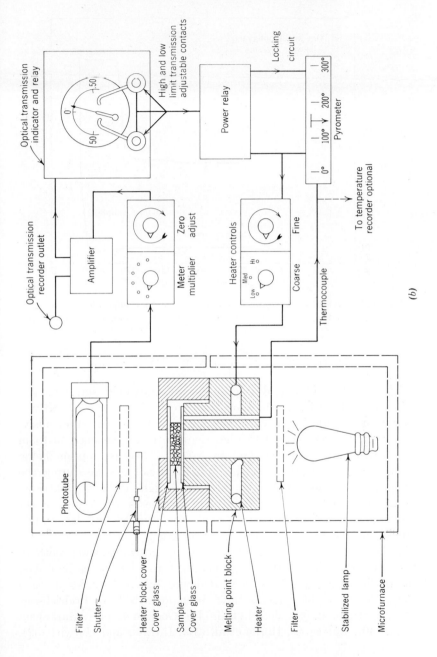

(b)

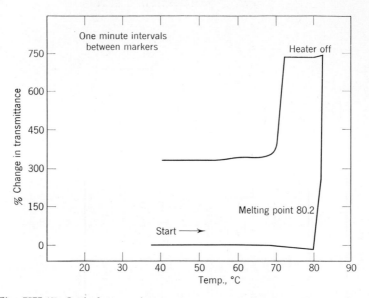

Fig. XII.17. Optical transmittance–temperature–time curve for a substance with a sharp melting point (42). Melting and solidification points are clearly shown.

3. HIGH-TEMPERATURE X-RAY DIFFRACTION

The usefulness of x-ray diffraction for the study of crystal structure, *solid–solid* phase transformations, and so on, is increased greatly if provision is made for varying the sample temperature. Previously, many metals were heated to high temperatures, quenched to room temperature, and then studied by x-rays. The assumption being made that the structure of the metal did not change during the quenching process. With the advent of high- (2000°C) and low- (−270°C) temperature x-ray diffraction cameras, this type of technique need not be reverted to since the sample may be studied continuously in any desired temperature range.

A large number of high- and low-temperature cameras, both of the powder diffraction and single crystal types, have been described in the literature, and have been reviewed by Goldschmidt in 1955 (44). More recent cameras have been described by Fridrichsons (45), Austin et al. (46), Jetter et al. (47), Goon et al. (48), Markowitz et al. (49), Bond (50), Horne et al. (51), Intrater and Hurwitt (52),

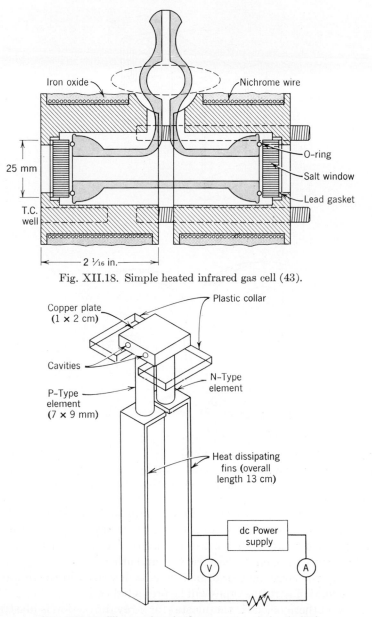

Fig. XII.18. Simple heated infrared gas cell (43).

Fig. XII.19. Thermoelectric thermostat and circuit (51).

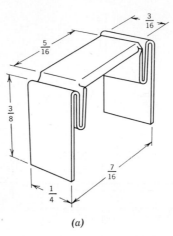

(a)

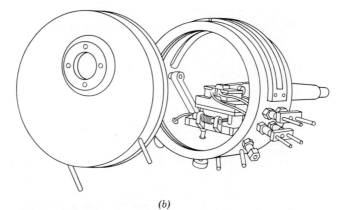

(b)

Fig. XII.20. High-temperature x-ray camera. (a) Platinum–40% rhodium heater strip; (b) schematic view of complete instrument (52).

Katz and Kay (53), Intrater (54), Shimura (55), Intrater and Appel (56), and others. High- and low-temperature cameras are also available commercially from the R. L. Stone Co., Philips Electronic Instruments, the General Electric Co., and others.

Due to the large number of instruments described in the literature, only several illustrative types will be presented here.

A novel thermoelectric thermostat for x-ray diffraction is illustrated in Figure XII.19 (51). The thermostat is a simple thermoelectric

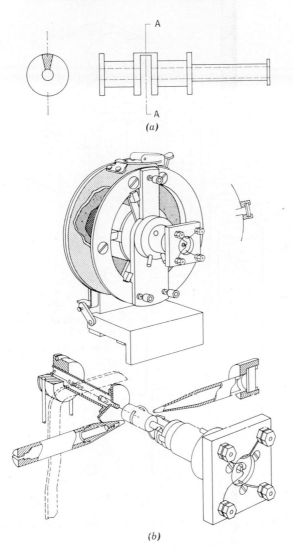

(a)

(b)

Fig. XII.21. High-temperature powder camera. (*a*) Heater core; (*b*) schematic view of entire assembly (50).

couple made up of a *p*-type and a *n*-type element, and two copper heat-dissipating fins. The *n*-type material was a doped bismuth telluride, the *p*-type, a doped antimony–bismuth telluride semi-

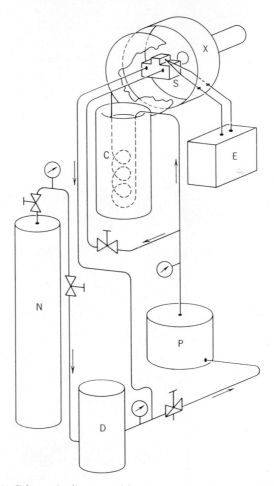

Fig. XII.22. Schematic diagram of low-temperature camera. Nitrogen tank, N; drying tower, D; pump, P; vacuum-type chamber, X; hollow sample holder, S; heat exchanger, H; Dewar flask, C; potentiometer, E (56).

conductor.   When current flows counterclockwise through the couple, the temperature of the copper plate falls; when the current is reversed, the temperature of the plate increases.   The temperature range covered by the thermostat was −5 to 70°C.

A high-temperature, high-vacuum x-ray camera capable of operation up to 1500°C has been described by Intrater and Hurwitt (52) and is illustrated in Figure XII.20. The sample is placed on a strip heater whose temperature stability was found to be better than $\pm 2°C$ for one hour at 1400°C. The heater strip is clamped in the camera by two sets of water-cooled copper blocks. Copper tubing served as both electrical and water leads to the furnace clamp blocks and leads out of the aluminum shell through vacuum seals. The camera shaft connects directly to the Norelco wide range goniometer. Temperature measurement is a problem for a heater such as this. A thermocouple in contact with the heater acts as a heat sink and the area in the immediate vicinity of it will be at a lower temperature than the average strip temperature. Greater temperature measurement accuracy can be obtained by correlation of the thermocouple readings with known transition points of pure metals or from lattice d- spacing measurements of the strip heater itself.

Bond (50) has described the conversion of a Debye-Sherrer type powder camera for high temperature operation. It is illustrated in Figure XII.21. The camera is built around a heater core which is 0.25 in. in diameter and constructed of Nichrome. The long stem of the core terminates in a flange which is clamped between Micalex washers to reduce heat conduction to the main part of the housing. The core has a central hole through which the sample is placed and in which the sample can rotate about an axis without touching the outer wall. The sample is heated by a resistance wire winding placed on the insulated core. The camera has been used at temperatures up to 950°C.

A system for use at low temperatures ($-195°C$) has been described by Intrater and Appel (56) and is illustrated schematically in Figure XII.22. The system consists of a temperature controller and a camera which is cooled by the circulation of cooled nitrogen gas through the sample block. The nitrogen gas is cooled by passage through a heat exchanger immersed in liquid nitrogen. The apparatus is said to maintain any temperature from ambient to $-195°C$ to within $\pm 2°C$ for at least 20 min.

The high-temperature x-ray camera may be used to follow the effect of elevated temperatures on the chemical system by two methods. The first is to thermostat the sample at a fixed or static temperature and detect changes in structure by change in d- spacing values. A second method is to study the effect of increasing temperature on a single d- spacing value. The diffraction peak will either increase or decrease with an increase in temperature, thus indicating a structural change in the substance. Both methods are illustrated in Figure XII.22. In Figure XII.23 a, changing the temperature from T_1 to T_2 gives an entirely different set of d- space values, while in Figure XII.23 b, a single d- space value changes as the temperature is continually increased at a slow, constant rate.

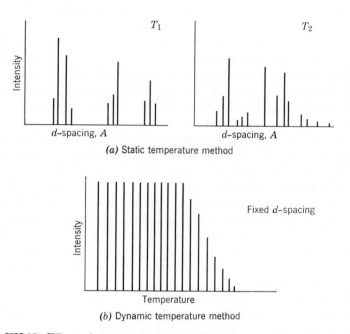

Fig. XII.23. Effect of temperature on a crystalline sample as determined by x-ray diffraction.

If the sample undergoes a volume change, either shrinking or expansion, during the heating cycle, the x-ray diffraction patterns may be misleading if a diffractometer is employed. The volume change will change the sample surface, thus increasing the scattering of the x-rays. This may be remedied by continually smoothing the surface exposed to the x-rays so as to give a perfectly flat surface. It should also be noted that the high temperature form of the sample should also be crystalline to give a diffraction pattern.

The most important applications of high-temperature x-ray diffraction are for detection of: (a) structure changes; (b) phase changes; (c) thermal expansion of sample; and (d) lattice defects.

References

1. Deribere, M., *Argile*, **188**, 5 (1938); *Rev. Sci.*, **76**, 383 (1938).
2. Garlick, G. F., *Luminescent Materials*, Oxford Univ. Press, London, 1949.
3. Kohler, A., and H. Leitmeier, *Z. Krist.*, **87**, 87 (1934).
4. Royer, L., *Compt. Rend.*, **204**, 602, 991 (1937).
5. Saurin, E., *Compt. Rend. Soc. Geol. France*, **1939**, 209.
6. Northrup, M. A., and O. I. Lee, *J. Opt. Soc. Am.*, **30**, 206 (1940).
7. Saunders, D. F., *Bull. Am. Assoc. Petro. Geol.* **37**, 114 (1953).
8. Parks, J. M., *Bull. Am. Assoc. Petrol. Geologists*, **37**, 125 (1953).
9. Daniels, F., C. A. Boyd and D. F. Saunders, *Science*, **117**, 343 (1953).
10. Lewis, D. R., *J. Phys. Chem.*, **60**, 698 (1956).
11. Bose, S. N., J. Sharma, and B. C. Dutta, *Trans. Bose Res. Inst., Calcutta*, **20**, 117 (1955).
12. Ingerson, E., *Econ. Geol., 50th. Anniv. Volume*, **1956**, 341.
13. Zeller, E. J., *Congr. Geol. Intern. Compt. Rend. 19ᵉ Algiers*, **12**, 365 (1952).
14. Mott, N. F., and R. W. Gurney, *Electronic Processes in Ionic Crystals*, Oxford Univ. Press, London, 1940.
15. Fonda, G. R., and F. Seitz, *Cornell Symposium of the American Physical Society*, Wiley, New York, 1948.
16. Kroger, F. A., *Some Aspects of the Luminescence of Solids*, Elsevier, Amsterdam, 1948.
17. Leverenz, H. W., *An Introduction to the Luminescence of Solids*, Wiley, New York, 1950.
18. Pringsheim, P., *Fluorescence and Phosphorescence*, Interscience, New York, 1949.
19. Boyd, C. A., *J. Chem. Phys.*, **17**, 1221 (1949).
20. Urbach, F., *Sitzber. Akad. Wiss. Wein. Math. Naturw. Kl., Abt. IIa*, **139**, 363 (1930).
21. Randall, J. T., and M. H. F. Wilkins, *Proc. Roy. Soc. (London)*, **A184**, 347 (1945).
22. Garino-Canina, V., and S. Cohen, *J. Am. Ceram. Soc.*, **43**, 415 (1960).
23. Boyd, C. A., and J. Hirschfelder, U. S. Patent No. **2,573,245**, October 30, 1951.
24. Morehead, F. F., and F. Daniels, *J. Phys. Chem.*, **56**, 546 (1952).
25. Ellsworth, H. V., *Canad. Dept. Mines Geol. Survey, Econ. Geol. Ser. No.* **11**, 55 (1932).
26. Alt, M., and H. Steinmetz, *Z. Angew. Mineral.*, **2**, 153 (1940).
27. Ashby, G. E., *J. Polymer Sci.*, **50**, 99 (1961).
28. Chevenard, P., *Rev. Metall.* **14**, 610 (1917).
29. Jetter, L. K., and R. F. Mehl, *Trans. AIME*, **152**, 166 (1943).
30. Barford, J., *J. Sci. Instr.*, **40**, 444 (1963).

31. Turnbull, J. C., *J. Am. Ceram. Soc.*, **33**, 54 (1950).
32. Saunders, J. B., *J. Res. Natl. Bur. Std.* (*U.S.*) **23**, 179 (1939).
33. Vanderman, E. J., *Rev. Sci. Instr.*, **22**, 757 (1951).
34. Berg, L. G., and N. P. Burmistrova, *Russ. J. Inorg. Chem.*, **5**, 326 (1960).
35. Garn, P. D., and S. S. Flaschen, *Anal. Chem.*, **29**, 268 (1957).
36. Glaser, F. W., and D. Moskowitz, *Powder Met. Bull.*, **6**, 178 (1953).
37. Reisman, A., S. Triebwasser, and F. Holtzberg, *J. Am. Chem. Soc.*, **77**, 4228 (1955).
38. Colner, W. H., and O. Zmeskal, *Trans. Am. Soc. Metals*, **44**, 1158 (1952).
39. Shimizu, S., *Tohoku Imp. Univ. Sci. Rept.*, **22**, 633 (1933).
40. Morton, H. A., *Laboratory Technique in Organic Chemistry*, McGraw-Hill, New York, 1938, p. 23.
41. Muller, R. H., and S. T. Zenchelsky, *Anal. Chem.*, **24**, 844 (1952).
42. Furst, A., and J. J. Shapiro, *Anal. Chem.*, **26**, 1082 (1954).
43. Burns, E. A., *Anal. Chem.*, **35**, 1106 (1963).
44. Goldschmidt, H. J., in *X-Ray Diffraction by Polycrystalline Materials*, H. S. Peiser, H. P. Broobsy, and A. J. C. Wilson, eds., The Institute of Physics, London, 1955, Chapter 9.
45. Fridrichsons, J., *Rev. Sci. Instr.*, **27**, 1015 (1956).
46. Austin, A. E., N. A. Richard, and C. M. Schwartz, *Rev. Sci. Instr.*, **27**, 860 (1956).
47. Jetter, L. K., C. J. McHargue, R. O. Williams, and H. L. Yakel, *Rev. Sci. Instr.*, **28**, 1087 (1957).
48. Goon, E. J., J. T. Mason, and T. R. P. Gibb, *Rev. Sci. Instr.*, **28**, 342 (1957).
49. Markowitz, M. M., J. M. Kishel, and R. F. Cree, *Rev. Sci. Instr.*, **29**, 248 (1958).
50. Bond, W. L., *Rev. Sci. Instr.*, **29**, 654 (1958).
51. Horne, R. A., W. J. Croft, and L. B. Smith, *Rev. Sci. Instr.*, **30**, 1132 (1959).
52. Intrater, J., and S. Hurwitt, *Rev. Sci. Instr.*, **32**, 905 (1961).
53. Katz, L., and M. I. Kay, *Rev. Sci. Instr.*, **28**, 968 (1957).
54. Intrater, J., *Rev. Sci. Instr.*, **32**, 982 (1961).
55. Shimura, Y., *Rev. Sci. Instr.*, **32**, 1404 (1961).
56. Intrater, J., and A. Appel, *Rev. Sci. Instr.*, **32**, 1065 (1961).
57. Pearce, J. H., and P. G. Mardon, *J. Sci. Instr.*, **36**, 457 (1959).

AUTHOR INDEX*

A

Abbott, A. E., 77 (ref. 35), 78 (ref. 35), *86*

Abrams, S. T., 155, *184*

Achhammer, B. G., 318 (ref. 32), 322 (ref. 39), *331*

Agarwala, R. P., 178, *184*

Aia, M. A., 99 (ref. 18), 100 (ref 18), *130*

Ali, S. I., 318 (refs. 36, 37), 319 (ref. 36), *331*

Aliferis, I., 20 (ref. 25), 21 (ref. 25), 27, *46*, 92, 93 (ref. 9), *130*

Alleman, T. G., 272 (ref. 4), 274, 289 (ref. 25), 290 (ref. 25), 291, *295*, *296*

Allison, E. B., 173, 176, *184*

Alt, M., 380 (ref. 26), *403*

Andersen, H. W., 325 (ref. 45), 326 (ref. 45), *331*

Anderson, C. J., 97 (ref. 17), *130*

Anderson, D. A., 249, *269*

Anderson, H. C., 234, *269*

Andrews, D. H., 346, 371

Angelis, G. de, 308 (ref. 14), *330*

Appel, A., 398, 400 (ref. 56), 401, *404*

Arens, P. L., 140, 142, 155, *183*

Arseneau, D. F., 238, 239 (ref. 12), *269*

Ashby, G. E., 380, *403*

Ashley, H. E., 135, *183*

Ashley, S. E. Q., 272 (ref. 7), *295*

Aston, J. G., 356, *372*

Austin, A. E., 396, *404*

Ayres, W. M., 301 (ref. 4), 302, 303 (ref. 4), 304 (ref. 4), 305, 307 (ref. 4), *330*

B

Badley, J. H., 346, 362 (ref. 15), *372*

Bailey, D. R., 190 (ref. 14), *228*

Baker, B. B., 327, *331*

Banerjee, S., 290 (ref. 43), *296*

Barcia Goyanes, C., 77, *87*

Barford, J., 382 (ref. 30), *403*

Barlow, A., 308 (ref. 22), *330*

Barnard-Smith, E. G., 356, 358, *372*

Barrall, E. M., 150 (ref. 50), 151, 156, 163, 165, 166 (ref. 76), 167, *183*, *184*, 312 (ref. 28), *330*

Barsh, M. K., 325, 326 (ref. 45), *331*

Bartlett, E. S., 80, *87*

Basolo, F., 31, *46*

Bauer, W. H., 254 (ref. 33), 255 (ref. 33), *269*

Baumgartner, P., 176 (ref. 92), 178, *184*

Bayliss, P., 140 (ref. 44), 142, 144 (ref. 44), 155, 161, 164, *183*

Beachell, H. C., 322, 324 (ref. 40), *331*

Bear, J. L., 37 (ref. 55), 47, 257, *269*

Beck, L. R., 243, 244 (ref. 20), *269*

Belcher, R., 106, *130*

Bell, J. M., 272, 287 (ref. 8), *295*

Bens, E. M. 301 (ref. 4), 302, 303 (ref. 4), 304 (ref. 4), 305, 307 (ref. 4), *330*

Ben-Yair, M. P., 291 (ref. 51), *296*

Berg, L. G., 225, *228*, 268, *270*, 387, 389, 390, *404*

Berkelhamer, L. H., 135 (ref. 29), 136, 152 (ref. 29), 153 (ref. 29), 156 (ref. 29), 162 (ref. 29), 163 (ref. 29), 169 (ref. 29), *183*

Berlin, A., 33, 35, *46*, 110, 111 (ref. 30), *131*

Bhadraver, M. S., 290 (ref. 48), *296*

Bhattacharya, A. B., 273 (ref. 12–15), 290 (refs. 12–14), 291 (ref. 15), *295*

Bhattacharyya, S. K., 134, *192*

Biffen, F. M., 101, 102 (ref. 19), *130*

Billingham, E. J., 276 (refs. 28, 29), 288 (ref. 40), 294 (ref. 28), *296*

Bills, K. W., 325 (ref. 45), 326 (ref. 45), *331*
Bjerrum, J., 290 (ref. 49), *296*
Blair, G. R., 335 (ref. 13), *344*
Blazek, A., 82, 85, *87*
Blumberg, A. A., 176 (ref. 90), *184*
Boersma, S. L., 138, 139, 142-144, 145 (ref. 37), 172, *183*
Bohon, R. L., 189, 191 (ref. 24), 217, 219, *228*
Bollin, E. M., 220, 221, *228*, 267 (ref. 45), 268, *270*
Bond, W. L., 396, 399 (ref. 50), 401, *404*
Borchardt, H. J., 176–178, *184*, 221, *228*
Boryta, D. A., 37, *47*, 77, *87*
Bose, S. N., 373, *403*
Bostock, W., 75, *86*
Boyd, C. A., 373 (ref. 9), 374, 375, 376 (ref. 9), 378 (ref. 9), 379 (refs. 9, 23), *403*
Brabson, J. A., 113 (ref. 36), 114, *131*
Bradt, P., 318 (ref. 33), *331*
Brauer, G. M., 308 (refs. 16, 24), 309 (ref. 24), 312 (refs. 16, 24), 313 (ref. 24), 315 (ref. 24), *330*
Breger, I. A., 191 (ref. 18), 209, 210, *228*, 250, *263*
Brewer, L., 190 (ref. 6), 191 (ref. 6), *227*
Bricker, C. E., 275 (ref. 27), 283 (ref. 27), 287 (ref. 27), 289 (ref. 27), 292 (ref. 27), *296*
Brundin, 107
Bryant, J. M., 107, 109 (ref. 29), *131*
Bryden, J. G., 82, *87*
Buehler, A. A., 298, *330*
Burgess, G. K., 135, 180, *183*, 192, *228*
Burmistrova, N. P., 225, *228*, 387, 389, 390, *404*
Burnham, H. D., 308 (ref. 12), *330*
Burns, E. A., 393, 397 (ref. 43), *404*
Burriel Marti, F., 77, *87*
Burton, H., 343, *344*
Bussiere, P., 227, *228*

C

Caley, 107
Campbell, C., 27, 33, *46*, 49–51, 52 (ref. 2), 53 (ref. 2), 67, 74, 77, 78, 80, 81, *86*, *87*, 88 (ref. 1), *130*, 134, 180, 181 (ref. 103), *182*, *185*, 191 (ref. 12), 214, *228*, 264, 265 (ref. 42), 266 (ref. 42), *270*, 305 (ref. 6), *330*
Campbell, P. F., 97, *130*
Card, C. S., 11, 13 (ref. 18), 14 (ref. 18), *46*, 75, 76 (ref. 34), *86*
Carleton, L. T., 346, 347 (ref. 16), 35.6 357, 365 (ref. 16), 366, 367 (ref. 16), *372*
Carpenter, C. D., 74 (ref. 24), *86*
Carroll, B., 35, 37 (ref. 48), 40, *46*
Carthew, A. R., 162, 164, 167, *184*
Charles, R. G., 259, 261 (ref. 38), 262, *269*
Chatterji, K. K., 272 (ref. 6), 273 (ref. 19), 287 (ref. 34), 290 (refs. 46, 47), 291 (ref. 19), *295*, *296*
Chevenard, P., 63, *86*, 382 (ref. 28), *403*
Chiang, Y., 134, *182*
Chihara, H., 163 (ref. 74), *184*, 191 (ref. 23), *228*
Chiu, J., 201, *228*, 236, 237 (ref. 10), *269*
Churchill, H. V., 272 (ref. 7), *295*
Cines, M. R., 346, 363 (ref. 3), *371*
Clampitt, B. H., 191 (ref. 13), *228*, 242 (ref. 19), 243, *269*
Clapper, T. W., 254 (ref. 33), 255 (ref. 33), *269*
Clark, C., 335 (ref. 10), *344*
Clarke, J. T., 356, 369 (ref. 20), 370, *372*
Claudel, B., 227 (ref. 44), *228*
Cleverly, B., 308 (ref. 23), *330*
Cobb, J. C., 293 (ref. 61), *296*
Cobb, J. W., 136, *183*
Cohen, S., 379, *403*
Coiffi, F. J., 293, *296*
Colner, W. H., 389, *404*
Cowell, C. F., 272, 287 (ref. 8), *295*

Cox, D. B., 190, *227*, 263, *269*
Crandall, W. B., 161, *184*
Cree, R. F., 396 (ref. 49), *404*
Croft, W. J., 396–398 (ref. 51), *404*
Cueilleron, J., 75, *88*
Curtiss, E. M., 240 (ref. 17), 241 (refs. 17, 18), *269*

D

Daniels, F., 176 (ref. 91), 177, *184*, 221, *228*, 325 (ref. 42), *331*, 373, 374 (ref. 9), 375, 376 (ref. 9), 378 (ref. 9), 379 (ref. 9), 380 (ref. 24), *403*
Das, S. S., 134 (ref. 9), 144 (ref. 9), *182*
Davis, B., 135 (ref. 29), 136 (ref. 29), 152 (ref. 29), 153 (ref. 29), 156 (ref. 29), 162 (ref. 29), 163 (ref. 29), 169 (ref. 29), *183*
Dean, L. A., 165, *184*
Dean, P. M., 271 (refs. 2, 3), 273, 288 (ref. 2), *295*
Dearth, L. R., 335 (ref. 8), *344*
De Bala, S., 56 (ref. 8), *86*
DeClerq, M., 8, 9, *46*
De Keyser, W. L., 27, *46*, 80, 81 (ref. 53), *87*, 181
Dekker, A. O., 325 (ref. 46), *331*
Demassieux, N., 8 (ref. 11), *46*
Deribere, M., 373, *403*
De Sorbo, W., 356 (ref. 20), 369 (ref. 20), 370 (ref. 20), *372*
Dhar, S. K., 31, *46*
Diehl, H. C., 272 (ref. 7), *295*
Dilling, E. D., 136, *183*, 192, *228*
Dimick, K. P., 308 (ref. 25), 309 (ref. 25), 311 (ref. 25), 312, *330*
Dimtroff, J. M., 335 (ref. 11), *344*
Dixon, H. D., 353 (ref. 18), 354 (ref. 18), 356 (ref. 18), 363 (ref. 18), *372*
Dornte, R. W., 346, 362 (ref. 14), 363 (ref. 14), *372*
Douglass, R. M., 56 (ref. 7), *86*, 126 (ref. 53), 128 (ref. 53), *131*
Dow Chemical Co., 121 (ref. 42), *131*
Doyle, C. D., 37, 38 (ref. 58), 39, 40, 43, 44 (ref. 61), 45, *47*, 240 (ref. 17), 241 (refs. 17, 18), *269*

Duhaut, P., 176 (ref. 92), 178, *184*
Dumbaugh, W. H., 284 (ref. 32), 285 (ref. 32), 287 (ref. 32), *296*
Dunne, J. A., 221 (ref. 35), *228*, 268 (ref. 44), *270*
Dupuis, J., 105, *130*
Dupuis, T., 92, 94, 95, 105, 106, 111, 113, *130*, *131*
Dutoit, P., 273, 289, *295*
Dutta, B. C., 373 (ref. 11), *403*
Duval, C., 1, 6–9, 15, 17, 19, 20, *45*, *46*, 49, 63, 73, 74, *86*, 88 (ref. 3), 89, 90 (ref. 3), 91, 92, 94, 95, 105–107, 110, 111, 113, 121, 126, 129, *130*, *131*
Dux, J. P., 308 (ref. 17), *330*

E

Eadie, F. S., 75, *86*
Edelman, D., 180, 182 (ref. 102), *185*, 266, *270*
Edwards, K. L., 191 (ref. 17), *228*
Edwards, O. W., 114, *131*
Eggleston, J. A., 292 (ref. 52), *296*
Ellsworth, H. V., 380 (ref. 25), *403*
Enagonio, D., 353 (ref. 18), 354 (ref. 18), 356 (ref. 18), 363 (ref. 18), *372*
Erdey, L., 27, 28, *46*, 72 (ref. 16), 73 (refs. 16, 17) 77, 80, 82 (ref. 16), 85 (ref. 16), *86*, *87*, 92, 94, 95, 103, 106 (ref. 25), *130*, 180 (ref. 100), *185*, 264, *270*
Ettre, K., 308–310 (ref. 21), 312 (refs. 21, 27), 315–317 (ref. 21), *330*
Ewing, G. W., 272 (ref. 5), 292 (ref. 5), *295*
Eyraud, C., 77, *86*
Eyraud, I., 77, *86*

F

Farquharson, K. R., 139 (ref. 39), *183*
Fauth, M. I., 235, 236 (ref. 9), *269*
Felton, H. R., 298, *330*
Fenner, C. N., 136, *183*
Fink, H. L., 356, *372*
Fisch, J., 273, 288 (ref. 10), 292 (ref. 10), *295*
Fisch, K. R., 328, 329 (ref. 49), *331*

Fischer, R. B., 332 (ref. 2), *344*
Flagg, J. F., 7, 8, 9 (ref. 9), 19 (ref. 9), *46*
Flaschen, S. S., 231 (ref. 4), 252, 253 (ref. 4), 254 (ref. 4), *269*, 388 (ref. 35), 389, 390 (ref. 35), *404*
Flengas, S. N., 295 (ref. 64), *296*
Foldvari-Vogl, M., 136, 161, *183*
Fonda, G. R., 374, *403*
Forman, E. J., 293, *296*
Forziati, A. F., 308 (ref. 16), 312 (ref. 16), *330*
Fotis, P., 322 (ref. 40), 324 (ref. 40), *331*
Franke, P. H., 338 (ref. 17), 340 (ref. 17), *344*
Frederickson, A. F., 264, *270*
Freeman, E. S., 35, 37 (ref. 48), 40, *46*, 180, 182 (ref. 102), *185*, 249, 266, *269*, *270*
Fridrichsons, J., 396, *404*
Fruchart, R., 7, 8, *46*
Fujii, C. T., 74, *86*
Furman, N. H., 272 (ref. 7), *295*
Furst, A., 390, 392, 394 (ref. 42), 396 (ref. 42), *404*
Furukawa, G. T., 353 (ref. 18), 354 (ref. 18), 356 (ref. 18), 363 (ref. 18), *372*

G

Gale, R. H., 74, *86*
Gamel, C. M., 250, *269*
Ganguly, N. D., 134, *182*
Garino-Canina, V., 379, *403*
Garlick, G. F., 373, *403*
Garn, P. D., 11, 12, 13 (ref. 16), 14 (ref. 16), 15, 16, *46*, 56, 77, *86*, *87*, 134, 179, *182*, *184*, 231 (ref. 4), 252, 253 (ref. 4), 254 (ref. 4), *269*, 388 (ref. 35), 389, 390 (ref. 35), *404*
Garner, W. E., 29 (ref. 40), *46*
Gasson, D. B., 221, *228*
Gast, T., 75, *86*
Gaur, H. C., 273 (refs. 12, 13), 290 (refs. 12, 13), *295*

Geith, C. R., 56 (ref. 8), *86* *
Gendrel, P., 6 (ref. 5), *45*, 49 (ref. 5), *86*, 88 (ref. 2), *130*
George, T. D., 255 (ref. 34), 256 (ref. 34), *269*
Gerard-Hirne, J., 140, 142, *183*
Ghosh, A. K., 272 (ref. 6), 287 (ref. 34), *295*, *296*
Gibb, T. R. P., 396 (ref. 48), *404*
Gita, G., 139 (ref. 41), *183*
Glaser, F. W., 389, *404*
Glasgow, A. R., 346, 353, 354 (ref. 18), 356, 358, 363, 371, *372*
Goldschmidt, H. J., 396, *404*
Goon, E. J., 396, *404*
Gordon, L., 92, 94, *130*
Gordon, S., 27 (ref. 38), *46*, 49–51, 52 (ref. 2), 53 (ref. 2), 67, 74, 77, 78, 80 (ref. 57), 81 (ref. 57), *86*, *87*, 88 (ref. 1), *130*, 134, 180 (ref. 103), 181 (ref. 103), *182*, *185*, 191 (ref. 11), *228*, 230 (ref. 1), 264–266 (ref. 42), *269*, *270*, 305 (ref. 6), *330*
Graham, R. P., 272 (ref. 7), *295*
Grassie, N., 325 (ref. 43), *331*
Gray, P. S., 27, *46*
Greathouse, L. H., 292 (ref. 56), *296*
Griffith, E. J., 66 (ref. 11), 67, *86*, 95, 96 (ref. 14), *130*
Grim, R. E., 134, 136, 155, *182*, *184*
Grimshaw, R. W., 162, *184*
Grobet, E., 273, 289, *295*
Groot, C., 77, *87*
Gruver, R. M., 142, 161, 163 (ref. 45), 167, *183*
Guar, J. N., 290 (ref. 48), *296*
Guiochon, G., 6 (ref. 5), 12, 18, 19, *45*, *46*, 49 (ref. 5), *86*, 88 (ref. 2), *130*
Gunn, S. R., 351, 352 (ref. 37), *372*
Gurney, R. W., 374, *403*

H

Haldar, B. C., 273 (ref. 11), 290 (refs. 11, 42, 44), *395*, *296*
Hall, J. W., 178, *184*
Hallett, L. T., 272 (ref. 7), *295*

Hammell, L., 157, *184*, 191 (refs. 15, 16), 201, 212, 213, *228*, 258, 259, *269*
Handley, R., 356, *372*
Harden, J. C., 146 (ref. 48), 147, 154, *183*, 218, 219, *228*, 237, 238 (ref. 11), *269*
Hardy, J. D., 335 (ref. 10), *344*
Harms, D. L., 321, 322, 323 (ref. 38), *331*
Hartmanshenn, O., 75, *86*
Hauser, R. E, 144, 146, 161, *183*
Haydel, C. H., 292 (ref. 56), *296*
Heaton, E., 162 (ref. 70), *184*
Henning, J. M., 353 (ref. 18), 354 (ref. 18), 356 (ref. 18), 363 (ref. 18), *372*
Herington, E. F. G., 367, 368 (ref. 33), *372*
Hermann, R., 308 (ref. 23), *330*
Hesford, J. R., 71, *86*
Hewitt, G. C., 308 (ref. 19), 312 (ref. 19), *330*
Hickam, W. M., 85 (ref. 62), *87*
Hill, J. A., 191 (ref. 10), *228*, 247, 249 (ref. 27), *269*, 307 (ref. 9), *330*
Hirschfelder, J., 379 (ref. 23), *403*
Hodgson, A. A., 161, *184*
Hoffman, A. S., 308 (ref. 20), 312 (ref. 20), *330*
Hoffman, I., 96, *130*
Hoffman, W. M., 114, *131*
Hogan, V. D., 191 (ref. 11), *228*
Hoiberg, J. A., 239, *269*
Holdcraft, A. D., 135, *183*
Holtzberg, F., 389 (ref. 37), *404*
Honda, K., 1, 6, *45*, 73, *86*
Hooley, J. G., 74, *86*
Horne, R. A., 396, 397 (ref. 51), 398 (ref. 51), *404*
Horton, A. T., 353 (ref. 18), 354 (ref. 18), 356 (ref. 18), 363 (ref. 18), *372*
Horton, G. R., 122 (ref. 48), *131*, 249–251 (ref. 29), 255 (ref. 34), 256 (ref. 34), 259, 260 (ref. 37), 261 (ref. 37), 262, *269*
Houldworth, H. S., 136, *183*
Hucks, J., 322 (ref. 40), 324 (ref. 40), *331*

Huffman, H. M., 356, *372*
Hume, D. N., 271 (ref. 1), 272 (ref. 1), 273 (ref. 21), 274 (ref. 21), 281, 282 (ref. 31), 283, 284 (ref. 21), 286–288 (ref. 21), 293, 294 (ref. 31), *295*, *296*
Hurwitt, S., 396, 398 (ref. 52), 400, *404*
Huss, J., 335 (ref. 11), *344*

I

Ingerson, E., 373, *403*
Intrater, J., 396, 398, 400, 401, *404*
Ippoliti, P., 308 (ref. 14), *330*
Iwata, S., 77, *87*
Izvekov, I. V., 74, *86*

J

Jacobs, P. W. M., 33, *46*
Jacobs, T., 37 (ref. 50), *46*
Jacque, L., 6 (ref. 5), *45*, 49, *86*, 88 (ref. 2), *130*
Jacquez, J. A., 335 (ref. 11), *344*
Jaffe, H. H., 179, *184*
Janak, J., 308 (ref. 13), *330*
Janssen, H. J., 292 (ref. 56), *296*
Jennings, E. C., 308 (ref. 25), 309 (ref. 25), 311 (ref. 25), 312, *330*
Jetter, L. K., 382 (ref. 29), 396, *403*, *404*
Johnson, J. F., 308 (ref. 20), 312 (refs. 20, 28), *330*
Johnston, H. L., 356 (ref. 20), 369 (ref. 20), 370 (ref. 20), *372*
Johnston, J., 346 (ref. 7), *371*
Jolly, W. L., 293 (ref. 60), *296*
Jonas, E. C., 161, *184*
Joncich, M. J., 190 (ref. 14), *228*
Jong, G. J. de, 155 (ref. 59), 156, 165, 168 (ref. 59), 171 (ref. 59), 172, 173, *184*
Jordan, J., 271, 272 (refs. 4, 66), 274, 276, 281 (ref. 18), 283 (ref. 17), 284 (refs. 18, 32), 285 (refs. 17, 32), 286 (ref. 17), 287 (ref. 32), 288 (ref. 40), 289 (ref. 25), 290 (ref. 25), 291, 292 (ref. 18), 294, *295*, *296*

K

Kashdan, W. H., 247 (ref. 23), *269*
Kateman, G., 356, *372*
Katz, L., 398, *404*
Kauffman, A. J., 136, *183*, 192, *228*
Kay, M. I., 398, *404*
Ke, B., 174, *184*, 245 (ref. 21), 246, 247, 248 (ref. 26), *269*
Keily, H. J., 281, 282 (ref. 31), 283, 293 (ref. 31), 294 (ref. 31)
Keim, W., 190 (ref. 9), *228*
Kerr, P. F., 136, *183*, 189, 192, 220, 221, *227*, *228*, 267 (ref. 45), 268, *270*
Kessler, J. E., 11, 12, 13 (ref. 16), 14 (ref. 16), 15, *46*
Kienitz, H., 369, *372*
Kimball, A. P., 308 (ref. 10), *330*
King, M. E., 20 (ref. 26), 21 (ref. 26), *46*
Kinjyo, K., 77, *87*
Kirk, P. L., 308 (ref. 26), 312, *330*
Kishel, J. M., 396 (ref. 49), *404*
Kissinger, H. E., 15, *46*, 134, 153, 154 (ref. 52), 155, 175 (ref. 52), 176, 179 (ref. 55), 180 (ref. 55), *182*, *183*
Klick, C. C., 335 (ref. 12), *344*
Klute, C. H., 174, *184*
Kmetko, E. A., 322 (ref. 41), *331*
Kohler, A., 373, 380 (ref. 3), *403*
Kohmann, G. T., 346 (ref. 7), *371*
Kortum, G., 333, 334 (ref. 6), 335, *344*
Kosters, B., (ref. 18), *330*
Kozyrev, B. P., 335 (ref. 14), *344*
Kracek, F. C., 230, *269*
Kraus, D. L., 75, *86*
Kroger, F. A., 374, *403*
Kronig, R., 170, *184*
Kropotkin, M. A., 335 (ref. 14), *344*
Kruger, J. E., 82, *87*
Kubelka, P., 332, *344*
Kulp, J. L., 136, 163 (ref. 75), *183*, *184*, 189, 192, *227*
Kuppenheim, H. F., 335 (ref. 11), *344*

L

Lamy, C., 140, 142, *183*
Langer, A., 85 (ref. 62), *87*

Laware, R., 106, 107, *130*
Le Chatelier, H., 1, 135, *183*
Lee, O. I., 373, *403*
Legate, C. E., 308 (ref. 12), *330*
Lehmann, F. A., 308 (ref. 24), 309 (ref. 24), 312 (ref. 24), 313 (ref. 24), 315 (ref. 24), *330*
Lehmann, H., 134, 144, *182*
Lehrle, R. S., 308 (refs. 11, 22), 312 (ref. 11), *330*
Leitmeier, H., 373, 380 (ref. 3), *403*
Leonard, G. W., 190 (ref. 8), 222, 223 (ref. 8), *228*, 240, *269*
Lermond, C. A., 332 (ref. 1), *344*
Levandowsky, J., 192 (ref. 27), *228*
Leverenz, H. W., 374, *403*
Lewin, S. Z., 49, *86*
Lewis, D. R., 157, *184*, 373, 375, 377 (ref. 10), *403*
Linde, H. W., 273, 274 (ref. 21), 283, 284, (ref. 21), 286 (ref. 21), 287 (ref. 21), 288, *295*
Lingane, J. J., 273, *295*
Liptay, B., 27 (ref. 39), *46*, 103 (refs. 20, 21), 106 (ref. 25), 130
Lodding, W., 157, *184*, 190 (ref. 7), 191 (refs. 15, 16), 201, 212, 213, *228*, 258, 259, *269*
Lukaszewski, G. M., 6 (ref. 4), 7, 8 (ref. 4), 9, 10 (ref. 4), 11, 15–17, 20, 21, 29, 30 (ref. 41), 37 (refs. 52, 53), *45–47*, 48, 71, *86*, 89, *130*, 134, *182*
Lumme, P., 37 (ref. 54), *47*

M

McCullough, J. P., 350 (ref. 17), 359, 362, *372*
McCurdy, W. H., 275 (ref. 27), 283 (ref. 27), 287 (ref. 27), 289 (ref. 27), 292 (ref. 27), 296
McGlynn, J. F., 190, *227*, 263, *269*
McHarque, C. J., 396 (ref. 47), *404*
McKeehan, W., 335 (ref. 11), *344*
Mackenzie, R. C., 134, 136, 139 (ref. 39), 140, 141 (ref. 46), 142, *182*, *183*
McMurdie, H. F., 15 (ref. 23), *46*, 155

(ref. 55), 179 (ref. 55), 180 (ref. 55), *183*

Madorsky, S. L., 318 (refs. 30, 34), *330, 331*

Magne, F. C., 371 (ref. 36), *372*

Mair, B. J., 346, 356 (ref. 9), *372*

Malard, C., 8 (ref. 11), *46*

Malotaux, R. N. M. A., 346, 356, *372*

Mardon, P. G., 227, *228*, 382 (ref. 57), *404*

Markin, T. L., 126 (ref. 54), 128, *131*

Markowitz, M. M., 37, *47*, 77, *87*, 396, *404*

Martin, A. J., 191 (ref. 17), *228*

Martin, S. B., 329, *331*

Martinez, E., 17, 18 (ref. 24), *46*, 163 (ref. 72), *184*

Mason, J. T., 396 (ref. 48), *404*

Mastrangelo, S. V. R., 346, 362 (ref. 14), 363 (ref. 14), *372*

Mathieu, M. P., 346, 363 (ref. 4), *371*

Mayr, C., 273, 288 (ref. 10), 292 (ref. 10), *295*

Mazee, W. M., 356, 370 (ref. 23), 371, *372*

Mazieres, C., 190 (ref. 5), 213, *227*

Mehl, R. F., 382 (ref. 29), *403*

Meier, J., 276 (refs. 28, 29), 294 (ref. 28), *296*

Mellor, J. W., 135, *183*

Melville, H. W., 325 (ref. 43), *331*

Menzies, A. W. C., 328 (ref. 48), *331*

Metz, D. F., 56 (ref. 7), *86*, 126 (ref. 53), 128 (ref. 53), *131*

Meussner, R. A., 74 (ref. 24), *86*

Michel, A., 7, 8, *46*

Mielenz, R. C., 20, 21, *46*

Miller, F. J., 286, 287 (ref. 33), *296*

Milner, O. I., 92, 94, *130*

Mockrin, I., 11, 23 (ref. 19), 24, 26, *46*, 67 (ref. 13), *86*

Mod, R. R. 371 (ref. 36), *372*

Moe, G., 325 (ref. 45), 326 (ref. 45), *331*

Mohler, F. L., 318 (ref. 33), *331*

Mondain-Monval, P., 287 (refs. 35, 36), 288 (refs. 35, 39), 290 (refs. 35, 39), *296*

Morehead, F. F., 380 (ref. 24), *403*

Morita, H., 232–234, *269*

Morton, H. A., 390 (ref. 40), *404*

Moskowitz, D., 389, *404*

Mott, N. F., 374, *403*

Muller, R. H., 274, *296*, 390, 391 (ref. 41), 392 (ref. 41), *404*

Munk, F., 333, *344*

Munroe, M. A., 77 (ref. 35), 78 (ref. 35), *86*

Murphy, C. B., 134, *182*, 191 (ref. 10), *228*, 240, 241, 247, 249 (ref. 27), *269*, 307, *330*

Murray, P., 155, *183*

N

Naik, M. C., 178, *184*

Nathans, M. W., 32, *46*, 156, *184*

Nayar, M. R., 273 (ref. 20), 291 (ref. 50), *295*, *296*

Nedumov, N. A., 223, *228*

Nelson, D. F., 308 (ref. 26), 312, *330*

Newcombe, E., 271 (ref. 3), 273, *295*

Newkirk, A. E., 6, 7, 9, 11, 13, 14 (ref. 8), 18, 20, 21, 22 (ref. 8), 23–25, 27, 32, *45*, *46*, 67 (ref. 12), *86*, 92, 93 (ref. 9), 106, 107, *130*

Newkirk, T. F., 214, 215, *228*

Newman, S. B., 134, *182*

Northrup, M. A., 373, *403*

Norton, F. H., 134, 136, 162, *182*

Notz, K. J., 179, *184*

Novikov, G. I., 224, *228*

O

Oldham, M. S., 335 (ref. 9), *344*

Oro, J. F., 308 (ref. 10), *330*

Ortner, M. H., 97 (ref. 17), *130*

Oster, G., 335 (ref. 16), *344*

P

Padmanabhan, V. M., 37 (ref. 51), *47*, 178, *184*

Paetsch, H. H., 134 (ref. 9), 144 (ref. 9), *182*

Pakulak, J. M., 190 (ref. 8), 222, 223 (ref. 8), *228*, 240, *269*

Palei, P. N., 89, *130*

Palm, J. A., 240 (ref. 17), 241 (refs. 17, 18), *269*

Pande, C. S., 273 (ref. 20), 291 (ref. 50), *295, 296*

Papailhau, J., 82, *87*

Paris, R., 287 (refs. 35–38), 288 (refs. 35, 39), 290 (refs. 35, 39), *296*

Parks, G. S., 346, 356, *372*

Parks, J. M., 373, 375, 379, 380 (ref. 8), *403*

Pask, J. A., 134, 135 (ref. 29), 136 (ref. 29), 143 (ref. 5), 144, 152 (ref. 29), 153 (ref. 29), 156 (ref. 29), 162 (ref. 29), 163 (ref. 29), 169 (ref. 29), *182, 183*

Paulik, F., 27, 28 (ref. 31), *46*, 72 (ref. 16), 73, 80 (refs. 16, 55), 82, 85, *86, 87*, 92, 94, 95, 103 (refs. 20, 21), 106 (ref. 25), *130*, 180 (ref. 100), *185*, 264, *270*

Paulik, J., 27, 28 (ref. 31), *46*, 72 (ref. 16), 73, 80 (refs. 16, 55), 82, 85, *86, 87*, 180 (ref. 100), *185*

Payne, R. E., 75, *86*

Pearce, J. H., 227, *228*, 382 (ref. 57), *404*

Peltier, S., 6 (ref. 7), *45*

Pendergast, J., 276 (refs. 28, 29), 294 (ref. 28), *296*

Penner, S. S., 325 (ref. 42), *331*

Periale, J., 293 (ref. 61), *296*

Petricciani, J. C., 254, 255 (ref. 33), *269*

Petrocelli, A. W., 75 (ref. 33), *86*

Pilcher, G., 356, *372*

Polyachenok, O. G., 224, *228*

Porter, R. S., 308 (ref. 20), 312 (refs. 20, 28), *330*

Poulsen, I., 290 (ref. 49), *296*

Powell, D. A., 82, 83 (ref. 59), *87*, 180 (ref. 101), *185*

Prettre, M., 227 (ref. 44), *228*

Price, J. C., 75 (ref. 33), *86*

Pringsheim, P., 374, *403*

Prout, E. G., 31, *46*

Purkayastha, B. C., 290 (refs. 41, 45), *296*

R

Rabatin, J. G., 11, 13 (ref. 18), *46*, 74, 75, 76 (ref. 34), *86*

Radell, E. A., 308 (ref. 15), 312 (ref. 15), *330*

Ramachandran, V. S., 134, *182*

Ramstad, R. W., 329, *331*

Randall, J. T., 375, *403*

Rase, H. F., 173, 178, *184*, 191 (ref. 25), 193 (ref. 25), 194 (ref. 25), *228*

Rassonskaya, I. S., 268, *270*

Redfern, J. P., 6 (ref. 4), 7, 8 (ref. 4), 9, 10 (ref. 4), 11 (ref. 4), 29, 30 (ref. 41), 37 (refs. 52, 53), *45–47*, 48, *86*, 89, *130*, 134, *182*

Reilly, M. L., 353 (ref. 18), 354 (ref. 18), 356 (ref. 18), 363 (ref. 18), *372*

Reiney, M. J., 318 (ref. 32), 322 (ref. 39), *331*

Reinhart, F. W., 318 (ref. 32), 322 (ref. 39), *331*

Reisman, A., 77, 79, 82, 84, *87*, 162, *184*, 191 (ref. 22), 216, 218, *228*, 389, *404*

Renouf, J., 227 (ref. 44), *228*

Richard, N. A., 396 (ref. 46), *404*

Richer, A., 11, 17, *46*

Richmond, H. D., 292 (ref. 52), *296*

Rideal, E., 295 (ref. 64), *296*

Rieke, R., 135, *183*

Riley, R. F., 129, *131*

Robb, J. C., 308 (refs. 11, 22), 312 (ref. 11), *330*

Robert, J., 287 (ref. 37), *296*

Roberts, A. L., 162 (ref. 70), *184*

Roberts-Austen, W. C., 1, 135, *183*

Robinson, R. J., 33, 35, *46*, 110, 111 (ref. 30), *131*

Robinson, W. R., 37 (ref. 56), *47*, 340 (ref. 20), *344*

Rogers, L. B., 150 (ref. 50), 151, 156, 163, 165, 166 (ref. 76), 167, *183, 184*, 273 (ref. 21), 274 (ref. 21), 283 (ref. 21), 284 (ref. 21), 286–288 (ref. 21), *295*, 332 (ref. 1), *344*

Rogers, R. N., 298, 300 (ref. 1), 301 (ref. 1), *330*

Ropp, R. C., 99 (ref. 18), 100 (ref. 18), 130

Ross, G. S., 353 (ref. 18), 354 (ref. 18), 356 (ref. 18), 363 (ref. 18), 372

Rossini, F. D., 346, 349, 356, 358 (ref. 10), 372

Rowland, R. A., 155, 157, 161, 184

Royer, L., 373, 403

Rudin, A., 161, 184, 191 (ref. 21), 228, 247, 269

Ruehrwein, R. A., 356, 372

Rynasiewicz, J., 7, 8, 9 (ref. 9), 19 (ref. 9), 46

S

Sacovy, N., 192 (ref. 27), 228

Saito, H., 11, 17, 46

Sanderson, J. A., 335 (ref. 15), 344

Saraiya, S. C., 37 (ref. 51), 47, 178 (ref. 94), 184

Satava, V., 74, 86

Saunders, D. F., 373, 374 (ref. 9), 375, 376 (ref. 9), 378 (ref. 9), 379, 403

Saunders, J. B., 382 (ref. 32), 404

Saurin, E., 373, 403

Saxena, R. S., 273 (refs. 14, 15), 290 (ref. 14), 291 (ref. 15), 295

Saylor, C. P., 353 (ref. 18), 354 (ref. 18), 356 (ref. 18), 363 (ref. 18), 369, 372

Scala, L. C., 85, 87

Schacher, G. P., 307 (ref. 9), 330

Schieltz, N. C., 20 (ref. 26), 21 (ref. 26), 46

Schlyter, K., 272 (refs. 22, 23), 274, 295

Schnitzer, M., 96 (refs. 15, 16), 130

Scholten, P. C., 77, 87

Schreyer, G., 333, 344

Schrieber, H. P., 161 (ref. 68), 184, 191 (ref 21), 228, 247 (ref. 25), 269

Schultz, R. D., 325 (refs. 45, 46), 326 (ref. 45), 331

Schwab, F. W., 366, 372

Schwartz, C. M., 396 (ref. 46), 404

Schwenker, R. F., 184, 243, 244 (ref. 20), 269

Scott, N. D., 247, 269

Segatto, P. R., 277, 278 (ref. 30), 269

Seitz, F., 374, 403

Seki, S., 163 (ref. 74), 184, 191 (ref. 23), 228

Sen-Sarma, R. N., 290 (ref. 45), 296

Sentyurin, I. G., 89 (ref. 6), 130

Sewell, E. C., 155, 183

Shapiro, J. J., 390, 392, 394 (ref. 42), 396 (ref. 42), 404

Sharma, J., 373 (ref. 11), 403

Shillcox, W. M., 335 (ref. 8), 344

Shimizu, S., 389, 404

Shimura, Y., 398, 404

Shulman, J. H., 335 (ref. 12), 344

Sillen, L. G., 272 (ref. 22), 295

Simons, E. L., 20, 21 (ref. 25), 46

Simpson, B. S., 15 (ref. 23), 46, 155 (ref. 55), 179 (ref. 55), 180 (ref. 55), 183

Sisko, A. W., 174, 184, 247, 248 (ref. 26), 269

Skau, E. L., 346, 371, 371, 372

Skinner, K. G., 155, 183, 214, 228

Sklyarenko, I. S., 89 (ref. 6), 130

Smit, W. M., 77 (ref. 45), 87, 345, (ref. 1), 346, 356, 357, 359–362, 364, 371

Smith, A., 328 (ref. 48), 331

Smith, C. L., 27 (ref. 38), 46, 80 (ref. 57), 81 (ref. 57), 87, 180 (ref. 103), 181 (ref. 103), 185, 264–266 (ref. 42), 270

Smith, G. G., 308 (ref. 18), 330

Smith, G. W., 74 (ref. 23), 86

Smith, J. P., 338 (ref. 17), 340 (ref. 17), 344

Smith, L. B., 396–398 (ref. 51), 404

Smothers, W. J., 134, 182, 250, 269

Smyth, H. T., 147–149, 150 (ref. 49), 151, 183

Snoodijk, F., 170, 184

Somiya, T., 292, 296

Soulen, J. R., 11, 23 (ref. 19), 24, 26, 40, 46, 47, 67 (ref. 13), 86

Speil, S., 135, 136, 152, 153 (ref. 29), 156, 162, 163, 169, 183

Spina, N., 308 (ref. 14), 330

Spingler, K., 325 (ref. 44), *331*
Splitek, R., 77, *87*
Steinmetz, H., 380 (ref. 26), *403*
Stembridge, C. H., 318 (refs. 36, 37), 319 (ref. 36), *331*
Stephenson, J. L., 74, *86*
Stolten, H. J., 274, *296*
Stone, R. L., 158, 159, 160 (ref. 64), 173, *184*, 191 (refs. 19, 25, 26), 193, 194 (refs. 19, 25, 26), *228*, 251, 252 (ref. 32), *269*, 302, 305 (ref. 5), *330*
Stoneking, D. J., 77 (ref. 35), 78 (ref. 35), *86*
Strassburger, J., 308 (ref. 16), 312 (ref. 16), *330*
Straub, J., 346, 356, *372*
Strauss, S., 318 (refs. 30, 34), *330, 331*
Streiff, A. J., 346 (ref. 10), 356 (ref. 10), 358 (ref. 10), *372*
Stross, F. H., 155, *184*
Strutz, H. C., 308 (ref. 15), 312 (ref. 15), *330*
Stull, D. R., 355, *372*
Sturm, E., 173, *184*, 190 (ref. 7), *228*, 306 (ref. 8), 307 (ref. 8), *330*
Sturtevant, J. M., 346, *371*
Sundaram, A. K., 37 (ref. 51), *47*, 178 (ref. 94), *184*
Svehla, G., 27 (ref. 39), *46*, 103 (refs. 20, 21), *130*
Swann, W. B., 308 (ref. 17), *330*

T

Takahashi, H., 163 (ref. 72), *184*
Tamas, D., 77, *87*
Tardy, P., 287 (ref. 38), *296*
Teetzel, F. M., 77, 78, *86*
Tenenbaum, M., 356, 371, *372*
Thomas, C. O., 327, *33*
Thomas, S. B., 346, 356, *372*
Thomason, P. F., 286, 287 (ref. 33), *296*
Thompson, D., 318 (ref. 34), *331*
Tompkins, F. C., 31, 33, *46*
Trambouze, Y., 227 (ref. 44), *228*, 292, *296*
Trantham, H. V., 74 (ref. 23), *86*
Triebwasser, S., 389 (ref. 37), *404*

Trites, A. E., 163 (ref. 75), *184*
Troutner, V. H., 77, *87*
Tryhorn, F. G., 79, *87*
Tryon, M., 308 (ref. 16), 312 (ref. 16), *330*
Tsang, N. F., 139, *183*
Tullage, R. de la, 63 (ref. 9), *86*
Turnbull, J. C., 382 (ref. 31), *404*
Tyson, B. C., 275, 283, 287 (ref. 27), 289, 292 (ref. 27), *296*

U

Urbach, F., 375, *403*

V

Vallet, P., 11, 17, *46*
Van der Akker, J. A., 335 (ref. 8), *344*
Vanderman, E. J., 382 (ref. 33), *404*
Van Nordstrand, R. Z., 74, *86*
Van Tassel, J. H., 37 (ref. 49), *46*, 122 (ref. 48), *131*, 249–251 (ref. 29), *269*
Varadi, P. F., 308–310 (ref. 21), 312 (refs. 21, 27), 315–317 (ref. 21), *330*
Vassallo, D. A., 146 (ref. 48), 147, 154, *183*, 218, 219, *228*, 237, 238 (ref. 11), *269*, 300, 308 (ref. 3), *330*
Verderame, F. D., 328, 329 (ref. 49), *331*
Viehmann, W., 174, *184*
Vieweg, R., 75, *86*
Vinejar, R., 335 (ref. 10), *344*
Vogel, J., 333, 335, *344*
Vold, M. J., 137, 156, 168, 169 (ref. 36), 170 (ref. 36), 173, 176, *183*
Vratny, F., 332 (ref. 2), *344*

W

Wache, S., 63 (ref. 9), *86*
Waddams, J. A., 27, *46*
Waddington, G., 350 (ref. 17), 359, 362, *372*
Waldman, M. H., 161 (ref. 68), *184*, 191 (ref. 21), *228*, 247 (ref. 25), *269*
Wall, L. A., 318, *330, 331*
Wallach, H., 135, *183*
Warne, S. St. J., 140 (ref. 44), 142, 144 (ref. 44), 155, 161, 164, *183*

Warner, M. F., 134, 143 (ref. 5), 144, *182*

Waterbury, G. R., 56, *86*, 126 (ref. 53), 128, *131*

Waters, P. L., 27, 40, 41 (ref. 60), 42, *46*, *47*, 75, 80, *86*, *87*

Watts, O. O., 271 (ref. 2), 273, 288 (ref. 2), *295*

Weaver, E. E., 190 (ref. 9), *228*

Webb, T. L., 139 (ref. 40), 140–142, *183*

Weingarten, G., 33, *46*, 191 (ref. 12), 214, *228*

Wendlandt, W. W., 25, 32, 37 (refs. 49, 55, 56), *46*, *47*, 75, 79, 80, *86*, *87*, 107, 108 (refs. 27, 28), 109 (ref. 29), 112–115, 117–119 (ref. 39), 120 (ref. 43), 121, 122 (refs. 44, 47, 48), 123, 124 (ref. 49), 125 (ref. 49), 127 (refs. 55, 56), 129 (ref. 55), *130*, *131*, 134, 156, 176 (refs. 20, 89), *183*, *184*, 186 (ref. 1), 191 (ref. 20), 209, 211, 212 (ref. 31), *227*, *228*, 239, 249, 250 (ref. 29), 251 (ref. 29), 255, 256 (ref. 34), 257, 259, 260 (ref. 37), 261 (ref. 37), 262, *269*, 304 (ref. 7), 305, 306 (ref. 8), 307 (ref. 8), 318, 319 (ref. 36), *330*, *331*, 338, 340 (refs. 17–22), 341 (ref. 21), 342 (ref. 19), 343 (refs. 19, 21), *344*

West, R. R., 161, *184*

Wetzel, W. H., 308 (ref. 18), *330*

White, J., 155, *183*

White, P. T., 356, 358, *372*

White, W. P., 346, 356, *371*

Whitehead, W. L., 191 (ref. 18), 209, 210, *228*, 250, *269*

Whitham, B. T., 308, (ref. 19), 312 (ref. 19), *330*

Wholin, R., 135, *183*

Wichers, E., 366, *372*

Wijner, M. D., 77 (ref. 45), *87*

Wilburn, F. W., 71, *86*

Wilfong, R. E., 325, *331*

Wilkins, M. H. F., 375, *403*

Williams, D. N., 80, *87*

Williams, R. O., 396 (ref. 47), *404*

Williamson, J. A., 77 (ref. 35), 78 (ref. 35), *86*

Williamson, L., 318 (ref. 34), *331*

Wilson, A., 134 (ref. 14), *182*

Wimberley, S. E., 254 (ref. 33), 255 (ref. 33), *269*

Wittels, M., 163, 164, 168 (ref. 77), 169, *184*

Wright, J. R., 96 (refs. 15, 16), *130*

Wunderlich, B., 247 (ref. 23), *269*

Wyatt, W. F., 79, *87*

Y

Yagfarov, M. S., 173, *184*, 226, 227, *228*

Yakel, H. L., 396 (ref. 47), *404*

Yang, W. Y., 37 (ref. 56), *47*, 340 (ref. 20), *344*

Yasuda, S. K., 298 (ref. 1), 300 (ref. 1), 301 (ref. 1), *330*

Z

Zagorski, Z., 77, *87*, 89 (ref. 7), *130*

Zavitsanos, P., 190 (ref. 6), 191 (ref. 6), *227*

Zeller, E. J., 373, *403*

Zemany, P. D., 318, 321 (ref. 29), *330*

Zenchelsky, S. T., 271, 277, 278 (ref. 30), 293, *295*, *296*, 390, 391 (ref. 41), 392 (ref. 41), *404*

Zinn, J., 298 (ref. 1), 300 (ref. 1), 301 (ref. 1), *330*

Zlatkis, A., 308 (ref. 10), *330*

Zmeskal, O., 389, *404*

SUBJECT INDEX

A

Acetone, DTA of, 236

Acetone hydrazone derivative, DTA of, 236

Alkaline earth oxalate hydrates, analysis of by TGA, 101

Aluminum oxide, ignition temperatures of, 92

Americium(III) oxalate 7-hydrate, TGA of, 126

Aminoguanidine picrate, DTA of, 236

Ammonium perchlorate, DTA of, 160, 254

Ammonium perchlorate, GEA-DTA of, 302

Ammonium phosphomolybdate, TGA of, 112

Ammonium tetraphenylborate, TGA of, 121

Amplifiers, dc, for DTA, 192

Atmosphere, furnace, self-generated, 12

Automatic thermogravimetric analysis, definition of, 89

examples of, 90, 91

of binary mixture, 91

B

Bacterial dextrans, DTA of, 234

Balsam fir wood, DTA of, 239

Barbituric acids, pyrolysis of, 312

Barium, analysis by TGA, 101

Bausch and Lomb Spectronic 505, 336

Benzoic acid, DTA of, 154

variation of peak temperature of, 154

Biphenyl, DTA of, 247

Bis(pyridine)cobalt(II) chloride, DRS of, 342, 343

reflectance of, 340, 341

Black gun powder, kinetics of, 33

Borchardt and Daniel's equation, 177

Burcite, variation of peak temperature of, 154

n-Butane, DTA of, 236

C

Calcite, glow curves of, 377

variation of peak temperature of, 154

Calcium, analysis of by TGA, 101

Calcium carbonate, kinetics of, 35

Calcium silicate hydrates, analysis of by TGA, 101

Camera, X-ray diffraction, high temperature, 396

low temperature, 400

Catalysts, oxidation of carbonaceous deposits on, 178

Cellulose and its derivatives, DTA of, 240

Cerium(III) nitrate 6-hydrate, TGA of, 97

Cesium nitrate, TGA of, 97

Cesium tetraphenylborate, TGA of, 121

Chemical reactions, elucidation of by thermal methods, 3

Chevenard thermobalance, dash pot errors, 25

weight-gain of curve, 20

Clays and soils, thermogravimetry of, 96

Coal, DTA of, 250, 251

heating values of, DTA method, 251

Cobalt(II) bromide 6-hydrate, reflectance of, 340, 342

Copper sulfate 5-hydrate, peak areas of, 155

Copper(II) sulfate 5-hydrate, GEA-DTA of, 305

Copper(II) sulfide–copper(I) sulfide system, by pyrosynthesis, 268

Cupferron metal chelates, analysis by mass spectrometry, 318, 319, 320

Cyclohexylamine stearate, thermal analysis of, 371

417

D

Derivative differential thermal analysis, comparison with DTA, 180
  history of, 180
  methods used in, 181
trans-o-Diaminocyclohexanetetraacetic acid, TGA of, 115
Diethylenetriaminopentaacetic acid, TGA of, 115
Differential scanning calorimeter, 206
Differential thermal analysis, applications of, 230
  applications of analytical chemistry, 231
  combined with mass spectrometry, 307
  correlation with TGA, 178
  definition of, 132
  factors affecting, 139
    amplifier sensitivity, 161
    comparison between static and dynamic atmospheres, 158
    furnace atmosphere, dynamic, 157
      static, 156
    furnace geometry, 161
    furnace heating rate, 152
    heating rate and peak area, 156
    sample diluent, 165
    sample heat capacity, 166, 167
    sample holder geometry, 143
    sample holder material, 140
    sample packing, 167
    sample particle size, 162
    sample size, 163
    sample thermal conductivity, 167
    thermocouples, 144
    thermocouple location, 147
  heat transfer in, 138
  history of, 134, 135
  instruments, Apparatus Manufacturers, 198
    Bohon, 219
    Bollin and Kerr, 221
    Campbell and Weingarten, 214
    components of, 186
    Deltatherm, 200

Differential Thermal Analyzer, Dupont, 201
    Harrop, 202
    high heating rate, 268
    Lodding and Hammell, 213
    micro, Mazieres, 213
    multiple, types of, 224
      with dilatometry, 227
      with electrical conductivity, 225
      with heat capacity and others, 227
      with radioactivity emission, 227
      with SHM, 203
    Newkirk, 214
    non-contact, 223
    Reisman, 218
    Rigaku Denki DTA-SHM, 203
    solution, 221
    Stone, 193
    thermistor, 222
    Thermoanalyzer, 201
    vapor pressure determination, 224
    Vassallo and Harden, 219
    Wendlandt, 209
    Whitehead and Breger, 209
  origin of thermal effects, 132
  quantitative, 168
    application of Vold's theory, 168
    calibration factor, 170, 173
    De Jong's equation for, 172
    heats of adsorption, 173
    heats of fusion of polymers, 174
    heats of polymerization of polymers, 174
    Sturm's equation, 173
    Wittel's equation for, 170
  reviews on, 134
  theory of Boersma, 138
    theory of Speil et al., 136
    Vold, 137
  uses of, 134
Differential thermal analysis curve, comparison with thermal analysis curve, 133
  peak area of, 134
  example of, 133

Differential thermal analysis peaks, factors affecting, 229
  origin of, 229
Differential thermogravimetric analysis, advantages of, 28
  comparison with other curves, 27
  definition of, 27
  history of, 27
  uses of, 28
Differential thermometric titrimetry, heats of reaction equation, 281
Dilatometer, Harrop, 385
  Linseis, 385
  rapid quenching type, 385
  Rigaku Denki, 382
  transducers for construction of, 381, 382
Dilatometer curve, 386, 387
Dilatometry, differential, 381
  definition of, 381
  normal, 381
Dilituric acid, TGA of, 110
Disodium calcium (ethylenedinitrilo)-tetraacetate, TGA of, 115
Dolomite, glow curves of, 377
Dotriacontane, DTA of, 246
Dynamic reflectance spectroscopy, definition of, 343
  uses of, 343

E

Electrical conductivity, 387
  apparatus for, 388
  coupled with DTA, 390
Enthalpimetric sensitivity index, 284
Entropy of fusion, of polymers, 174
Epoxides, DTA of, 235
(Ethylenedinitrilo)tetraacetic acid, TGA of, 115
N-Ethylguanidine picrate, DTA of, 236

F

Flash pyrolysis, 329
Fractional thermogravimetric analysis, 46
  coking coal, 42
  errors in, 42
  NaHCO₃, 40

Fresnel's law, 333
Furnaces, atmosphere controls, 191
  heater elements, temperature limits of, 191
  temperature programmers, 191
  types of, 191
  vented and non-vented, comparison, 13

G

Gas cell, heated, infrared, 393
Gas evolution analysis, 297
  advantages of GEA-DTA, 307
  apparatus for, 300, 298
  comparison with DTA, 303, 305, 306
  effect of operating variables upon, 299
  multiple instruments, with DTA, 305
Germanium dioxide—aluminum oxide mixtures, thermoluminescence of, 397
Gibbsite, DTA of, 258
Glow curve, 376
Goethite, DTA of 258
Guanidine picrate, DTA of, 236
Guanylurea picrate, DTA of, 236

H

Heats of fusion, of polymers, 174
Heats of polymerization, of polymers 174
Heats of transition, by DTA, 174
Hydrated salt mixtures, analysis of, 95
Hydrazine picrate, DTA of, 235
Hydroxyethyl(ethylenedinitrilo)-triacetic acid, TGA of, 115
2-(o-Hydroxyphenyl)benzoxazole metal chelates, TGA of, 121

I

Illitic shale, DTA of, 158
Integral procedural decomposition temperature, 43
  of some polymers, 45

K

Kaolin, effect of particle size in DTA of, 162

Kaolinite, DDTA of, 264
　DTA of, 141, 153
Kinetics of volatilization, Doyle's
　method, 37
Kubelka-Munk function, 335

L

Lanthanum sulfate, kinetics of, 32
Lead diliturate 2-hydrate, TGA of, 110
Lignite, DTA of, 159
Linear pyrolysis, apparatus for, 325
　rates of decomposition of solids, 325
　types of compounds studied, 326
Lithium stearate, DTA of, 263
Lubricating greases, DTA of, 263

M

Magnesite, variation of peak tempera-
　ture of, 154
Magnesium, analysis of by TGA, 101
Magnesium carbonate, DTA of, 252
Magnesium diliturate 8-hydrate, TGA
　of, 110
Manganese(II) carbonate, DTA-TGA
　of, 180
Marlex 50, variation of peak tempera-
　ture of, 154
Melting point apparatus, automatic,
　390
Meltometer, 392
Microcalorimeter, 168
Metal bipyridine complexes, kinetics of,
　31
Metal 5,7-dihalo-8-quinolinol chelates,
　DTA of, 259
Methods of impurity determination,
　345
N-Methylguanidine picrate, DTA of,
　236
2-Methyl-8-quinolinol tetraphenyl-
　borate, DTA of, 249
Milk, effect of heat on, 343
Moisture content of solids, by DTA,
　251

N

Naphthalene, thermal analysis of, 365
Neoprene W, DTA of, 243

Niagara limestone, glow curves of,
　379
Nitrilotriacetic acid, TGA of, 115
5-Nitrobarbituric acid, TGA of, 110
Nitrobenzene, heat of vaporization of,
　394
Nitroglycerin, GEA-DTA of, 302
p-Nitrophenylhydrazine, DTA of, 236
Normal alkanes, thermal analysis of,
　371
Nylon 66, DTA of, 243
　pyrolyzate analysis, 323, 322

O

Organic acids, DTA of, 239
Organic compounds, melting points of
　by DTA, 238
　boiling points of by DTA, 238
Organic derivatives, by DTA, 236
Oxalic acid 2-hydrate, DTA of, 239
Oxine phosphomolybdate, TGA of, 113
Oxyluminescence, definition of, 380
　use of, 380, 381
　use in evaluating antioxidants, 381

P

Peak assymetry, Kissinger's, 175
Pentaborane, thermal analysis of,
　370
Pentaerythritol tetranitrate, GEA of,
　300
n-Pentane, thermal analysis of, 370
n-Pentane–iso-octane mixture, ther-
　mal analysis of, 370
Plutonium(IV) oxalate 1.5 hydrate,
　TGA of, 126
Polyani-Wigner equation, 33
Polyadipamides, DTA of, 247
Polyesters, unsaturated, DTA of, 249
Polyethylene, DTA of, 243
Polyethylenes, degree of crystallinity
　of, 247
Polyglucosans, DTA of, 233
Polymers, analysis of pyrolyzates by
　mass spectrometry, 318
　pyrolysis of, 312, 313
　pyrolyzate analysis by infrared
　spectroscopy, 323, 324

Polysebacamides, DTA of, 247
Polystyrene, pyrolysis of, 313
Poly(vinyl alcohol), pyrolysis of, 315
   pyrolysis products of, 314, 315, 316, 317
Polyvinyl formal, pyrolyzate analysis, 324
Potassium diliturate, TGA of, 110
Potassium ethyl sulfate, GEA-DTA of, 306
Potassium hexacyanoferrate(III), reflectance spectra of, 334
Potassium hydrogen phthalate, TGA of, 106
Potassium niobate, electrical conductivity of, 389
Potassium nitrate, DDTA curve of, 180, 264
   DTA curve of, 180
Potassium nitrate–potassium perchlorate, DDTA of, 265
Potassium perchlorate, DDTA of, 265
Potassium tetraphenylborate, TGA of, 121
Procedural decomposition temperature, 43
Prout-Tompkins equation, 31
Pyrolysis, applied to airborne solids, 327
Pyrolysis chambers, boat-combustion tube type, 310
   boat type, 309, 310
   gas chromatographic, 308, 309
   hot wire, 308
      color temperatures of, 309
Pyrolytic techniques, definition of, 297
Pyrolyzates, analysis of, 297
   analysis of by gas chromatography, 308
   analysis of by infrared spectroscopy, 321
   analysis of by mass spectrometry, 317
   detection of, 297
Pyrosynthesis, 268

Q

Quinolinium phosphomolybdate, TGA of, 114

8-Quinolinol, DTA of, 166
8-Quinolinol tetraphenylborate, DTA of, 249

R

Rare earth chloride hydrates, DTA of, 257
Rare earth cupferrates, TGA of, 107
Rear earth neocupferrates, TGA of, 107
Rare earth oxalate hydrates, TGA of, 128
Rare earth oxalate hydrate mixtures, DTA of, 255
Reaction kinetics, Berlin and Robinson method, 33
   computer program for, 40
   differential enthalpic analysis in, 177
   DTA, Borchardt's method for, 176
   DTA, homogeneous solutions, 177
   DTA, Kissinger's method for, 153, 174
   DTA, oxidation of carbonaceous deposits by, 178
   dynamic method, Newkirk, 32
   Freeman and Carroll method for, 35
   GEA, 298
   isothermal weight-change method, 30
   nature of solid state, 29
   non-isothermal weight-change method, 32
   nucleation in, 30
   thermogravimetry in, 29
   various compounds studied by, 37
Recorders, potentiometric, for DTA, 192
   X–Y function, for DTA, 192
Recording balance, Ainsworth, 56
   Cahn RG Electrobalance
   cantilevered beam, 50
   deflection-type, 50
   detection of off-balance condition, 51
   Fisher, 53
   helical spring, 50, 74
   Mauer, 61
   null-type, 50
   requirements of, 49
   review of, 49
   Sartorius, 71

sensing elements of, 51
Sharples, 62
strain gage, 51
torsion, 51
Reflectance spectra, diffuse, 323
regular, 333
Reflectance spectroscopy, heated sample holder for, 338
high temperature, apparatus for, 339
instruments for, 335
theory of, 332
Rubidium tetraphenylborate, TGA of, 121
Ruthenium dioxide, TGA of, 97

S

Salicylaldehyde metal chelates, analysis by mass spectrometry, 318
Salicylic acid, effect of diluent on peak area, 165
Sample holders, DTA, construction materials, 186
DTA, multiple sample, 189
sample size, 190
types of, 186, 187
Sample temperature, errors in, 24
Scandium oxalate 6-hydrate, TGA of, 129
Sequestrene AA, TGA of, 115
Sequestrene Na 2, TGA of, 115
Sodium carbonate, drying and decomposition of, 92
Sodium phosphate hydrates, thermogravimetry of, 95
Sodium thiosulfate, peak areas of, 155
Starch, DTA of, 232
Stearic acid, DTA curve of, 170
Strontium, analysis of by TGA, 101
Strontium and cadmium phosphates, TGA of, 98
Strontium nitrate, TGA of, 97
Sturm's equations, 173

T

Talc, DTA of, 253
Talc A, DTA curve of, 143
Temperature detectors, DTA, thermistors, 190

DTA, thermopiles, 190
types of thermocouples, 190
Thermal analysis, apparatus for,
adapted wall cell, 357, 358
adiabatic calorimeter, 353
constant wall cell, 356, 357
calculations of, 355
comparison of static and dynamic methods, 363
definition of, 346
dynamic or thermometric method, 346
errors and limitations of, 359
Gunn's method, 351
limitations of dynamic method, effect of stirring, 361
influence of contact between layers, 361
rates of diffusion, 360
rate of heat transport, 361
solid-liquid transitions, 359
solid phase transitions, temperature differences during, 360
limitations of static method, application of solid-solution theory, 363
evidence of solid-solution formation, 362
uncertainty of impurity values, 362
recommendations for good results in, 364
reviews of, 346
static or calorimetric method, 346
theory of, 346
Thermal methods of analysis, definition of, 1
various techniques used in, 2
Thermal analysis curve, analysis of, 346, 347
Thermal stability determination, apparatus for, 328
Thermobalance, Brabender, 71
Chevenard, 63
components of, 48

definition of, 48
Derivatograph, 72
differential, De Keyser, 80
  R-C circuit for, 80
  various types of, 80
factors to be considered in construction of, 48
gas circulating system and, 85
Harrop, 61
Mettler balance converted to, 78
modifications of, 67
multiple instruments, with DTA, 82
  with DTA and DTG, 82, 85
pressure or vacuum type, 75
Stanton, 69
straing-gage, 80
Thermo-Grav, 60
torsion type, 75
Ugine-Eyraud, 67
Wendlandt, 79
Thermodilatometric analysis, definition of, 381
Thermography, non-contact, 223
Thermogravimetry, applications of, 88
  applications of, analytical chemistry, 89
  definition of, 4
  drying temperatures, 9
  errors in, 20
    furnace convection currents, 21
    sample condensation, 26
    sample container air buoyancy, 20
    sample holder, 26
    temperature measurement, 23
    thermobalance construction, 25
  factors affecting, 6
    amount of sample, 19
    furnace atmosphere, 11
    gases dissolved in solids, 19
    geometry of sample holder
    heating rate, 7
    recording or chart speed, 9
    sample heat of reaction, 18
    sample holder sink, 15
    sample packing, 19
    sample particle size, 17

sample thermal conductivity, 19
  historical aspects, 6
  quasi-static technique, use of, 5
Thermoluminescence, apparatus for, 375
  applications of, 373
  definition of, 373
  kinetics of decay of, 374
  origin of in crystals, 374
  substances which exhibit, 376
  theory of, 374
  use in evaluating catalysts, 378, 379
  use in radiation damage, 380
Thermometric titrimetry, acid–base reactions, 284
  apparatus for, 272, 273
  applications, 283
  complex formation reactions, 289
  definition of, 271
  differential, apparatus for, 275
  differentiating circuit for, 277
  errors in, 284
  fused salts in, 276
  history of, 272
  non-aqueous solvents, 292
  oxidation–reduction reactions, 291
  precipitation reactions, 288
  reviews on, 271
  synonyms for, 272
  temperature detection in, 274
  titration of H_3BO_3, 286
  titration of HCl, 285
  titration of KCl with $AgNO_3$, 285
  types of recorders for, 275
Thermometric titration curves, theory of, 278
Thorium o-aminobenzoate, TGA of, 123
Thorium benzoate, TGA of, 123
Thorium cinnamate, TGA of, 123
Thorium m-cresoxyacetate, TGA of, 123
Thorium 2,4-dichlorophenoxyacetate, TGA of, 123
Thorium m-hydroxybenzoate, TGA of, 123

Thorium mercaptobenzothiazole, TGA
    of, 123
Thorium phenylacetate,TGA of, 123
Thorium pyrogallate, TGA of, 123
Thorium stearate, TGA of, 123
Thymine, pyrolysis of, 311
Titrathermomat, 278
Toluene, DTA of, 154
Tremolite, quantitative DTA of, 163,
    164

V

Vibrin 135, DTA of, 240

W

Weight-loss curve, resolution factor, 10
    self-generated atmosphere, 12
    typical, 5
Wheatstone bridge, unbalance
    potential equation, 274

X

X-ray diffraction, high temperature,
    applications of, 401, 402

Z

Zirconyl nitrate 2-hydrate, TGA of, 97